# ENERGY, RESOURCES AND ENVIRONMENT

This book is the third in a series published by Hodder and Stoughton in association with The Open University.

*Environment and Society*
edited by Jonathan Silvertown and Philip Sarre

*Environment, Population and Development*
edited by Philip Sarre

*Energy, Resources and Environment*
edited by John Blunden and Alan Reddish

*Global Environmental Issues*
edited by Paul M. Smith and Kiki Warr

The final form of the text is the joint responsibility of chapter authors, book editors and course team commentators.

The books are one component of the Open University course U206 *Environment*. Details of the course are available from the Student Enquiries Office, The Open University, PO Box 71, Milton Keynes MK7 6AG.

# ENERGY, RESOURCES AND ENVIRONMENT

*EDITED BY*
*JOHN BLUNDEN AND ALAN REDDISH*
*FOR AN OPEN UNIVERSITY COURSE TEAM*

Hodder &
Stoughton

LONDON   SYDNEY   AUCKLAND   TORONTO

IN ASSOCIATION WITH

The Open
University

*British Library Cataloguing in Publication Data*
Energy, resources and environment.
  I. Blunden, J.   II. Reddish, A.
  333.79

  ISBN 0–340–53361–7

First published in the United Kingdom 1991

Designed by the Graphic Design Group of the Open University

Index compiled by Editech, Ipswich, Suffolk

Typeset by Wearside Tradespools, Fulwell, Sunderland

Printed in the United Kingdom for Hodder and Stoughton Educational, a division of Hodder and Stoughton Ltd, Mill Road, Dunton Green, Sevenoaks, Kent by Butler & Tanner Ltd, Frome and London

# Contents

# Introduction

This book is the third in a series of four which present an interdisciplinary and integrated explanation of environmental issues. Throughout it is stressed that environmental issues are complex and that to understand them we must combine scientific evidence and theory, analysis of social processes, knowledge of technological possibilities and awareness of underlying value positions. The series considers a range of environmental issues, some local, many transnational and some global. It aims to widen readers' *awareness* of environmental issues, to increase their ability to *analyse* them and to equip them to *evaluate* policies to influence such issues. It stresses that solutions to particular problems should be complementary with, and ideally contribute to, the solution of international and global problems, including global warming.

The first book identified the basic processes that support the huge variety of life on earth, the impacts of society over millennia and changing beliefs as to how society should relate to environment. The second book examined the relationship between population growth, economic development and environmental change, with particular reference to agriculture and urbanisation. In so doing it began to identify the role of advanced technology in transforming the way society related to environment.

This book makes a new start by considering a few familiar machines in common use in developed countries, and shows that they depend on extensive supply systems for energy and materials. These systems, from natural origin through processing and use to disposal, are the concern of later chapters. Throughout, the book stresses that energy and materials systems are interlinked, not least because mining and mineral processing use large amounts of energy, and that these systems for *supplying* energy and materials should not be thought of in isolation from our *demand* for them, which can change with more efficient use or with our way of life. The book also emphasises the idea that our current notions of the exploitation of finite sources of energy and minerals may not be tenable in the longer term. A change in the way and the rate at which we use these resources may not only be necessary for developed countries and for any future attempts to improve living standards in the developing world, but also may be essential if we are to come to terms successfully with environmental problems, many of which are global.

The first two chapters outline the current systems of production and consumption of energy and minerals. As far as energy is concerned, the dominance of fossil fuels is a reminder that energy is being used at a rate which cannot be sustained indefinitely. Moreover, the disparities in levels of consumption between countries is so great that it would be disastrous for the environment if the less developed countries began to use energy in the same way that developed countries do. Similar disparities exist in consumption of minerals, though here the global trade in minerals means that some less developed countries have valuable resources.

The next three chapters explore in greater detail the impacts of current energy and materials systems, from visual disturbance, noise and dust around mines, through transport spills, acidification of water, air and soil, and chemical pollutants from smelting and manufacturing processes, to waste dumping. For both energy and minerals, various improvements are considered, from cosmetic changes to mines and spoil heaps, through new technologies of supply and greater efficiency of use, to recycling and reduction of waste. Such changes would require a change in society's priorities as well as technical change.

The last three chapters consider political responses to the impacts of energy, minerals and manufacturing. Two sides are analysed. First, the past and present role of government in regulating harmful emissions: here the UK's historic method of negotiating the best practicable levels is contrasted both with European Community imposition of maximum levels and new proposals to make polluters pay. Second, the role of public opinion and pressure groups: frequently public protest arises from risk of accidents or from aversion to waste, whether unsightly, toxic or radioactive. The technical and political difficulties of handling hazardous waste suggest strongly that more priority should be given to strategies of efficient use and recycling which will reduce pollution and waste as well as reducing the consumption of finite resources.

The fourth book in the series considers two sets of issues: first, the resource and pollution impacts which have recently forced environmental issues on to the global political agenda and, second, the suitability of the concept of sustainable development as a guide to policy at national and international level. The oceans and atmosphere are considered as natural systems and as the scene of changes which have made them global issues and stimuli to international collaboration over ocean management, ozone depletion and the threat of global warming. The concept of sustainable development, which has been so central to the post-Brundtland debate, is critically analysed and shown to be at best an agenda which may bring together the disparate range of environmental issues considered in the series, from habitat and genetic loss, through problems of population growth, agriculture and urbanisation, to the costs and benefits of the technologies of energy and mineral supply.

In thinking out the concept of sustainable development it will be necessary to recall two basic principles from Book One: The biosphere depends on a throughput of energy from the sun and also depends on the recycling of a finite stock of materials. These are also vital for this book.

# 1    Introduction

Raise your eyes from this book and look around you. How much of what you can see is the natural world as it might have been without human intervention, and how much the result of human ingenuity and industry? Even if you are sitting in a garden or the countryside the living things will have been much arranged and organised by human hands. If, as is more likely, you are sitting in your home, the office, a bus or a train, almost everything in sight will be the product of complex manufacturing processes which have transformed the materials of the world into forms we find useful or attractive. Walls and windows, furniture and fabrics, clothes and cutlery, lamps and looking glasses, machines of every kind from cars to refrigerators and television sets – these are all reminders of how far we are from simple survival and how much we depend on the skills of others. (Recently, a group of hardy experimenters, used to twentieth century UK conditions, tried to live as though they were in the Iron Age, and they apparently missed above all else good pairs of Wellington boots – so it is not only the obviously advanced products that we take for granted.) A social, industrial and economic organisation of extreme complexity provides this standard of living. Perhaps it is not so surprising that it sometimes shows strain – maybe we should be more astonished that it works as well as it does. The complexity does mean, however, that it is not always at all obvious where environmental problems originate. This book will try to tease out some of the interconnections between the resources used, the services provided and the problems encountered. In the first two chapters we will look at two primary resources, energy and minerals, and then go on in later chapters to the environmental problems created by the ways we use them at present, and some of the choices available for the future.

This first chapter is about energy, which not only makes our present machines turn, but has always been a major influence on the form taken by human society (as described by Simmons in *Silvertown & Sarre, 1990*, Chapter 5). More fundamentally, the energy of the sun drives the ecosystem (Silvertown in *Silvertown & Sarre, 1990*, Chapters 2–4) and, as we shall see, the internal structure of materials implies various forms of energy storage. Most of us have played the 'animal, vegetable or mineral' game to classify different materials; the environmental implications of our production of some of the animals and vegetables by various agricultural processes have been examined by Grigg, Woodhouse and Bowler in *Sarre, 1991*, Chapters 2–4. The remaining category, mineral, forms the subject of the next chapter, but it is not altogether distinct from 'energy'. On the one hand, some important energy resources (coal, oil, uranium) are themselves minerals; on the other, mineral extraction and processing require energy, to drive digging and crushing machinery, and to modify chemical structure, e.g. in the smelting of natural ores to produce useful metals.

# 2   *Energy use in three machines*

The distinction that is being made between energy and minerals can be clarified, in a preliminary way, by looking at three familiar machines – a car, a refrigerator and a television set. All are complex structures of metals, plastics, glass and more specialised materials (e.g. lead–acid batteries, alumina sparking plugs, quartz–halogen lamps, synthetic rubber tyres; glass wool insulation and chlorofluorocarbon refrigerants; silicon chips and ferrite cores) of wonderfully varied *mineral* origins, and much chemical and manufacturing ingenuity. But they won't do anything (except provide status symbols, and slowly rust away) until supplied with *energy* in a suitable form.

## 2.1   *A car*

For a car, the energy source is (at present) almost invariably petrol or diesel fuel, a 'fossil fuel' store of *chemical* energy that burns explosively in the conditions inside the engine to produce *heat*. This is in turn converted into *mechanical* energy in the engine, and hence into movement of the wheels, the vehicle and its occupants, which can all be set in motion from rest and be driven up hills (two basic indicators that energy has been supplied.) Some of the energy produced by the engine is also converted into *electrical* energy and stored in the battery to operate the fuel ignition system, the lights and various electric motors (the starter motor, fuel pump and smaller motors such as in windscreen wipers).

   The primary heat-to-mechanical **energy conversion** is characteristic of a **heat engine**. Other examples are the paraffin-fuelled gas turbine of a jet aircraft, or the coal-fired steam turbine of a power station (or indeed the eighteenth-century steam engines that powered the industrial revolution). In a power station the heat engine stage, converting the heat energy of steam into the mechanical energy of steam jets and rotating turbine blades, is followed by a further, mechanical-to-electrical, conversion in the electricity generator attached to the turbine.

## 2.2   *A refrigerator*

A refrigerator (of the usual domestic type) has energy supplied as *electricity* from the mains which drives a motor and compressor, an electrical-to-mechanical energy conversion. This compresses the refrigerant, which is a gas such as ammonia or the chlorofluorocarbons (CFCs) which were introduced as they were thought to be more innocuous (until their effect on the ozone layer was observed – see Warr in *Smith & Warr, 1991*, Chapter 3). The compression leads to liquefaction and heating of the gas. It is cooled back to the temperature of the room by passing it through an external radiator. It is then allowed to evaporate and expand in pipes surrounding the food storage space where it cools further before returning to the compressor and repeating the cycle. The net effect is that heat is taken *from* the internal cold space *to* the warmer external air. It is an important principle (the famous **Second Law of Thermodynamics**) that this can only be done by supplying energy from some other source to make a 'heat engine in reverse'.

In a refrigerator we are more interested in the cooling effect on the food than the heating effect on the kitchen. But the same principle can be used for heating a building by taking heat from the (already colder) outside air, a nearby river or groundwater, in which case the equipment is called a heat pump.

## 2.3   A television set

A television set also requires a supply of *electrical* energy from the mains, to be converted, among other things, into *light* from the screen and *sound* from the loudspeaker. But this can only form a meaningful picture and message if there is a further supply of electrical energy, to the aerial socket at the back of the set. This can either be, as originally intended, from an aerial picking up energy from *electromagnetic* radio waves sent out by television transmitters, or it can be from a video recorder producing a similar energy pattern from programmes stored on magnetic tape. In both cases this second energy supply is called a **signal** because the amount of energy involved is tiny compared with that supplied from the mains, but it fluctuates in a patterned (coded) way; this ensures that a particular transmitter (or video channel) can be separated out from the others, and the conversion of mains energy into light and sound can be controlled so that the required pictures and speech or music are reconstructed.

Thus a television set is another energy conversion device, to set alongside the machines and heat engines which have contributed so much to the industrial and social fabric of the developed world over the last three centuries. But it is also an **information** device. The feature which is unchanged through all the energy transformations, from the light and sound of the original scene to electrical effects in the television camera, the transmitter, the radio waves, the receiver and back to light and sound, is the distinctive pattern that constitutes information. This sets television alongside earlier information storage methods such as books, pictures and discs, communication methods such as letters and telephones, and the newer access and processing methods of computers. Information transfer too has always been an important factor in the development of society; the great increases in speed and range provided by electronics over the last half-century have already modified work patterns and may gradually transform settlement patterns from those we have come to expect. As we examine the environmental problems of present practice and future options about energy and minerals in the rest of this book, we should also bear in mind the changing possibilities offered by these unprecedented fast, long-distance information transfers.

## 2.4   Summary

The relationship between mineral and energy requirements is illustrated with three familiar machines. All are structurally complex, based on many minerals, and all require energy to operate them: a car uses the chemical energy in petrol to operate a heat engine; a refrigerator uses mains electricity to operate a heat engine in reverse; a television set uses mains electricity to produce light and sound, and a further electromagnetic signal determines the programme content. While they are all 'energy conversion' devices, the television set is also an 'information' device.

*Activity 1*

Before reading any further, pause to reflect on other objects and equipment around you and what you know of their mineral origins, the energy used in making or operating them, and any environmental problems they might cause. Make notes for comparison with ideas that will emerge in later parts of the book.

# 3    *Energy – what does it mean?*

I have already been using the word 'energy', and implying that it can be converted between various forms, without further explanation, which perhaps has left you feeling rather bemused. The earlier books in this series have similarly made frequent reference to energy of various forms without particularly explaining the terms and units used.

*Activity 2*

Book 1 of this series (*Silvertown & Sarre, 1990*) made references to coal, nuclear and solar energy, to photosynthesis and energy flow through food webs, to human organisation and its dependence on energy use, and to energy release in earthquakes. Book 2 (*Sarre, 1991*) referred to energy use in the production of various crops, and their dietary energy value. Make notes on how you think these various usages of 'energy' are related, for reconsideration after Section 4.

Maybe this isn't a problem for you, particularly if you have a background in science or technology. In that case you may be able to skip fairly rapidly to Section 6 of this chapter. But if it all seems obscure and impenetrable I hope Sections 4 and 5 can shed some light on the ideas involved – obviously the material of many textbooks can't all be compressed into two sections of one chapter, but it will be worth catching a glimpse of some general terms and principles to help make sense of current problems. There is no reason to feel surprised or guilty if the ideas seem baffling – 'energy' is an abstract idea of some subtlety, sharper in its scientific definition and richer in its implications than in everyday usage. Much that is now treated as obvious was by no means so two or three centuries ago, and some very able minds have agonised over these concepts. But unifying the terminology and units in different applications continues to be a headache. So take heart, and share in grappling with slippery ideas.

## 3.1   Different usages

I think there are two kinds of difficulty with the word 'energy'. The first is that it is used along with related words in everyday language in ways which shade into each other. We might describe someone's personality as 'forceful, hard-working, hot-headed, energetic and powerful' and know more or less what we mean by each of these lively adjectives, but we would be hard pressed to disentangle from this exactly how the corresponding five abstract nouns 'force, work, heat, energy and power' were to be distinguished. In scientific language each of these five words is sharply defined and they are by no means interchangeable; we need to watch their use carefully. In Section 4 the main emphasis will be on *energy* in its various forms, but it will be related back to the underlying ideas of *force, work* and *heat*. The important distinction from *power* will emerge in Section 5.

The second difficulty is that this sharper scientific use of 'energy' has been adopted by the UK government and picked up by the media and the rest of us, but only up to a point. We have a Department of Energy where we used to have a Ministry of Fuel and Power; the newspapers will write of an 'energy crisis' or of 'energy policy' rather than the specific problems of oil, coal or nuclear power stations. So some of the unifying ideas linking specific **fossil fuels** (coal, gas, oil, which store chemical energy) and nuclear fuels (such as uranium and plutonium) with ways of producing electricity (by heat engines driving generators) are generally recognised, but others, which will emerge below and may be crucial for the future, have often been neglected. So it will be worth trying to get a more general grasp of underlying energy principles so that the continuing debate about future policies (energy efficiency, use of solar or renewable energy versus fossil and nuclear fuels, pollution, the ozone hole, the greenhouse effect and so on) can be better followed.

## 3.2   Fossil fuel reserves – a first look

Before embarking on this more abstract analysis we can stay briefly with the conventional idea of energy resources by looking at the way 'proved reserves' of oil, gas and coal were distributed around the world in 1989 (Figures 1.1a, 1.2a and 1.3). Since the industrial revolution, national prosperity has been intimately linked with ready access to these fossil fuels. For Britain in the eighteenth century, coal was crucial; it soon became equally important throughout the world, as it still is. For the USA at the end of the nineteenth century, oil also became vital, supporting the development of the automobile, again soon a world issue. Throughout the developed world in the mid-twentieth century, natural gas has been adopted as a cleaner domestic and industrial fuel. So current perceptions about the amounts of these three fuels now available give an instant image of powerful economic and political influences at work at the end of the twentieth century.

Figures 1.1a, 1.2a and 1.3 (which were produced by the oil industry) show the map of the world redrawn with the heights of the different blocks scaled in proportion to their **proved reserves** of the three fuels. This is a term to be treated warily; it does not represent the total resource judged to be ultimately available, but only that part which can be extracted 'under existing economic and operating conditions'. That is, it depends on the state of exploration and extraction technology, and on world prices, which all the main operators in the energy industries try to keep favourable. The

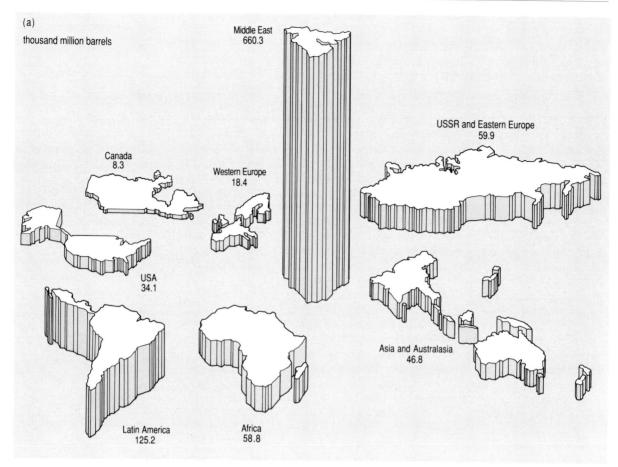

▲    Figure 1.1(a)    Oil: proved reserves. Map representing global distribution, 1989.

◀    Figure 1.1(b)
Oil: proved reserves.
Changes since 1970.

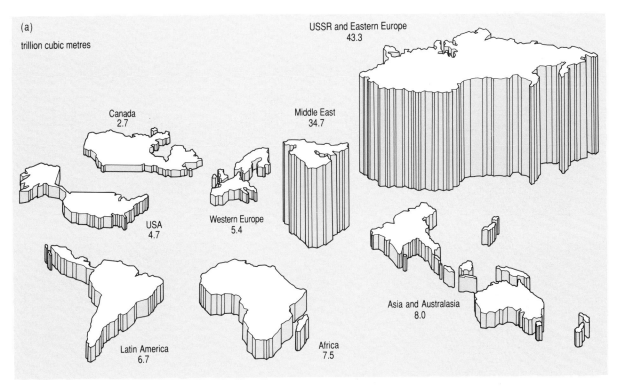

▲   *Figure 1.2(a)    Natural gas: proved reserves. Map representing global distribution, 1989.*

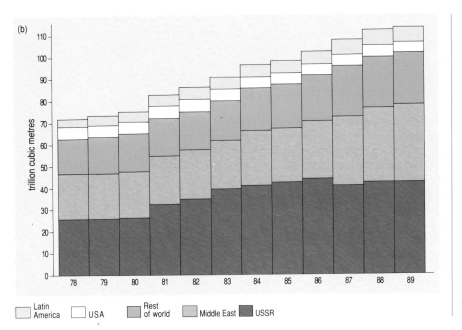

◄   *Figure 1.2(b)*
*Natural gas: proved reserves.*
*Changes since 1970.*

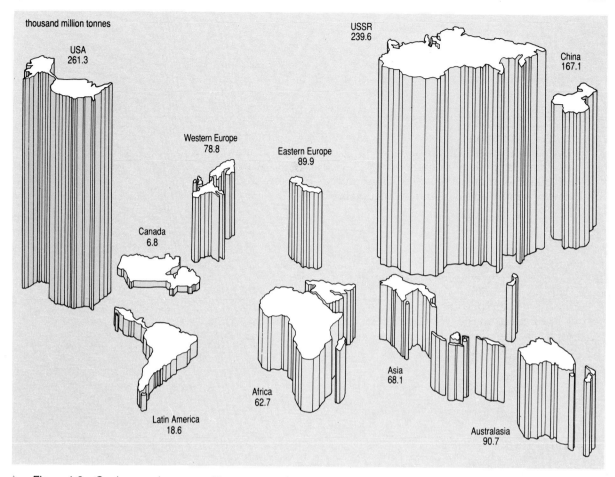

▲  *Figure 1.3    Coal: proved reserves. Map representing global distribution, 1989.*

quoted proved reserves of oil and gas have actually *increased* over the past 20 years as a result of exploration and changing economic conditions, in spite of the large consumption (Figures 1.1b and 1.2b). Even so, the most spectacular, oil, is fairly hair-raising; the overwhelming dominance of the Middle East gives an immediate reason for political instability in that region.

What these maps do not show is the relation of these reserves to world demand. This is conveyed by a figure for how long the reserves would last at current extraction rates. This turned out to be for oil (in 1989) 44 years averaged over the whole world, but ranging from a mere 5 years for the UK reserves and 10 for North America to over 100 years for several Middle Eastern states, which again emphasises the political volatility of the oil issue. For natural gas, the picture presented in Figure 1.2 is not much more comfortable: the USSR now outstrips the Middle East. For the world, the 'life' at current extraction rates is about 56 years, but again the UK and North America have only about 13 years, while the USSR has 51 years and several Middle Eastern states have over 100 years. Only for the original industrial fuel, coal (Figure 1.3), is the distribution more even throughout the world, with projected lives at current consumption rates of 200 to 400 years.

These figures have all to be viewed with some scepticism, as there is much uncertainty and commercial or political calculation involved, but they do present an immediate first impression of one part of the energy problem – and a reason why coal-rich countries view any constraint on coal burning (arising from the greenhouse effect, for example) with such alarm.

There is much more comparison between these and other energy sources (nuclear, solar) to be done before a more general assessment can be made. Are they interchangeable? Can the system be made sustainable? Not least, we need a common way of comparing the energy available with energy demand. These three maps, for example, all use different physical measures – barrels of oil, cubic metres of gas, tonnes of coal (all by the thousand million or more). We will reach a common measure, and a more global view of supply and demand, in Section 5.

## 3.3    Summary

Two sources of confusion about the use of the word 'energy' are suggested. There is the overlap in everyday language with words like force and power; the media tend to use it to cover only fuels and power stations.

A first impression of some current energy resource problems is conveyed by figures on the world distribution of oil, gas and coal reserves; these emphasise the need for a more general basis of comparison with other energy resources and with demand.

# 4    Forms of energy and energy conversion

For present purposes it is useful to distinguish five forms of energy – mechanical, electromagnetic, thermal, chemical and nuclear – which will be discussed in turn. The most familiar energy process, burning fuels to produce heat, is chemical-to-thermal energy conversion in these terms. These two forms of energy can now be related to the first two in the list, but it is convenient to continue to keep them separate. Each of the five forms covers a wide range of effects, including some kinds of energy conversion within the form; other kinds of conversion take place between forms.

These many kinds of energy conversion can be summarised in a table (Table 1.1), which we can build up as we proceed.

There are potentially 25 'boxes' to be filled in as we consider ways of converting from one of the five forms, listed at the left, to the same or a different one of the five listed along the top – though there will be no need to work patiently through each of them in turn (you will be glad to hear). The boxes along the diagonal represent conversions *within* one form, the rest conversions *between* forms. I shall start at the top left with conversions within the mechanical form, which introduces some fundamental ideas. Then as I consider each new form of energy in turn, I can fill in the conversions within it, and also with each preceding form, completing a larger part of the table each time, as you will see.

*Table 1.1   Conversion between different forms of energy*

| From \ To | Mechanical | Electromagnetic | Thermal | Chemical | Nuclear |
|---|---|---|---|---|---|
| Mechanical | | | | | |
| Electromagnetic | | | | | |
| Thermal | | | | | |
| Chemical | | | | | |
| Nuclear | | | | | |

## 4.1   Mechanical energy

Mechanical energy is associated with machines of all kinds; old-fashioned clockwork is a good example. It also arises in everyday experiences with rolling and bouncing balls, in musical instruments, and in less mellifluous producers of noise and turbulence such as pneumatic drills, waterfalls and earthquakes.

A raised weight, a wound-up spring or the stretched elastic in a catapult has **potential energy**. 'Work' has been done against a 'force' to provide this energy: the gravitational force pulls the weight back to Earth and the internal forces inside the spring or elastic try to restore its normal shape. Conversely, anything storing energy, of the many kinds to be considered, is able to do work in this sense, moving something against a force. One weight falling can raise a heavier one by means of a system of pulleys, for example. The heavier weight must move a shorter distance, showing that two factors are involved in work and potential energy: the force and the distance moved. (Try telling a weightlifter that he only does work when he lifts a barbell, not when he is 'just' holding it above his head (Figure 1.4) – so much for precise scientific language!)

This potential energy can be converted into the **kinetic energy** of movement, as when a ball, or a stream of water, picks up speed as it runs down a hill, or a stone is released from a catapult. The kinetic energy of a moving stream of water, air or high-pressure stream can be converted into the *rotational* kinetic energy of a water wheel, windmill or turbine. Conversely, energy must be supplied (from the rotating shaft driven by the engine) to get a stationary car moving, or to raise it to the top of a hill. Similarly, energy must be supplied (from a pump) to move or raise water or (from a fan) to move air.

▲    *Figure 1.4*
*A weightlifter doing no work!*

### Vibrations and waves

The conversion of potential to kinetic energy needn't take place once and for all: it can be recovered (nearly), as when a ball bounces back into your hand. Or it can be converted regularly back and forth, as when a ball rolls up and down the sides of a bowl, or a weight hanging on a rod or string forms the pendulum of a clock or a child's swing (Figure 1.5). In these cases potential energy at the extreme positions is converted into kinetic at the intermediate position, and back again. These various types of oscillation about a central position are similar to the vibrations that can arise in all kinds of things when they are disturbed from their resting position. The time taken by each vibration can vary over a wide range, from several seconds for large systems (bridges or the water of the sea) to ever smaller fractions of a second in musical instruments producing higher and higher notes. In ultrasonic dog whistles and medical scanners the notes are too high for us to hear, and each vibration can take only a few millionths of a second.

Of course, a swing (or any other vibrating system) left to itself won't go on for ever converting potential and kinetic energy back and forth. The vibrations die down, because of friction between moving parts, air resistance, or similar effects in liquids and solids. It is a basic principle, the **law of conservation of energy** (or more grandly, the First Law of Thermodynamics) that any energy which seems to be missing must be accounted for in some other form. So where does it go? The usual way energy can seem to be lost, or dissipated, is as heat or **thermal energy**, a different form of energy I shall come back to below. This dissipation is the main reason why mechanical energy conversion 'machines' (windmills, musical instruments) have less than perfect **efficiency**, which is a measure of how much of the energy supplied is converted into the form required. The whole of this section is based on the idea that energy is never destroyed, only converted from one form to another, in all kinds of complicated ways. The use of a common unit for measuring energy, which we shall come to in the next section, is likewise only possible because of this principle.

So when you strike a gong, pluck a string or blow a whistle, you convert kinetic energy (of the mallet, your finger or the air stream) into **vibrational energy**, which is alternately potential and kinetic, but dies away as thermal energy unless energy continues to be converted to compensate. Such a conversion can be very orderly – the steady fall of a weight or unwinding of a spring can be used to maintain the regular oscillations of a pendulum in a clock; the steady motion of a violin bow, or a flautist's breath, can produce the regular vibrations, in the string or the air, of a pure note. Or it can be disordered – the hammering in a machine shop, the crash of dropped crockery, producing the confused sounds we call **noise**. In either case there is energy conversion 'within the mechanical form', from steady effects to rapid vibrations of some kind.

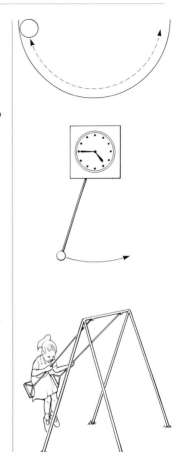

▲   Figure 1.5   Oscillations – ball, pendulum, swing.

The reason you can hear the sounds of musical instruments or breaking crockery is because **sound waves** travel from them through the air to your ear. You may have seen the demonstration of an electric bell ringing in a glass jar from which the air can be pumped away; as it is sucked out the sound dies away, though the hammer can be seen to be striking the bell as before. This emphasises that air has to be present for sound to be heard at a distance, and is an example of a more general energy transfer process.

When a vibration, or indeed any kind of mechanical disturbance, is set up in one place in a gas, liquid or solid, energy can be 'handed on' progressively *through* the material as waves. These are of various kinds depending on the exact conditions. For each kind of wave there is a distinctive speed at which the disturbance travels, though the material at each point only vibrates around a fixed position. We normally experience sound waves in air, but they travel similarly in other gases, and in liquids and solids. You can hear sound under water, or by putting your ear to the ground – the speed of sound is then greater than in air.

There are other types of mechanical wave, each with their own speeds. Most obvious are those we first learned to call waves at the seaside, those on the surface of water. Others arise in the strings and drumskins of musical instruments, and, more disturbingly, in the Earth, carrying away the energy from earthquakes (Smith in *Silvertown & Sarre, 1990*, Chapter 6).

Waves, too, die away as their energy is dissipated as thermal energy. Think of the sequence of events when a bucket of water is poured into a water-butt. The original potential energy of the raised water is successively converted into the kinetic energy of the falling water, the turbulent motion (and sound) of the splash, and waves travelling outwards, then back and forth as they bounce off the sides. As the ripples die down all the energy initially supplied is finally turned into thermal energy (shown by a slightly increased water temperature, which in turn falls back to normal as heat is lost to the surroundings).

The conversions 'within the mechanical form' covered in this section can now be incorporated into the table (Table 1.2); dissipation as thermal energy can also be included as a first example of conversion 'to another form'.

Table 1.2

| From \ To | Mechanical | Electromagnetic | Thermal | Chemical | Nuclear |
|---|---|---|---|---|---|
| Mechanical | potential/kinetic turbine vibration sound waves turbulence | | dissipation (friction etc.) | | |
| Electromagnetic | | | | | |
| Thermal | | | | | |
| Chemical | | | | | |
| Nuclear | | | | | |

## 4.2   *Electromagnetic energy*

This rather long-winded term 'electromagnetic' is used rather than 'electrical' to emphasise that the electricity we all use every day is only part of a large family of related forms of energy. The familiar sources of electricity are batteries (in portable equipment such as torches and radios, and in cars) and the mains that link our homes and workplaces to power stations. They are used to operate all kinds of equipment – radios and television sets, lights, the motors of vacuum cleaners and washing machines, heaters and cookers.

When we use them to operate radios, microwave cookers and lights we are taking advantage of 'energy conversions within the electromagnetic form'. The ideas of mechanical vibrations and waves described above have electromagnetic equivalents, but with some important differences. The most basic is the question of 'what is doing the vibrating?', which cannot be answered simply. The answer given now for most materials is **electrons**, which are minute constituents of matter, part of its basic structure. They can move fairly freely through conductors such as metals to form an electric current. This can flow steadily in one direction (direct current, d.c.), which is what happens when a wire is connected across a battery. Or it can change direction many times a second: in a wire connected across the alternating current (a.c.) mains, the current reverses 50 times a second – a frequency of 50 hertz (Hz). But vastly higher frequencies are possible – for example your radio and television will have some way of indicating the frequencies of different transmitters, from kHz (kilohertz, thousands of Hz) to MHz (megahertz, millions of Hz). These imply that each transmitter involves its own oscillator, converting electrical energy from a battery or the low-frequency a.c. mains into currents fluctuating at these high frequencies (much higher than the mechanical vibrations of sound). Furthermore, such currents in the aerial of the transmitter produce **electromagnetic waves** of corresponding frequency which travel away and can be picked up by your receiving aerial. These waves differ profoundly from sound, or other mechanical waves: their speed is vastly greater ('the speed of light', $3 \times 10^8$ metres per second, apparently the highest speed which can be reached by any means) and they can travel through vacuum, a fact on which our survival crucially depends.

Why is this? The clue is the reference to the speed of *light*. Fluctuations of currents at radio frequencies, and the corresponding electromagnetic waves, are by no means the end of the story. Electrons are so light and mobile that in various circumstances they can move between or within atoms so as to produce electromagnetic waves of much higher frequency still, all travelling through a vacuum at this same speed. All these waves together form the so-called spectrum of **electromagnetic radiation** – radio frequencies up to about 1000 MHz ($10^9$ Hz); the microwaves used in cookers, radar and satellite communications ($10^9$ to $10^{12}$ Hz); the infra-red radiation from hot objects ($10^{12}$ to $10^{15}$ Hz); visible light from red to violet in a narrow band near $10^{15}$ Hz; ultra-violet, x-rays and gamma-rays at even higher frequencies. (These different wavebands are also often described by their *wavelengths*, which decrease as the frequency increases. Thus infra-red to ultra-violet is from some $10^{-4}$ m to $10^{-7}$ m, as mentioned by Ross in *Smith & Warr, 1991*, Chapter 2.) The sun, our primary source of energy for the Earth, radiates a wide range of electromagnetic waves from infra-red to ultra-violet, which only reach us because they can carry energy across the vacuum of space. (A television set in a bell-jar would not stop working when the air was pumped out; the radio waves would still reach it, and we could see, but not hear, it.)

When we switch on a traditional light bulb, the flow of current makes a tungsten filament white-hot, producing a similar wide range of radiation. A fluorescent lamp is more efficient as a light source because the materials used have been chosen to provide effects limited to narrower bands of frequencies, channelling more of the electrical energy into visible light and less into infra-red ('heat'). An x-ray tube similarly converts d.c. electricity into the even higher frequencies of x-rays. Conversely, a solar cell has materials chosen to convert the high-frequency energy of sunlight into d.c. electricity like that from a battery.

When we use a battery or the mains to drive an electric motor we are moving out of the electromagnetic form to 'conversion to mechanical energy', the kinetic energy of a rotating shaft. This process depends on the subtle relationship between electric currents, magnets and forces that was disentangled, particularly by Michael Faraday, in the first half of the nineteenth century. The process is used in reverse in a **generator**, which is the normal way that electricity is produced in a power station, or in your car, from the rotations of a shaft driven by a steam turbine, or a petrol engine. (Different versions produce d.c. or a.c.) The same principles are also used in some types of loudspeakers and microphones to convert higher frequency electric currents to and from the mechanical vibrations of sound, carefully matching the detailed fluctuations of music, speech or other noise.

Finally, there is one of the commonest uses of electricity: conversion to thermal energy in electric fires and cookers. I could have described this first, as an inevitable process whenever a current flows. Electrons are not completely free to move in metals and other conductors: they encounter resistance, which dissipates electrical energy as heat, much as friction and similar effects dissipate mechanical energy. I kept it to the end for three reasons. First, to emphasise that it is a 'loss' process which limits the efficiency of other types of conversion, as friction does for machines. Second, so that infra-red could be mentioned first, alongside other electromagnetic waves. The fact that it is produced by all hot objects says something about the nature of thermal energy. Third, because in terms of total energy policy it is a wasteful way to use electricity, as we shall see, though it may be convenient in other ways.

We can now fill in these various new conversion processes in the table (Table 1.3).

Table 1.3

| From \ To | Mechanical | Electromagnetic | Thermal | Chemical | Nuclear |
|---|---|---|---|---|---|
| Mechanical | X | generator<br>microphone | X | | |
| Electromagnetic | motor<br>loudspeaker | oscillator<br>lamp<br>x-ray tube<br>solar cell | dissipation<br>(resistance) | | |
| Thermal | | | | | |
| Chemical | | | | | |
| Nuclear | | | | | |

## 4.3   Thermal energy

This term is used rather than 'heat energy' to acknowledge that there have been some shifts of usage of the word 'heat' over the time that it has been studied more carefully. Three forms of heating have been known about for a long time – that from the sun, long before there were humans to experience it (let alone to describe it as we do now, as the arrival of electromagnetic radiation); that from the burning of fuels such as wood (the release of stored chemical energy), and that dissipated during mechanical work, during thousands of years of human experience. The reverse process, of producing work from heat, has only been available for the two hundred years or so since the industrial revolution, with the invention of the steam engine and other forms of heat engine.

The starting point for more careful consideration of heat is the idea of **temperature**. We can get a direct impression of 'hotness' by touch, and can turn this into a more precise measurement by using a thermometer. The temperature reading obtained in this way must not be confused with the amount of thermal energy that needs to be supplied or removed to *change* the temperature. Everyday experience with cookers shows that it takes longer to boil a pan of water than to get the empty pan red-hot (or even to melt!). The amount of energy needed to produce a particular temperature change depends on the amount, and the nature, of the material being heated.

If two objects at different temperatures are brought into contact, but 'isolated' from the rest of the world, so that they can exchange thermal energy with each other, but not with anything else, the hotter object cools, and the colder warms up until they are both at the same temperature. Think of hot tea in a vacuum flask (the best thermal isolation we can provide). When cold milk is added, the mixture rapidly reaches a uniform intermediate temperature. This is normally described as *heat* transfer from the hot tea to the cold milk, though it could equally be described as a conversion of some of the internal thermal energy of the tea into that of the milk. It is *not* described as a transfer of 'cold' from the milk to the tea! Even cold milk has a thermal energy content – it could be even colder. Heat 'flows' from higher to lower temperatures.

A further normal experience is that (even in a vacuum flask) the uniform temperature of the milky tea gradually falls as heat is transferred to the surroundings. The law of conservation of energy requires that no energy should actually be lost, but as energy is shared with the cooler surroundings the temperature of the tea falls – sometimes described as a reduction in the 'quality' of the thermal energy. One version of the Second Law of Thermodynamics is that there is no *spontaneous* process by which the opposite can happen – energy cannot flow of its own accord from the cool surroundings into the tea to warm it up! Put like that it might seem pretty obvious, but there is nothing in the First Law, that of energy conservation, to say that it can't. The Second Law points out that there is a direction, that of falling temperature and energy 'quality', which is always followed in purely thermal processes.

But these conversions purely 'within the thermal form' are only a small part of the story. We have already seen that unwanted dissipation as thermal energy always occurs to some extent in mechanical and electromagnetic conversions, because of friction and resistance. Such processes are irreversible, and together with the cooling just described, point to a general tendency for energy to degrade from mechanical and electromagnetic forms to thermal energy, which then further degrades to progressively lower temperature. The example of water poured into a water-butt described mechanical energy converting into turbulence, and the ripples dying away into thermal energy. In a comparable way microwave radiation in a microwave cooker is absorbed in foodstuffs (mainly in their water content) and turned into thermal energy. The sun's radiation is absorbed by the Earth's atmosphere and surface, heating them to a temperature at which they re-radiate just as much energy back into space as they receive (with complications producing the greenhouse effect, as described by Ross in *Smith & Warr, 1991*, Chapter 2) – in which case the temperature remains constant. The principle mentioned above, that hot objects give out infra-red radiation is, more correctly, that all objects give out radiation over a wide frequency band depending on their temperature, mainly microwave at low temperatures, reaching further into the infra-red, visible (red-hot and white-hot), and ultra-violet at progressively higher temperatures. The radiation arriving from the sun covers the range of frequencies appropriate to its high temperature; the same *quantity* of energy leaving the Earth is in the much lower range of frequencies appropriate to its lower temperature, i.e. of lower *quality*.

These effects all lead to the view that the internal thermal energy associated with the temperature of an object is a combination of mechanical and electromagnetic fluctuations within the material, differing from the orderly vibrations described previously in their 'noisy', random character. Thus the temperature of a gas can be directly related to the random motion of its **molecules**, which dart about between collisions with each other and the walls of the container at speeds comparable to the speed of sound. In liquids and solids the molecules are not so free to move, but there are also possible electron movements within the material, so that the thermal energy is a combination of random mechanical vibrations and high-frequency currents dependent on the temperature and the particular structure, with much diversity in the details.

While this picture makes it plausible that mechanical or electrical work done on a material can lead to an increase of internal thermal energy, because of the *irreversible* effects of friction or resistance, it doesn't yet explain how a heat engine can perform the converse operation of turning heat into work. The thermodynamic ideas involved were first developed to explain the steam engine, which like other heat engines involves a cycle of compression, heating, expansion and cooling of a gas in a cylinder with a moving piston. The average effect of the random thermal motions of the molecules is to exert pressure, a force balancing that applied from outside to the piston. When the piston moves to compress the gas, *work* is done on the gas, increasing its internal thermal energy (and temperature). Conversely, in expansion, work is done by the gas at the expense of its internal thermal energy. The internal thermal energy can also be increased, of course, by supplying heat from some external source, and conversely decreased by removing heat to an external cooling system. These processes are in principle *reversible*, and in practice nearly so. When the implications are followed through, it turns out that heat supplied from the external source *can* be converted into work, but that even in the most favourable circumstances, only a fraction of the heat supplied can be converted, the remainder being 'rejected' at the lower temperature of the cooling system.

This is a basic thermodynamic constraint on the efficiency of any thermal-to-mechanical energy conversion system, like a car engine or the steam turbine of a power station (the subsequent mechanical-to-electrical conversion in the generator is a separate operation, not limited by these thermodynamic ideas). This means in practice that present types of power station only convert 30–40% of the thermal energy available from the burning of fuel into electricity, and the rest is 'rejected' as heat. This can either be wasted, lost to the atmosphere via cooling towers as is usual in the UK, or it can be used in a combined heat and power (CHP) system, pumped as hot water round buildings in the surrounding area (district heating), as is often done elsewhere. Furthermore, as this inevitable 'thermodynamic price' has been paid to produce high-grade electricity, it is wasteful to degrade it immediately to heat (in electric fires etc.) without using it to do useful work (motors, lights, electronics, etc.) first. Of course, the irreversible effects of friction and resistance mean it will all turn to heat in the end.

The same thermodynamic principles also show that heat can be transferred from a low to a high temperature after all – but only if external work is supplied, driving a heat engine in reverse, to satisfy the Second Law: this is the principle of refrigerators and heat pumps.

Finally, thermodynamics can be extended beyond thermal-mechanical effects in gases to electromagnetic effects in other materials as well. This has wide implications. An example that can be included in our conversion table is that thermal-electrical conversion can take place *directly*, without the moving parts of heat engines and generators, in the 'thermoelectric effect'. If two suitable conducting wires are joined end to end to form a loop, an electric current flows if the junctions are held at different temperatures – a type of generator. Conversely, if a current is driven through the loop by a battery, one of the junctions is cooled – a type of refrigerator. This effect has so far only found small-scale applications, and is subject to similar fundamental efficiency constraints to those of heat engines, but may have more importance in the future.

Again the table can be filled in (Table 1.4).

Table 1.4

| To<br>From | Mechanical | Electromagnetic | Thermal | Chemical | Nuclear |
|---|---|---|---|---|---|
| Mechanical | X | X | (dissipation)<br>refrigerator<br>heat pump | | |
| Electromagnetic | X | X | (dissipation)<br>thermoelectric<br>cooling | | |
| Thermal | heat engine | thermoelectric<br>generation | heat transfer<br>cooling | | |
| Chemical | | | | | |
| Nuclear | | | | | |

When heat is supplied or work is done to a material, it does not always change the temperature (and the internal thermal energy) in the way described above. It may also produce further internal energy changes. One type is called phase change, such as the melting of ice or the boiling of water, in which the material retains its chemical identity (molecules of hydrogen and oxygen, symbol $H_2O$), but the interaction between the molecules changes, to the progressively greater freedom of the liquid and gaseous states. This can be accommodated by introducing another kind of internal energy, called latent heat, which is the amount of energy needed to produce the phase change, or released when the change is made in the reverse direction, without changing the temperature. Such phase-change effects contribute to the operation of refrigerators and steam engines.

## 4.4   Chemical energy

A more deep-seated form of internal energy is that bound up in the structure of the molecules themselves. Chemistry recognises about a hundred distinct elements that make up the molecules. Each has a characteristic atomic structure on a minute scale – **atoms** have a diameter of only about one ten thousand millionth of a metre (which can be written more conveniently as $10^{-10}$ m; see Box 1.2 later in the chapter). The implication of this submicroscopic scale is that normal quantities of material contain unimaginably large numbers of atoms. They are indestructible by normally available processes (exceptions form the subject of the next section). The wide range of different materials arises from the innumerable possible combinations of such elementary atoms into similarly minute molecular structures held together by **chemical bonds**, subject to various rules about the possible pairs of atoms which can bond together. Each type of bond requires the supply of a certain amount of energy to break it (or, conversely, releases a certain amount of energy when it is formed). Chemical reactions between bulk materials involve rearrangements of the atoms in the reacting molecules to form product molecules of different structure; that is, the chemical bonds break and re-form. The detailed sequence of events on the molecular scale may be quite complicated, but the final state is a collection of molecules with a different total energy in all the bonds from that in the initial state. The difference can be positive or negative; that is, the reaction may either give out or absorb energy on balance (and is called exothermic or endothermic respectively).

In our conversion diagram it is scarcely possible to find any conversions wholly 'within the chemical form' because chemical reactions always involve a balancing release or absorption of energy in this way. Often this is thermal energy, i.e. the disordered combination of mechanical and electromagnetic fluctuations described above. Conversions of this kind are studied in **thermochemistry**.

## *Fuels and photosynthesis – the carbon cycle*

Those materials that react with air to give out heat are candidates for consideration as fuels. For example, when coal burns, carbon (C), its main constituent, combines with the oxygen of the air ($O_2$) to form the strong carbon–oxygen bonds in carbon dioxide ($CO_2$), with considerable energy release. Hydrocarbon fuels like natural gas (methane, $CH_4$) already contain carbon–hydrogen bonds which must first be broken during combustion, permitting the formation of carbon–oxygen and hydrogen–oxygen bonds in the products (carbon dioxide and water) – again with net energy release because of the way the bond energies add up.

The process of **photosynthesis** in plants is in a sense the converse of this. Plants are able to take carbon dioxide from the atmosphere and use energy supplied from sunlight to break up its carbon–oxygen bonds so that the constituent atoms can be recombined, along with other elements, to form the enormous range of organic compounds, such as sugars and carbohydrates, needed for biological processes; some oxygen is released back to the atmosphere. Some of these compounds are useful 'energy stores' for the process of respiration, which uses atmospheric oxygen to provide energy release within the organism when required. Like burning, this produces carbon dioxide. Normal decay also returns carbon dioxide to the atmosphere, but organic materials that are buried without access to air can retain some of their stored energy, and are slowly converted into coal, oil or gas – fossil fuels. So the energy transferred through the ecological food webs and that available from fossil fuels both derive from solar energy, but with a difference of millions of years in the storage times.

## *Chemistry and electromagnetism*

Burning and photosynthesis are reactions taking place in opposite directions, forming and breaking up carbon dioxide respectively. There is another important difference between them. The energy release from burning fuels is typical of a thermochemical process, producing disordered thermal energy. In photosynthesis the energy is supplied as electromagnetic radiation in an appropriate frequency range; this is characteristic of **photochemistry**. Again this can involve either the supply or release of energy in electromagnetic form – some reactions require light or other radiation, while other reactions give it out. (This is not to say that materials formed photochemically cannot be broken up thermally – this happens whenever we burn wood.)

A further link with electromagnetic energy is in **electrochemistry** – the branch of chemistry from which the study of electricity developed in the first place. This studies the way electrical currents passed through solutions can break up chemical compounds (electrolysis), or, conversely, chemical energy can be stored in batteries and fuel cells to be converted into (d.c.) electrical energy when required. Primary batteries, such as torch batteries, use up the chemical energy originally stored in their materials, which change as the battery is discharged by supplying current. Fuel cells have provision for removing spent materials and replacing them with fresh. Secondary batteries, like those in cars, can be recharged from a generator to reverse the chemical changes produced during discharge.

In the light of what we now believe about atomic structure and the nature of chemical bonds, these electromagnetic effects are nearer the heart of the matter. The atom is seen as a minute positively charged **nucleus** containing most of the mass (the chemically unchanging part) surrounded by negatively charged electrons occupying most of the volume, which are rearranged in forming and breaking chemical bonds. In a sense chemical energy *is* electromagnetic energy on the atomic scale, though this makes it so inaccessible to normal experience that it remains convenient to think of chemical energy as a distinct form. Much practical chemistry concerns bulk quantities of materials involving myriads of molecular reactions. The average behaviour is much easier to observe than individual molecular events, so thermochemistry continues to be much used. But the direct chemical-to-electromagnetic energy conversions of electrochemistry and photochemistry are not subject to the same thermodynamic constraints as the chemical–thermal–heat engine–electricity conversion route, so in principle batteries and fuel cells can be more efficient than power stations. In practice, more needs to be learned about the use of such primary molecular processes in a controlled and economic way if they are to replace existing methods.

## Life processes

All the above ideas are now generally believed to apply to the **biochemistry** of living materials as well as dead ones. The complexity, delicacy and virtuosity of life processes are extreme compared with much technical chemistry. For example, metabolism (the conversion of food into useful forms) involves long series of delicately controlled low-energy reactions, dependent on highly specific molecular interactions rather than heating. Genetics involves 'coding' in the complex molecular structure of DNA, using delicate distinctions which are easily damaged – by radioactive emissions, for example. Movement, from basic effects in cell walls to more complex processes in muscles, involves *direct* chemical to mechanical energy conversion, for which we have as yet no technical equivalent. Our vehicles mostly use heat engines, using the unwanted intermediate stage of thermal energy; those that instead use the intermediate stage of electricity are constrained by limitations in battery design, i.e. in electrochemical understanding. Look at birds, and how their foraging, metabolism, flight mechanism, voice production, self-maintenance and replication are so elegantly packaged!

The conversion table can again be filled in (Table 1.5).

*Table 1.5*

| To<br>From | Mechanical | Electromagnetic | Thermal | Chemical | Nuclear |
|---|---|---|---|---|---|
| Mechanical | X | X | X | ? | |
| Electromagnetic | X | X | X | electrolysis<br>battery (charge)<br>photosynthesis | |
| Thermal | X | X | X | thermochemistry<br>(endo-) | |
| Chemical | muscle | battery (discharge)<br>fuel cell<br>photochemistry | thermochemistry<br>(exo-) | 0 | |
| Nuclear | | | | | |

## 4.5   Nuclear energy

Nuclear energy was identified during the present century from the recognition that the 'indestructible' atoms of chemistry are not the end of the story – nothing ever is! The positively charged nucleus of the atom, the chemically unchanging part, is now believed to consist of positively charged **protons** (each balancing an electron's negative charge, but much heavier) and **neutrons** (not electrically charged, but of about the same mass as protons) held together by a distinct type of nuclear attractive force. Much energy must be supplied to prise them apart. This can be compared to the way molecules consist of atoms joined by chemical bonds (i.e. electromagnetic effects of electrons *outside* the nucleus), except that the scale of these effects *within* the nucleus is about a thousand times smaller and the energies required to separate the components are millions of times greater – which is why they were not so readily observed. These large binding energies imply that nuclei are stable, and at first sight this does not seem too promising as an energy source. But, as in the chemical case where energy can be released because some bonds are stronger than others, so in the nuclear case some nuclei are more stable than others, and the change from a less stable to a more stable form can involve a large energy release. There are three distinct ways this can happen.

### Radioactivity

Each chemical element is distinguished by the total charge in the atom; electrons outside, protons inside the nucleus. Its nucleus can contain varying numbers of neutrons, changing the nuclear mass, to form different **isotopes** of the same element. They are identified by adding a mass number (the total number of protons and neutrons) to the letter symbol for the element: $^{12}C$ for the commonest isotope of carbon, $^{14}C$ for a different one (sometimes written as C-14 etc.). The nature of the nuclear force means that the range of stable combinations of protons and neutrons is limited. There are a few possibilities for each element, but if there are too many or too few neutrons the nucleus sooner or later 'decays' to a more stable combination, spitting out unwanted bits with the appropriate amount of energy. This is the process of **radioactive decay**. (The emissions produced are often called radiation, though this is only true in the sense used previously for part of the process.) The exact moment of decay of each nucleus is not predictable, but the average decay time over all the atoms in a sample is a well-defined property of each radioactive isotope. The decay time is variable, from small fractions of a second to thousands of millions of years. Natural radioactivity arises from those long-lived isotopes that survive from whatever cosmic process created them in the first place. But many more isotopes which have never previously existed (or would have long ago decayed if they had) can now be made artificially in nuclear reactors. For large nuclei there are no stable forms, so no elements are found naturally with more than 92 protons (uranium is the largest). Larger nuclei, all radioactive, can be produced artificially; plutonium (94 protons, 138–152 neutrons in various isotopes) is a particularly important example.

The energy of the emissions produced by radioactive decay is dissipated, finally as thermal energy, in passing through matter. The gross heating effect of natural radioactivity contributes to the high temperature below the Earth's surface which can be exploited in geothermal energy supply systems. But there are more specific chemical and biochemical damage effects when particular emissions collide with molecules, including those of biological materials. Living things have evolved in the presence of natural radioactivity, so are to some degree adapted to it. Arguments for the safe disposal of artificial radioactivity (nuclear waste) often point to the low levels of emissions from them compared with the natural background, a reasonable argument if the radioactivity can be contained so that it remains external to living things. But radioactive isotopes not known in nature are chemically indistinguishable from their stable counterparts, and may find their way into living organisms and enter the food web. They may then concentrate radioactivity *within* organisms in ways which would not otherwise arise, and the natural background is irrelevant. This means that specific radioactive isotopes particularly related to life processes must be treated as individual poisons, to add to the chemical variety. Weapons tests, nuclear accidents and controlled releases of $^3$H (tritium), $^{60}$Co (cobalt-60), $^{90}$Sr (strontium-90), $^{131}$I (iodine-131), $^{137}$Cs (caesium-137), $^{239}$Pu (plutonium-239), for example, have caused particular concern because of the way these isotopes are taken up by the body.

## Fission

Some of the heavier elements can decay not only by radioactivity, but also by **fission**, the process which made possible the atomic bomb and all current types of nuclear power station. When an extra neutron is added to the nucleus of some fissile isotopes, notably of uranium ($^{235}$U) and plutonium ($^{239}$Pu), the resulting instability blows the nucleus apart into two roughly equal halves (i.e. isotopes, many radioactive, of elements of mass around 120) and other fragments, in particular neutrons, all with a great deal of energy. (These isotopes are therefore known as nuclear 'fuels', but this is not in the sense used above for chemical fuels.) The total energy release is much greater than from radioactive decay. The emitted neutrons can go on to produce further fission, producing the possibility of a chain reaction in a critical mass of the particular isotope which can be made to explode. In the reactors of power stations this is prevented by absorbing some of the emitted neutrons to control the fission process. Much heat is produced, which is used to produce steam to drive turbines and generators in the same way as in fossil fuel stations. The initial fissile isotope in the 'fuel' is gradually used up, to be replaced by (radioactive) fission products and radioactivity created by neutron bombardment, both in the fuel and the surrounding structure (the neutrons also cause physical damage to the material of the structure). The spent fuel can be removed and either stored or reprocessed to separate the various isotopes present. The surrounding structure eventually becomes so radioactive and/or weakened that the station must be shut down, leaving the problem of decommissioning – all controversial issues, as we shall see in Chapter 8 of this book.

Existing so-called burner reactors make use of the fissile isotope of uranium ($^{235}U$) that is only present in small proportions in natural uranium, with the implication that available supplies will soon be used up if the use of nuclear power continues to expand. It has long been argued that it would be preferable to modify the reactor conditions so that it 'bred' fissile plutonium instead from the main isotope of natural uranium ($^{238}U$). Such a 'fast breeder' reactor overcomes 'fuel' supply problems, but introduces others: not only technical difficulties in developing a reliable and economic reactor of this type, and continuing waste and decommissioning problems, but also the production of large amounts (many tonnes) of plutonium. This is both highly toxic (in milligrams) and a bomb material (in kilograms), so requires meticulous accounting and security to avoid plutonium being lost to the environment, or falling into the wrong hands.

*Fusion*

The fission of heavy elements releases energy because the fission fragments, elements in the middle of the mass range, are more stable than heavier ones. But intermediate mass elements are also more stable than lighter ones. So the bringing together, or **fusion**, of light elements can also release energy. In particular the fusion of isotopes of the lightest element, hydrogen, to form helium is believed to be the primary source of energy production in the sun, so we are fundamentally dependent on it. Extremely high temperatures are needed to bring nuclei close enough together to fuse. These have been achieved on Earth so far only in the hydrogen bomb, though much research continues to try to achieve stable fusion that could be used in a power station. The ready availability of hydrogen isotopes in sea water seems to overcome 'fuel' supply problems. The products of fusion are not themselves radioactive, unlike fission products, so the goal of controlled fusion has proved seductive to nuclear scientists and governments. However, even if successful, the neutrons produced in this process will also produce damage and radioactivity in the surrounding structure, making the economics and decommissioning problematic.

It should be noted that in all nuclear power production so far (existing burners, prototype fast breeders and projected fusion) the only energy conversion process proposed is from nuclear to *thermal* energy to electricity, as in conventional fossil fuel stations. This dependence on the unwanted intermediate of heat leads to thermodynamic efficiency constraints and the need for large-scale installations. The study of nuclear forces does not yet seem to suggest any equivalent for the direct chemical–electrical conversion of batteries and chemical–mechanical of muscles.

Thus, as we complete the conversion table, this thermal conversion is the only useful process at present; the others are either damage effects, or methods of studying nuclear processes. As with chemical energy, there are no conversions purely 'within the nuclear form' (Table 1.6).

*Table 1.6*

| To / From | Mechanical | Electromagnetic | Thermal | Chemical | Nuclear |
|---|---|---|---|---|---|
| Mechanical | X | X | X | X | (high-energy collision) |
| Electromagnetic | X | X | X | X | (high-energy collision) |
| Thermal | X | X | X | X | ?(fusion) |
| Chemical | X | X | X | 0 | ? |
| Nuclear | ?('radiation' damage) | ?(radioactivity) | reactor | ?('radiation' effects) | 0 |

## 4.6   Summary

Five distinct forms of energy have been discussed (mechanical, electromagnetic, thermal, chemical and nuclear) with the recognition that thermal is a *disordered* version of the first two, and that chemical is an *atomic* scale version of electromagnetic. The other three are at present seen as more fundamentally distinct. Various energy conversion processes within and between forms have been described. These are finally collected together in Table 1.7. The efficiency of conversion from one form to another in general depends on the extent to which unwanted dissipation as heat can be avoided. All other forms can be fully converted into thermal energy of progressively lower temperature (degraded); conversion from thermal energy to mechanical and electromagnetic forms (work) can never be complete, being subject to thermodynamic constraints.

*Table 1.7*

| To / From | Mechanical | Electromagnetic | Thermal | Chemical | Nuclear |
|---|---|---|---|---|---|
| Mechanical | potential/kinetic turbine vibration sound waves turbulence | generator microphone | friction refrigerator heat pump | ? | (high-energy collision) |
| Electromagnetic | motor loudspeaker | oscillator lamp x-ray tube solar cell | resistance thermoelectric cooling | electrolysis battery (charge) photosynthesis | (high-energy collision) |
| Thermal | heat engine | thermoelectric generation | heat transfer cooling | thermochemistry (endo-) | ?(fusion) |
| Chemical | muscle | battery (discharge) fuel cell photochemistry | thermochemistry (exo-) | 0 | ? |
| Nuclear | ?('radiation' damage) | ?(radioactivity) | reactor | ?('radiation' effects) | 0 |

*Activity 3*

Try to classify the various forms of energy identified in Activity 2 into the five forms described in this section.

# 5    *Energy and power*

Because energy ideas arose in a number of different fields that were originally studied separately, various ways of measuring energy are still in use and this can be confusing. There is, however, only one internationally recognised unit for **energy**, the joule (symbol J) and all other energy units in this chapter can be expressed in terms of it. All individual *stores* of energy (raised weights, spinning flywheels, charged batteries, chemical bonds, sacks of coal, barrels of oil, loaves of bread, consignments of uranium) have a certain energy content in joules.

One related idea, however, must be kept clearly distinct, and that is **power**, with its own unit, the watt (symbol W). Whenever a 'machine' of some kind (including in this context lamps, living organisms, power stations, the whole energy system of a country or the sun) converts energy from one form to another, or transfers energy from one store to another, it does so at a certain *rate*, in joules per second; this is what is meant by the power in watts.

The important distinction to grasp is that between energy and power. Only the corresponding units, joules and watts, are needed at this point. The *number* of joules involved in different energy storage systems, or watts in different conversion processes, varies over a wide range. When we have established the equivalence of other units we can relate local to global effects, using just two scales for energy and power. As we will see later in Figure 1.6, these will be logarithmic scales, where each interval represents multiplication by 10, in order to cover the wide range of numbers involved.

## 5.1    *Units of energy*

### *The primary mechanical unit*

The joule is a small unit – often described as about the amount of potential energy Newton's famous apple had when it was still on the tree, or the kinetic energy with which it hit his head (Box 1.1 will remind you of some facts about units if you have met these ideas before, though it is not necessary for the study of this book).

In practice, amounts of energy are often in multiple units, sometimes so large that we run out of the standard metric prefixes. Even the unusual, large ones (PJ, EJ; Box 1.2) used for national energy statistics are not always sufficient, as Figure 1.6 in the next section will show.

---

**Box 1.1**

The potential energy in joules is the mass in kilograms times the acceleration due to gravity, 9.81 m/s², times the height raised in metres:

potential energy $= m \times g \times h$

Thus a 102-g apple raised 1 m above Newton's head would have its potential energy raised by 1 J. This would be converted into kinetic energy when it fell through this distance.

---

**Box 1.2**

1000 joules
  $= 1 \times 10^3$ J  $= 1$ kJ (kilojoule)

1 000 000 joules
  $= 1 \times 10^6$ J  $= 1$ MJ (megajoule)

and so on:
  $1 \times 10^9$ J  $= 1$ GJ (gigajoule)
  $1 \times 10^{12}$ J  $= 1$ TJ (terajoule)
  $1 \times 10^{15}$ J  $= 1$ PJ (petajoule)
  $1 \times 10^{18}$ J  $= 1$ EJ (exajoule)

This can also be extended downwards to small quantities, using negative powers, as follows:

0.001 joules (thousandth of a joule)
  $= 1 \times 10^{-3}$ J  $= 1$ mJ (millijoule)

0.000 000 1 (millionth of a joule)
  $= 1 \times 10^{-6}$ J  $= 1$ μJ (microjoule)

0.000 000 000 1
  $= 1 \times 10^{-9}$ J  $= 1$ nJ (nanojoule)

and so on:
  $1 \times 10^{-12}$ J $= 1$ pJ (picojoule)

---

**Box 1.3**

● 1 coulomb of charge requires 1 joule to increase its potential by 1 volt; and

● a current of 1 ampere is 1 coulomb per second.

The practical effect of this is that when a battery, or the mains, causes a current in a resistive wire, or an equivalent appliance:

● the power, the rate of conversion of electrical energy into heat (in watts) is the voltage supplied by the battery or mains (in volts) times the current flowing in the particular appliance (in amperes): that is

$P = V \times A$

---

## Electrical energy

The primary electrical units have also been chosen to give energy in joules (Box 1.3 gives some examples to remind some of you).

Standard electrical appliances usually have power 'ratings' quoted in watts (W) or kilowatts (kW): for example, a 60-W electric light bulb, a 650-W microwave cooker, a 2-kW electric fire and so on.

The total amount of electrical energy used depends on the time the appliance is on, so the standard unit of electricity we buy is the kilowatt-hour (kWh), the energy used by a 1-kW appliance in one hour – which is a rather roundabout way of getting back to joules!

Q   How long will a 60-W bulb run on one unit, 1 kWh?

A   A 1-kW (= 1000 W) appliance would run for 1 hour, a 1-W appliance would run for 1000 hours, so a 60-W bulb would run for 1000/60 = 16.7 hours.

Q   How many joules are there in a kilowatt-hour?

A   A device operating at a power of 1 kW = 1000 W = 1000 joules per second running for 1 hour (= $60 \times 60$ seconds) converts

$$1000 \times 60 \times 60 \text{ J} = 3600\,000 \text{ J}$$
$$= 3.6 \times 10^6 \text{ J}$$
$$= 3.6 \text{ MJ}$$

of electricity into some other form such as thermal energy. So,

     1 kWh = 3.6 MJ

## Thermal energy

Thermal energy is now normally measured directly in joules, but there used to be heat units based on the properties of water:

●   the metric calorie (the energy needed to increase the temperature of 1 g of water by 1 °C), and

●   the British Thermal Unit, Btu (similarly, the energy needed to increase the temperature of 1 pound of water by 1 °F).

They are still to be found sometimes:

●   the Calorie in dietary requirements – in fact what is meant is 1000 calories, or 1 kilocalorie (1 kcal = 4.19 kJ).

●   the therm for gas supplies

     = $10^5$ Btu

     = 105 MJ

Q   Your electricity and gas bills tell you how much you pay for a unit, 1 kWh, of electricity and a therm of gas (e.g. 6 pence per kWh, 38.5 p per therm). How much are you paying per MJ of energy in the two forms?

A   Electricity:    1 kWh = 3.6 MJ costs 6p, so

                  (6/3.6)p = 1.67p per MJ

   Gas:            1 therm = 105 MJ costs 38.5p, so

                  (38.5/105)p = 0.37p per MJ

## Chemical energy

Individual chemical bond energies are typically a few $\times 10^{-19}$ J, a very small amount of energy reflecting the minute size of atoms and molecules. Their rearrangements on the molecular scale when multiplied up to more familiar dimensions correspond to calorific values for fuels measured in kilojoules per gram. For example, the combustion of pure carbon in air would give 33 kJ/g, while real coal of different qualities (which can include some hydrocarbons, as well as impurities) gives values from 15 to 35 kJ/g.

     Large-scale national energy statistics often use the unit 'million tonnes of coal equivalent', or mtce. A standard calorific value for coal is taken to be 26.4 kJ/g, which is in the middle of the above range, and the mtce determined accordingly.

Q   What is 1 mtce in joules?

A   Energy content of 1 million tonnes of coal

$$= \text{calorific value} \times \text{number of grams}$$
$$= 26.4 \times 10^3 \text{ J per gram} \times 10^6 \text{ (grams per tonne)} \times 10^6$$
$$= 26.4 \times 10^{15} \text{ J}$$
$$= 26.4 \text{ PJ}$$

The oil industry prefers to express comparative statistics in million tonnes of oil equivalent, or mtoe, which is equal to 41.9 PJ, a larger figure reflecting the higher calorific value of oil (though in the same general range as the mtce).

A conventional practical measure is the standard barrel of oil, which is $0.159 \text{ m}^3$, of approximate energy content $5.7 \times 10^9$ J, or 5.7 GJ.

Natural gas is quoted by the cubic metre ($\text{m}^3$), of energy content 38 MJ.

Estimates of the total energy available on Earth from fossil fuels (mainly coal, oil, gas) are obviously technically difficult to make, and are much influenced by commercial and political considerations, as mentioned in Section 3.2 above. It is important to distinguish between proved reserves, which it is considered 'could be extracted in the future under existing economic and operating conditions' and **total resources**, which are much less certain, but have been estimated on geological grounds. The figures quoted in 1989 (which will give a broad impression on the logarithmic chart of Figure 1.6 below) are set out in Table 1.8.

*Table 1.8*

|  | Proved reserve | | Total resource estimate |
|---|---|---|---|
| oil | $1.2 \times 10^{11}$ | $= 5 \times 10^{21}$ J | $1.5 \times 10^{22}$ J (?) |
| natural gas | $1.1 \times 10^{14} \text{ m}^3$ | $= 4 \times 10^{21}$ J | $1.0 \times 10^{22}$ J (?) |
| coal | $1.0 \times 10^{12}$ tonnes | $= 2.6 \times 10^{22}$ J | $3.0 \times 10^{23}$ J (?) |

Remember that these apparently small differences represent increases by significant multiples: coal reserve about 5 times oil, 6 times gas; coal resource about 12 times higher still.

## Nuclear energy

At the atomic scale, nuclear reactions involve energies measured in $10^{-11}$ J rather than the $10^{-19}$ J associated with chemical bonds. In the case of $^{235}$U fission, $3.2 \times 10^{-11}$ J per nucleus translates into $8 \times 10^{10}$ J per gram. Natural uranium contains only 0.7% of $^{235}$U, so the available energy from a burner reactor is reduced from this by about 150 times, to about $5 \times 10^8$ J per gram of uranium. This figure is some $2 \times 10^4$ times greater than that from combustion of the same mass of coal. (In a fast breeder reactor, which makes use of all the uranium, the energy per gram is more like the original figure, about $3 \times 10^6$ times greater than for coal.) This spectacular reduction in the tonnage of fuel required provides a primary argument for nuclear power, to be set against its problems.

Estimates of total available energy from uranium are even more commercially and politically sensitive. Although this is drastically oversimplifying to give a general impression, a figure of about $2 \times 10^6$ tonnes has been quoted as a 'reasonably assured resource'. This implies an available energy of about $10^{21}$ J if used in burners, but over $10^{23}$ J in breeders.

Fusion of deuterium, a possible hydrogen isotope for use in fusion reactors, releases about $10^{-12}$ J per nucleus. Allowing for the small proportion of this isotope present in normal hydrogen, this translates into about 12 TJ per cubic metre of sea water. Hence, from the known amount of sea water, there is an apparent world fusion resource of $3 \times 10^{30}$ J, well off the end of the scale in Figure 1.6.

## 5.2   Power ratings

In Figure 1.6 the first scale shows the energy equivalent of the various units and the amounts stored in various resources. The second shows the power rating of various conversion 'machines'.

Familiar domestic electric appliances have ratings from a few watts to a few kilowatts, and can be marked on the scale. But any energy unit transferred over any time period (e.g. car fuel consumption in gallons per hour, oil production in barrels per year, food intake in calories per day) is equivalent to a power in watts. In this way fuel-burning vehicles can have ratings similarly expressed, up to a hundred megawatts or so for a jet aircraft. Note that the power rating can be the average over a long or short period, and that the vehicle figures are only when they are in use, of course – not averages over a day or a year. A well-insulated house may have a total annual heating requirement expressed as 3000 kWh per year.

$Q$   What is this expressed as an average rating in watts?

$A$   3000 kWh = $3000 \times 3.6$ MJ

$\qquad\qquad$ = $1.08 \times 10^{10}$ J

1 year = $60 \times 60 \times 24 \times 365$ seconds

$\qquad\quad$ = $3.1536 \times 10^{7}$ seconds

So, an average power rating

$\quad$ = $1.08 \times 10^{10}$ J/$3.1536 \times 10^{7}$ s

$\quad$ = about 350 W

But the moment-by-moment heating rate will range from zero in summer to several kilowatts in winter.

This distinction between 'average' and 'instantaneous' power can be confusing. A large power station might have a power rating of 1 GW, which is the electrical power available when it is operating. The power stations of the UK have a total installed capacity of about 60 GW, when they are all operating. The total energy they are called on to supply in a year is about 250 TWh which, by a similar calculation to the above, is about 28 GW *average* power. This difference is a reflection of the varying demand through the day and year. The total energy consumption of all kinds in the UK has an average rate at present of about 285 GW, with the same proviso about variations over the year.

Another distinction which is sometimes made in quoting power ratings is between electrical power, in kW(e) or kW$_e$, and the thermal power needed to produce it, in kW(th) or kW$_{th}$. The latter is always greater because of the limited efficiency of power stations.

The total power rating of the world energy supply system (fossil fuel, hydropower and nuclear, with rather uncertain fuelwood) has risen from about 1 TW in 1900 to 10 TW in 1990. This increase by a factor of 10, and the

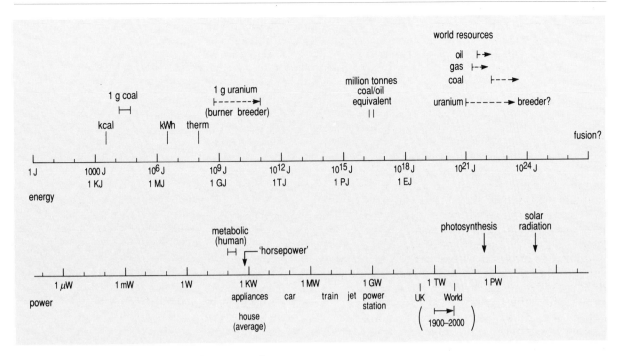

▲   Figure 1.6   Master log scales of energy and power.

expanding expectations of industrial society, is a major issue in world policy, and explains why 'energy' is on every national agenda. If it were to continue to increase at the same rate (say, to 100 TW in the next century) there would be major resource difficulties.

The power rating of our primary energy resource, radiation reaching the Earth from the sun, is more than 10 000 times larger than current energy demand, about $1 \times 10^{17}$ W. The rate of energy conversion by photosynthesis throughout the world is less than 1% of this, but still a few hundred terawatts.

The food energy requirements of human beings are usually expressed as about 2000–4000 kcal per day, depending on activity – this can likewise be expressed as a range of metabolic power ratings.

Q   What is this range in watts?

A   2000 kcal per day = 2000 × 4.19 kJ/60 × 60 × 24 s
                      = 97 W

The 2000–4000 kcal range is therefore about 100–200 W, or about 150 W on average.

If this is multiplied by the present world population of 5000 million we reach a primary global human metabolic requirement of 750 GW, doubling, on current projections, by the end of the next century.

The metabolic needs of horses are somewhat greater than those of humans – this is reflected in the old unit for power, the horse-power, which is now standardised at 746 W (not biologically accurate).

In industrial society we all have ready access to many kilowatts of energy from various sources. So we can think of this as access to many

'150 W slaves and 746 W horses' – but this is evidently not without limit. If we divide the total world energy use, at a rate of 10 TW, by the present population of 5000 million, we find an average of 2 kW per person throughout the world. But this is unequally distributed, from about 10 kW each in the US, through 4–5 kW in Europe and Japan to less than 1 kW in many less developed countries. If the growing world population follows the development path of industrialised countries, the pressure on existing energy resources will be overwhelming. Energy use on the present US scale by the projected 10 000 million population at the end of the next century would imply a power rating of $10 \text{ kW} \times 10^{10} = 100$ TW for the world energy system. This is the crucial bit of arithmetic for thinking about the energy future.

## 5.3   *The resource problem*

What this would mean in resource terms can be seen by comparing the two scales in Figure 1.6. In a sense these scales are independent of each other: so much energy in each store, a certain power rating for each converter. But of course they are related by the definition of power as a rate of energy conversion. The scales could have been lined up with 1 W opposite 1 J, 1 MW opposite 1 MJ, etc., which would have shown the energy used by each converter every second, which isn't very practical. What I have actually done is to line them up to show the *annual* energy required, or supplied, in each case, which fits in better with practical energy plans. Thus, a 1-W device converts 1 joule per second, or about 30 MJ per year (think of the number of seconds in a year). A 1-GW power station supplies about 30 PJ per year, i.e. about 1 mtce (but this is the electrical output; with the usual power station efficiency of about 30% it would take about 3 mtce of primary fuel to generate this output). Make sure you can identify these pairs of figures on the two scales in Figure 1.6.

If you look across from the world requirements (10 TW now, more projected in the future) to the world resources, the proximity of *annual* demand to *total* reserves of some fuels begins to explain recurrent crises and concerns. Oil, gas and uranium in burner reactors can only last tens of years at current rates. If world requirements reach 100 TW, even coal, and uranium in breeder reactors, begins to approach similar limits (not to mention other adverse effects). Only controlled fusion can be seen as a way of consuming *terrestrial* resources that would meet such expanding demands, which explains its appeal to those who think such an expansion in total energy use is a necessary feature of development. Apart from questions of feasibility, costs and more immediate environmental effects, such an expansion would in principle increase 'thermal pollution' because the extra energy would disturb the Earth's energy balance, as described below.

At present there is still a large gap, a factor of about 10 000, between human energy production and the power rating – the continuous rate of energy supply – of our 'extra-terrestrial fusion reactor', the sun. So on the one hand, the thermal pollution issue is not serious at present: on the other, the total solar energy resource is more than adequate for our future needs. Even the *annual* energy resource produced by photosynthesis is comparable to the *total* gas and oil reserves. But of course the solar (direct, indirect and biomass) resources are distributed over the Earth, not concentrated as in fossil or nuclear fuels, so their large-scale use would require a different approach to energy policy.

What this broad analysis of the global situation tries to show is the basic interrelationship between three major factors: world population, average energy use per head and the energy resources to be used.

1    The rapid growth of population since industrialisation is in a way a measure of 'success', in biological terms, in utilising resources, including energy. But such growth is bound to be limited sooner or later by resource exhaustion. Current projections of world population rely on less developed countries experiencing the same transition to stability with prosperity as already experienced in the developed ones – but will that require a similar energy consumption? The current projection of stability at a world population of about 11 000 million by the year 2100 already implies major stress on traditional energy resources.

2    Do we need 5–10 kW per head, or can we manage equally well on 1–2 kW, with more care about using energy efficiently?

3    Should we continue to use up terrestrial energy stores, fossil or nuclear, or seek the sustainability and freedom from pollution of a renewed dependence on the continuous energy supply from the sun (and other renewable resources)?

## 5.4   Summary

Various energy units have been shown to be expressible in terms of a single unit, the joule. The energy content of different energy stores can all be displayed on a single joule scale.

Energy converters are characterised by their power, the *rate* of conversion, in joules per second, or watts. They can all be similarly shown on a single watt scale.

A comparison of individual and world energy consumption with resources provides a broad summary of resource difficulties and policy options.

# 6    A glance at the detailed statistics

The information shown in Figure 1.6 provides a broad, but sketchy, survey of a wide range of effects. A vast amount of more detailed information is available about various parts of this range, each with its own flavour.

## 6.1   Global energy balance

The continuous energy supply to the Earth is almost entirely from the sun: some $1.7 \times 10^{17}$ W reaches the Earth, of which about 35% is reflected back into space by clouds, 20% is absorbed in the atmosphere, and 45% reaches the surface. Two much smaller additions are gravitational effects from the sun and moon interacting with the Earth's rotation to give tides, about $3 \times 10^{12}$ W, and internal heat from the Earth, $3 \times 10^{13}$ W.

Solar energy drives the hydrological (water circulation) and carbon cycles and, with the Earth's rotation, the weather system. These provide the range of renewable energy resources: hydropower, biomass, wind and wave power (solar); tidal and geothermal power (non-solar). These will be discussed further in Chapter 5.

The temperature of the Earth adjusts itself so that its low-frequency radiation balances the energy received. In the absence of an atmosphere this temperature would be about −18 °C, but the 'greenhouse effect' of frequency-dependent absorption properties in some low-concentration atmospheric gases raises the surface temperature to an average 15 °C, as further discussed by Ross in *Smith & Warr, 1991*, Chapter 2.

Any additional energy supply from fossil fuel or nuclear sources upsets this energy balance to some extent. The total heat added in principle constitutes thermal pollution, though this is not yet globally significant – but there are local effects in cities. If total non-solar energy use continues to increase, this could be a problem in the next century. Solar energy use of course does not affect this balance.

A more immediate concern is the *enhanced* greenhouse effect due to gaseous emissions, of which carbon dioxide from all fossil fuels is a major component, and which leads to predictions of global warming. Some uncertainty remains about the 'natural' mechanisms controlling carbon dioxide in the atmosphere, which varied significantly during the periodic glaciations of the last ice age without human intervention. However, the measured increase in atmospheric carbon dioxide (and other greenhouse gases) is much faster than deduced for earlier times and is generally attributed to fossil fuel burning (and other human activities). Strong international pressure is building up for a reduction in fossil fuel use in developed countries, and the encouragement of less energy intensive economies elsewhere.

## 6.2   Human needs

Except for the 150 W or so of metabolic requirements, human beings do not have any need for energy as such, but only for the services it can provide: space heating in cold climates, cooling in hot ones, hot water, cooking, lighting, food storage, domestic machinery, industrial processes, transport, etc. It is the sum of all these services which account for the 5–10 kW per head of energy use in industrial societies. The way energy consumption is built into society and its economic system is extremely complex, and considerable energy analysis has to be done to tease out the energy contribution to particular products and services. One example is illustrated in Figure 1.7, done some years ago, but still indicative of the many energy inputs involved. The processes shown in the production of a loaf, from farm, mill, bakery to distribution, add up to 20 MJ total energy 'cost'. (Note that the food energy value of a loaf is about 9 MJ, more than twice the energy expanded on the farm to produce the wheat, but less than half of all production costs.) All these processes can be carried out with varying energy efficiency – that is, with use of primary energy to a greater or lesser degree.

Day-to-day decisions are made on an economic basis. If energy is cheap there is little incentive to save it. The response to the oil price shocks of the 1970s was a reduction in energy use in the developed countries as a myriad minor efficiency improvements were introduced. Many studies have shown that the services we value can be provided for much less

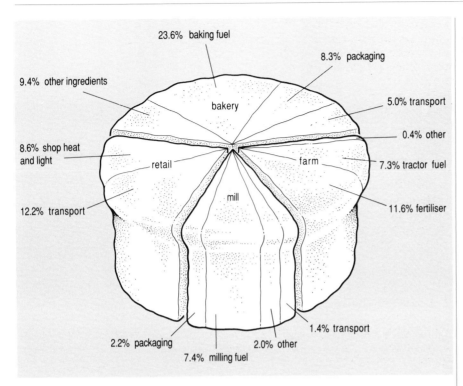

◀   Figure 1.7
Detailed breakdown of the
fuel cost of a white loaf.

23.6%  baking fuel

8.3%  packaging

9.4% other ingredients

bakery

5.0%  transport

0.4%  other

8.6% shop heat
and light

retail

farm

7.3% tractor fuel

mill

11.6% fertiliser

12.2%  transport

1.4% transport

2.2%  packaging

2.0% other

7.4%  milling fuel

energy, as we shall see in Chapter 5. Whether this happens will depend on the economic and regulatory framework, but perhaps also on individual awareness, as the environmental implications of energy profligacy become clearer.

## 6.3   National energy use

Total world energy use and its changes with time have been mentioned above, but more details of the distribution between different countries, and between different economic sectors, will give a better picture of present practice, with its powerful economic and political influence.

Information on world energy use is speculative before about 1900, but US developments have been traced back to 1850. Figure 1.8 shows the transition from wood to fossil fuels (later in the US than in older industrial societies), and Figure 1.9 traces the increasing consumption per head to the present 10 kW or more (note the logarithmic scale, where the approximate straight-line increase with time implies an underlying exponential, or geometric, growth over this earlier period: that is, a constant percentage increase, about 1%, per year. This annual growth increasing along with the total consumption is a 'runaway' process that has to be stopped by something).

Figure 1.10 gives one estimate of world consumption from 1900 to 1975, made by the UK Department of Energy, and a revealing scenario from that time for their view of how demand might increase from 1975 to 2050. Figure 1.11 is a more detailed breakdown, produced by the oil industry, for actual consumption in 1970–89. Both graphs show how the rise in total energy consumption was slowed down by the oil price rises of the 1970s.

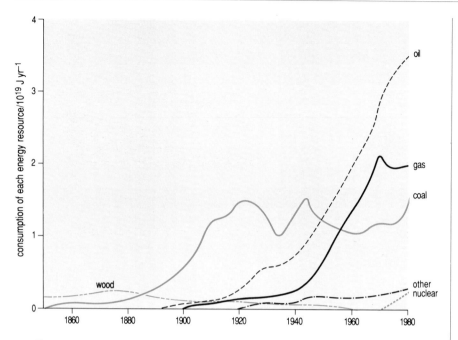

▲  *Figure 1.8    The main sources of power in the United States from 1850 to 1980.*

▲  *Figure 1.9    US per capita energy consumption since 1850.*

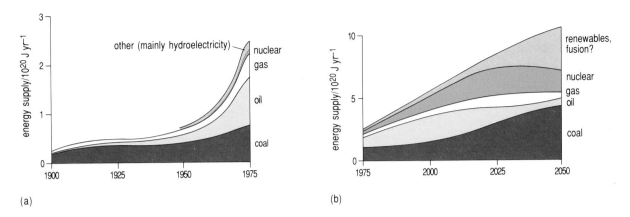

▲ Figure 1.10   World energy supplies from 1900 to 1975 and the projected demand for the period 1975 to 2050.

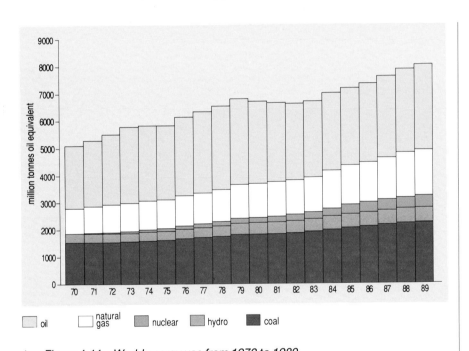

▲ Figure 1.11   World energy use from 1970 to 1989.

$Q$   How do the different scales on these two graphs relate to the standard used above, where average energy conversion rate is expressed in watts?

$A$   Figure 1.10 uses units of $10^{20}$ J yr$^{-1}$ (joules per year). There are $31.6 \times 10^6$ seconds in a year, so each unit represents

$$10^{20}/31.6 \times 10^6 \text{ W} = 3.16 \times 10^{12} \text{ W}$$
$$= 3.16 \text{ TW}$$

Thus the graph shows an increase from less than 1 TW in 1900 to about 8 TW in 1975 (and the projection implies about 12 TW in 1988, 30 TW in 2050).

Figure 1.11 uses million tonnes oil equivalent (mtoe) per year, i.e. 41.9 PJ per year.

$$= 41.9 \times 10^{15}/31.6 \times 10^{16} \text{ W}$$
$$= 1.33 = 10^9 \text{ W}$$
$$= 1.33 \text{ GW}$$

So the scale unit of 1000 mtoe represents 1.33 TW, and the value of over 8000 mtoe in 1989 represents about 10.7 TW.

These figures fill in the details on the rough statement made in Section 5.2 that world energy demand has increased from 1 TW to 10 TW during this century.

At present over 70% of the world's primary energy comes from fossil fuels. Biomass fuels (wood, animal wastes), many of which are not traded and do not appear in commercial statistics, are believed to provide 10–15%. The remainder is accounted for by hydroelectricity, nuclear power and, to a minor extent at present, other forms of renewable energy.

Figure 1.12 shows a comparison made in 1975 between energy consumption, in kilowatts per head, and an economic measure of wealth creation, the gross national product (GNP) per head, for different market

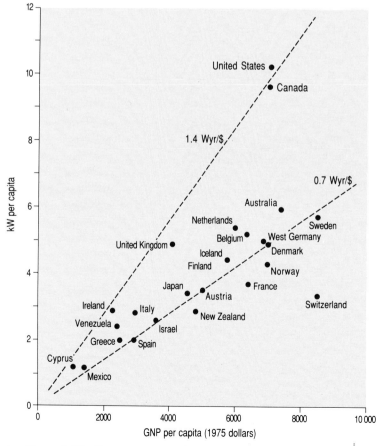

▲  Figure 1.12   *Energy consumption intensity per capita, kW vs GNP.*

economy countries. Such plots were formerly used in the argument that prosperity and energy use were indissolubly linked. While it is obviously true that rich countries use a lot of energy, there are two questions to consider before accepting that this is necessary. First it is clear that there is a wide range of energy uses associated with a particular GNP – compare the US and Switzerland, for example. It has therefore been increasingly recognised over the past two decades that a better measure of economic success is the energy *intensity*, the ratio of per capita energy use to GNP. The dashed lines in Figure 1.12 show two different values for this ratio differing by a factor of two, without any clear implication that the lower value is the minimum possible. Economic theorists will continue to argue how far energy use can reduce in the developed countries, and must rise in the less developed ones, to improve prosperity. But they are now recognising a second difficulty with this approach, the question of whether GNP is a good measure of quality of life, particularly where environmental effects are concerned. The 'sustainable development' objectives of the late 80s have emphasised how GNP increases can be at the expense of environmental damage and resource losses, which are not included in the economic statistics – a debate to which we will return in Chapter 5, and which is taken up by Smith in *Smith & Warr, 1991*, Chapter 6.

Whatever may be reasoned theoretically, the factual account of regional differences and recent changes is given in Figure 1.13. US consumption per head remains well above 10 kW, eastern Europe has risen to 6 kW, Japan and western Europe have settled at about 4 kW, and the rest of the world is rising steadily to 1 kW. What is the real need per person? If 1 kW is multiplied by a $5 \times 10^9$ world population this gives a total of 5 TW, less than at present; 10 kW multiplied by $10 \times 10^9$ gives a total of 100 TW, which is surely not sustainable by fossil or nuclear methods without serious environmental effects. This emphasises the need for detailed

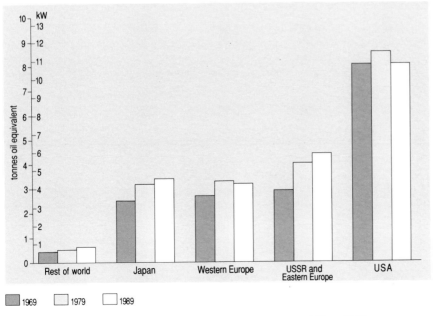

■ 1969    □ 1979    □ 1989

▲   Figure 1.13   *Energy production per capita by region, 1969 to 1989.*

scrutiny of energy use to see how far it can be reduced, and for the introduction of more benign energy sources to meet the demand that remains.

Finally, the way energy use is distributed between different end uses, for the UK economy as an example, is shown in Figure 1.14. Over 50% of the energy demand is for low-temperature heat, below the boiling point of water, and for space cooling. About 20% is to provide higher temperature heat, 20–25% for operating vehicles and other machines and only 5–10% for electricity-specific tasks such as lighting, electrolysis and electronic equipment. Human societies perform their various activities at definite times, so there is a daily, weekly and annual pattern in the energy demands of buildings, industry and transport. Many factors affect national energy use: climate, population density, amount and type of industry – Switzerland and Denmark have much less heavy industry than Germany and Sweden, for example. However, the UK pattern of energy use in 1986 is fairly typical of industrial countries. The breakdown for developing countries shows greater energy use for cooking, and less for space heating, but is otherwise similar.

Each national government has its own response to the energy policy required to satisfy this demand efficiently, either by leaving it to the market, or, because large-scale or long-term issues are being neglected, by modifying it in some degree through taxation, subsidy, regulation or more centralised planning. Increasingly, world environmental problems are seen to be linked to national energy policies in ways that will require international regimes of agreement to be developed, as we shall see in Chapter 4, and are taken up by Greene in *Smith & Warr, 1991*, Chapter 4.

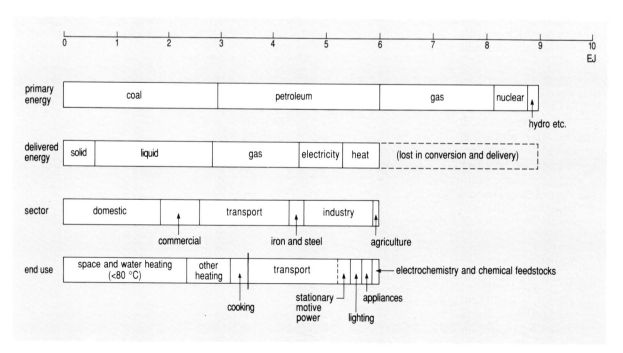

Figure 1.14   UK energy: end use by function (1986).

## 6.4  Summary

Some of the statistics available have been introduced on three scales: the global one of the Earth's energy balance, the individual one of human energy needs, and the intermediate one of national and international provision of energy to meet these needs. The scales overlap where the total provision for a growing population stresses the available resources, and impinges on the local and global environment. Reduction of energy demand by increased efficiency is an important option.

# 7  Conclusion

This chapter has ranged widely over the scientific principles of energy conversion to provide a background to broad considerations of energy policy, both to present practice and future options. The basic arithmetic of population, energy demand and resources implies growing stresses in the existing energy system, particularly when environmental effects are included: these will be taken up in Chapter 4. There are two related ways forward. The first is to clarify why energy is needed, in order to establish a desirable and equitable provision. The second is to provide what is needed in a benign way. These form the subject of Chapter 5.

Fossil fuels clearly cannot be exploited indefinitely; the long-term choice seems to be between nuclear and solar (i.e. extra-terrestrial nuclear). This is often presented as an ideological conflict between high-tech and low-tech, which is a pity. Present and proposed forms of nuclear energy conversion are undoubtedly a consequence of one path of industrial-scientific development, wedded to large scale and to centralised control. But there is still scope for better application of scientific advance in improved energy conversion and storage principles (chemical–electrical–mechanical–nuclear) without the emphasis being limited to large-scale *thermal* conversion in large power stations. A securer future may lie with smaller scale, more delicate and efficient methods, where the endless ingenuity of human invention is applied with more recognition of global consequences. Meanwhile, can a recognition of present problems and priorities be made politically acceptable, both within the west (particularly the United States) and worldwide? If not, can the world remain so divided without destructive conflict?

## References

SARRE, P. (ed.) (1991) *Environment, Population and Development*, Hodder & Stoughton/The Open University, London (Book Two).

SILVERTOWN, J. & SARRE, P. (eds) (1990) *Environment and Society*, Hodder & Stoughton/The Open University, London (Book One).

SMITH, P. M. & WARR, K. (eds) (1991) *Global Environmental Issues*, Hodder & Stoughton/The Open University, London (Book Four).

# Answers to Activities

*Activity 1*

There can be no general response; it will depend on personal circumstances. You might have considered your central heating system, which may use North Sea gas needing exploration, extraction, pipelines, risks of explosion, leakage (of a 'greenhouse' gas). Or crockery, based on china clay, with the environmental effects of its extraction and the former kilns of the 'Potteries' region. Or domestic refuse, with a considerable energy content in the paper and plastic packaging, which will probably not be recovered if the waste is only buried, also causing a land-fill gas hazard. And so on. The rest of this chapter and book will provide many further examples.

*Activities 2 and 3*

Coal – chemical energy
Solar – electromagnetic waves; photosynthesis – (photo)chemical
Food webs – (bio)chemical
Human energy use – fire = chemical, thermal, electromagnetic (radiation)
Agriculture – solar – electromagnetic; animals – biochemical
Industry – chemical (fossil fuel), thermal, mechanical, electromagnetic, nuclear
Earthquakes – mechanical
Fertilisers, pesticides – chemical
Machines and transport – mechanical, chemical, electromagnetic

# 1   Introduction

In the developed world people's lives are highly dependent on mineral resources that are extracted from the earth. They provide the substance of the places where people live and work: homes, hospitals, factories. They contribute to the infrastructure of the means of getting around – roads, railways and airfields – as well as to the vehicles, trains or aeroplanes themselves. They provide the fuel, because oil, gas and coal are minerals too, as Chapter 1 made clear. Indeed, minerals appear in almost everything people use, from cups and saucers to computers. Their contribution to high output agricultural production systems via machinery and fertilisers has been stressed in the previous book in this series (*Sarre, 1991*). Developed countries have come to depend more and more on a whole range of minerals, which are finite in quantity, and in the time since the industrial and agricultural revolutions, the needs they serve have increased at an exponential rate.

Sometimes a mineral requires little processing beyond that concerned with its extraction from the ground in order to meet a particular need: for example, the gravel to refurbish a drive-way, or the raw salt applied to a road to stop it from freezing in cold weather, or the ground limestone scattered over a field by a farmer to improve the pasture. In other cases minerals may need to be refined through sophisticated processes and then manufactured into items of equipment which may be further assembled into a complex machine before people's needs can be met; the car is an example of this.

Q   Can you list some of the many items the car contains which are made from minerals?

A   To begin with, it contains many different metals which are fabricated into items such as the body shell (steel – which is made from iron plus smaller amounts of other minerals such as manganese, phosphorus and silicon, and also carbon); the wheels (steel alloys); all the parts of electric motors used in the starter mechanism, the windscreen wipers and automatic window winders (iron, steel, copper, aluminium, etc.); the engine (iron, steel alloys, aluminium, zinc, etc.); the exhaust system (iron and steel, but if it is of modern design, also the precious metal, platinum, used as an agent of pollution control in catalytic converters); the battery (lead); and the electric wiring (copper and aluminium). Then there is the glass, made from sands, for the windows, and a mass of plastic materials derived from the chemicals industry that go into the production of headlining, seats, tyres, light covers, wiring insulation, etc. Finally, there is the paint on the exterior of the car which may include several chemicals, a plastic base, china clay and even powdered slate! Of course, you may add other items. You might, for example, include the petrol in the tank and the oil in the sump, along with the instruction manual which will contain a considerable amount of china clay, which produces the surface of the glossy paper on which it is printed.

Don't worry if you were not able to match the list provided. You will become more familiar with many minerals and their uses as this book progresses. The important point here is that all these manufacturing processes bring with them the possibility of environmental impact. The fabrication of steel and the manufacture of glass inevitably involve the venting of gases, and the processes of the chemicals industry lead to a wide range of wastes for disposal, some of which are highly toxic. The federal government of the USA records 12 000 of these toxic wastes, of which 15% are known to cause cancer. Although the release of all these effluents is now subject to some legislative constraint, there are still accidents and mistakes, and even sometimes a wilful disregard for the regulations, when personal gain is put above public health interests. Moreover, attempts at regulation are sometimes seen as inadequate. For instance, paint shop gases vented to the atmosphere from a car body shop is an environmental *cause célèbre* in parts of Oxford, where those affected allege damage to property and personal discomfort.

Apart from the impact on the environment caused by any one of these manufacturing and assembly processes, whether they involve the construction of a car or other manufactured goods, such items eventually reach the end of their useful lives and will need to be disposed of. In the case of cars, this is usually about ten years, and this, too, will have its environmental dimension, for they are either dumped in some refuse tip, or taken apart and the metals and plastics obtained fed back into the production process – in other words, the raw materials of the component parts will be recycled. Unfortunately, from an environmental point of view, such recycling is still not a matter of normal practice in what remains essentially a 'throw away' society.

In the chapters that follow, the use of minerals in manufacturing, the methods of waste disposal and the possibilities for recycling will be examined in relation to their environmental impact. But this is only one part of the story. The initial provision of minerals for use in industry also has a strong environmental aspect, so the rest of this chapter considers the range of minerals, how they are removed from the Earth's crust and the initial processes of refining. It also examines what determines *where* such activities occur and the extent to which they are stimulated or constrained, because the interplay of the supply of minerals and the demand for them does not operate in a free market. Governments can and do give incentives to mining companies engaged in minerals extraction in order to maximise production within their own state borders, usually by way of modest tax concessions. But in a climate of increasing environmental awareness, they may also wish to restrict or even prevent development at sites of great ecological or landscape value, especially if alternatives are available. At the same time it has to be understood that if there is a choice of sites and it is left for companies to decide, those sites of least cost are usually worked, or those that are unlikely to be subject to political interference of one kind or another. The need for heavy capital investment in a mine over several years makes a secure political environment for the company a factor of major significance. Thus we will see that the interplay between sets of factors influences the location of mines, the nature of activities at such locations and therefore their likely impact on the environment.

But let us first consider the ways in which minerals are extracted and undergo the initial process of refinement. To assist in this task a case study is used which involves one of the United Kingdom's most valuable mineral resources.

# 2    Identifying key issues

## 2.1    The landscape of china clay

For those who live in Britain, the landscape of Cornwall must be among the most familiar and appealing. But anyone who has travelled west by rail or road eagerly anticipating the beaches of Newquay or St Ives, cannot fail to have been struck by the awesome nature of the 'Cornish Alps'. These are not the aftermath of some gigantic earth movement of distant geological time, but the results of human activity – the extraction from the Earth's crust of china clay, i.e. the mineral called kaolin.

To appreciate just what has occurred as a result of human intervention in this, one of Britain's most extensive mining landscapes, it is necessary to do no more than turn a few kilometres north from St Austell on the coast or south from the village of Roche along the A30 road. Here, in a vast area of over 8000 hectares, the entire landscape, apart from the villages, has been transformed by mining. A few hours spent examining this area cannot explain everything about the impact of the extraction and processing of minerals on the environment, but it is a spectacular place to start.

As an introduction, it is not necessary to turn to a technical description of the area: that of the Cornish writer Daphne du Maurier (1907–89) will serve as well. Look at Box 2.1 and the extract from her book *Vanishing Cornwall*. When you read it, also consider carefully the photograph in Plate 1, which rounds out the picture she conjures up in words.

---

*Box 2.1*

In the china clay country is the strange, almost fantastic beauty of the landscape, where spoil heaps of waste matter shaped like pyramids point to the sky, great quarries formed about their base descending into pits filled with water, icy green like arctic pools. The pyramids are generally highest and the pools deepest, on land which is no longer used.

These clay heaps with their attendant lakes and disused quarries have the same grandeur as tin mines in decay but in a wilder and more magical sense, for they are not sentinels of stone or brick constructed to house engines, but mountains formed out of the rocky soil itself, and the pools, man-made, are augmented by water seeping from underground sources and by the winter rains. Sites in full production may work close at hand, cranes swing wide, trolley-buckets climb to the summit of a waste-heap . . . before unloading and returning to base, lorries pass in and out of entrances to the road, the precincts barred by wire and DANGER notices; but the discarded pyramids and pools seem as remote from industry near by as any lonely tor upon the moors.

Wild flowers struggle across the waste, seeds flourish into nameless plants, wandering birds from the moorland skim the lakes or dabble at the water's edge. Seagulls flying inland hover over the surface. There is nothing ugly here. Cornishmen are wresting a living from the granite as they have done through countless generations, leaving nature to deal in her own fashion with forgotten ground, which being prodigal of hand, she has done with a lavish and careless grace.   (du Maurier, 1972)

These images in words, although colourful, underline several important issues concerning the winning of china clay; these issues are also appropriate to many other minerals that are important to the lifestyles of those living in the developed countries. At the same time they identify some key environmental impacts that are the consequence of minerals extraction.

## 2.2    *A valuable resource*

In the extract in Box 2.1, the writer suggests that kaolin is not the only mineral substance to be extracted from the rocks of Cornwall. Tin mining might have been the most important Cornish industry in the eighteenth and nineteenth centuries, the relics of which are still to be seen in the derelict engine houses, but china clay has now come into its own. Even so, this, too, has been exploited for two centuries. It took the discoveries of William Cookworthy (made some time between 1745 and 1748) to turn what was a useless material that had lain in the earth for 290 million years into a valuable material which is ideal for making porcelain. And it took the discovery in this century of its value as a surface coating in the manufacture of high-quality paper to turn the extraction of Cornish china clay into a multi-million pound industry of major international significance, second only to North Sea oil in the value of exports

The realisation that a mineral can perform a valuable function makes it worthy of exploitation and therefore it becomes a resource. But it need not remain of intrinsic value for ever. Grimes Graves near Thetford in Norfolk was prized for a thousand years by Neolithic peoples as a site for flint axe heads which were essential to their lives. However, the discovery of more efficient bronze substitutes meant that the value of flint as a resource fell away to insignificance by 1400 BC. From being a centre of industry, pocked with shafts from which flint was hewn, Grimes Graves reverted to an uninhabited area of heather and birch forest.

*Q*    What is a mineral resource?

*A*    Defining the word 'mineral' presents no problem. A good dictionary will tell you that it is any substance which is not animal or plant, although it could have originated from once living material, as will be seen below. But for it to become a resource it must be subject to human appraisal and to be judged as having a value. Remember that resources are not fixed over time or space. The Bushmen of the Kalahari desert survive in a world in which minerals that are valued by industrial societies play no part. Their resources, which people in developed countries would hardly consider as such, are the succulent plants, grubs and insects which make their lives possible in an arid environment. Thus resources are as dynamic as society itself.

## 2.3    *Methods of extraction*

Of more significance in environmental terms are the images purveyed in the extract in Box 2.1 and in the photograph regarding the magnitude of china clay operations. In one year in this area alone, the operations will yield 26 million tonnes of china clay and 200 million tonnes of waste rock – all from pits which can be as deep as 85 m and cover 40 hectares. The method of excavation normally used here, **open-pit extraction**, is that most

commonly employed in the extraction of minerals. It is a method well
suited to any shallow deposit, whether it is china clay or sand and gravel.
A metal ore that (for reasons which will become apparent later) has been
disseminated through some other rock material will often be extracted in
this way, as will hard rocks such as granite. But this mode of extraction is
suitable only so long as the depths involved are not too great.

Open-pit extraction of the kind in Box 2.1 offers the advantage of
operating in a flexible way. Because the working surfaces of the mineral are
exposed over a wide area, it is easier to expand or contract production.
Open pits are also economically more attractive. This is because they allow
the application of large earth-moving machines on a scale which makes for
maximum cost-effectiveness. Not surprisingly, it is now the most
commonly used method of winning minerals, even if it is the most
environmentally disturbing.

Before a new pit is begun in Cornwall, as elsewhere, all the **overburden**
(overlying unwanted rock) must be cleared to expose the valuable material
beneath. When the overburden is added to other forms of waste which
come from the processing of china clay (quartz, and a fine mud-like
substance known as micaceous residues), the ratio of waste extracted to
valuable material can rise to between 7:1 and 8:1. For open pits where
metal ore is extracted, ratios can vary widely; indeed for the rare metals
they can be between 100:1 and an extreme of 500 000:1. For open-pit
operations extracting coal, ratios can be 15:1. These coal workings, referred
to as open-cast pits, are unusual in that the overburden is not removed
before the extraction of the mineral. Instead, **open-cast extraction** involves
the *progressive* removal of the overburden, prior to the extraction of the
mineral and the return of the overburden to the site. Coal workings of this
kind have become increasingly familiar in the East Midlands, north-east
Yorkshire and in central Scotland during the expansion of this form of
production in the 1980s.

**Strip mining**, for example for coal in the USA, is similar, but the
overburden and minerals associated with the coal are left exposed to the
weather.

**Underground mining**, the other major form of minerals extraction,
entails removing minerals from the end of often narrow tunnels where
there are obvious limits to the application of more human effort and
machines (Figure 2.1). Underground mining could not be used to extract
china clay because of the nature of the material and its location in deep
pockets of surrounding granite which are close to the surface of the land.
Where underground mining *can* be used, one of two methods is followed.
In the open-stoping approach, the rock body from which the valuable
material is extracted must be sufficiently strong to allow underground
cavities to remain after the ore has been removed through drilling and
blasting. The other method, that of filled-stoping, requires that waste
materials are used to fill those portions of the mine that have been worked
out. Where metallic ores have been extracted, the waste will include the
**tailings** (that is, the fine waste rock left after the valuable ore has been
processed, using chemical or mechanical methods). Sufficient ground
support is thus provided to allow further extraction of the ore, but it also
has the added environmental advantage of reducing surface waste tipping.

Another means of extracting certain minerals involves drilling
**boreholes** from the surface to permit the removal of the valuable material.
In the case of oil and natural gas, where these are trapped in sedimentary
rocks deep below the land surface, they usually emerge under pressure
and without pumping. Many of you will have seen oil gushers, even if only

▲   *Figure 2.1    Mechanical mining underground. Even though the use of a coal cutting 'shearer' can greatly increase productivity, such operations cannot approach the cost effectiveness of open-pit extraction. They also result in more waste material that will need to be disposed of.*

on film! For the winning of minerals such as salt and potash, however, the injection of water via the borehole creates a solution which can then be pumped to the surface. Sulphur can be extracted by the injection of super-heated water under pressure. This melts the sulphur which escapes to the surface via another borehole.

The environmental disturbances created by these methods of extraction in relation to the winning of the various minerals are discussed later in Chapter 3. For the moment it is worth emphasising that because the amount of wastes produced from underground workings is small compared to that from open pits, the former produce less surface disturbance as a result of their disposal. Coal mining is perhaps an important exception insofar as the surface tipping of wastes can be a major environmental disturbance.

## 2.4    *Minerals processing and wastes*

The method of winning china clay from massive open pits is among the simplest of all those used in extraction. Unrefined kaolin is removed from the pit walls by a powerful water jet. The resulting clay slurry, together with its attendant quartz fragments and micaceous residues, is pumped away to tanks where the valuable mineral settles out from the waste. Only the method for sand and gravel, which involves washing and perhaps some crushing after extraction, is more straightforward. This simple procedure contrasts with the methods used for the extraction of metallic ores. For these, the means by which the unwanted constituents of the ore body are removed (**minerals processing**) is carried out on site because of the low value of untreated ore compared with ore in its refined state. Only in the case of the most valuable minerals (or those mined in high concentrations such as iron-ore) would it be economic to transport untreated ores over long distances for processing at locations which would be convenient for their further fabrication.

The extraction of metallic ores from the parent rock is carried out in two stages in the **milling** process. First, the mined rock containing the metal ore is reduced in size by crushing or grinding. Secondly, it is concentrated, a means by which the desired metallic ore in the rock body is separated from other materials which are discarded as waste. Separation may be carried out by a number of different methods depending on the properties of the mineral. Gravity separation, the means used for china clay, can also be used to concentrate some metals (such as gold and silver), but for other minerals it has been largely replaced by **flotation**. This method of concentrating minerals is based on the principles of surface chemistry and is most widely used with metal sulphide ores. The chemicals which are used to 'float out' the ore from the fine rock particles are selected not only for their effectiveness, but also for those qualities that may do least harm to the environment should they be discharged into local water courses. Although most flotation plants are able to recycle the liquids used for processing, they all contain a **settling pond** stage which allows solid particles, including metals, to settle at the bottom by gravity, as well as permitting the treatment of any undesirable acid formed from sulphides (salts created by sulphur combining with metals) which may have been present in the parent rock. These are important issues which are discussed further in Chapter 3. A third approach to the extraction of metallic ore from the fine rock material uses a magnetic separation process, especially for iron-ore. Finally, where the ore is dry, electrostatic techniques (which involve the attraction or repulsion of electrically charged bodies) can be used, particularly on iron and titanium ores.

In the quotation in Box 2.1, no mention is made of the tailings. Later on in her book, though, du Maurier refers to the disposal of the fine materials left after refining the kaolin which caused 'the streams to run from the watershed milky white'. Because the quantities of these tailings long remained relatively small, the practice of discharging them into the local watercourses continued until the 1970s. Only then did increased environmental awareness bring about the ending of the practice. In the processing of metallic ores, whether they have been extracted by open-pit or underground techniques, the majority of waste rock finishes up in the pit known as a **tailings pond** as the residues of the milling process.

As the metallic ores extracted have become less rich in metal content over recent years, the amount of tailings to be disposed of has grown – indeed, it is evident that the lower the metal content of ore that can be worked economically, the higher the waste content. Thus, for example, uranium winning operations produce about 99% waste, most of which is in the form of tailings, compared with a chemical mineral such as potash where the percentage of waste is about the same as that of the valuable mineral. The fine materials resulting from processing minerals are now less densely packed than they were as part of the parent rock and are between 20% and 40% greater in volume. This exacerbates the disposal problem and frequently adds to the environmental problems they may cause (Figure 2.2).

Figure 2.2    Tailings at the Inco nickel mines, Sudbury, Ontario. Rock waste
from the milling of the nickel bearing ore deposited in a tailings pond at Inco's
Copper Cliff operation. The total area of these ponds is 1100 ha but is being
expanded to double the size.

China clay tailings are inert and their discharge to the wider
environment, in whatever way, is largely a problem of visual disturbance.
However, because tailings from the milling of metal ores are impregnated
with residual heavy metals and may contain sulphides or even radioactive
materials, a number of problems can be created. In particular, when the
tailings site reaches the end of its useful life and is abandoned, the
pollution of both air and water in the vicinity of the mine may occur. Also,
the further processing of some metallic ores beyond the milling stage to the
point at which they become metals can create a problem of environmental
significance.

## 2.5    Metals production and wastes

**Smelting** is the process by which most concentrated metal ores emerging
from the mill are transformed to a pure metal. The range of environmental
impacts that can arise varies greatly depending on the nature of the ore
itself.

Box 2.2 lists the most important metals and their uses. Although a few
of these, such as platinum, gold, silver and occasionally copper and
mercury, are found in the metallic state, they mostly occur in nature in
combination with oxygen as oxides, with sulphur as sulphides, with
oxygen and carbon dioxide as carbonates and with oxygen and silica as
silicates.

## Box 2.2   Metals and their uses

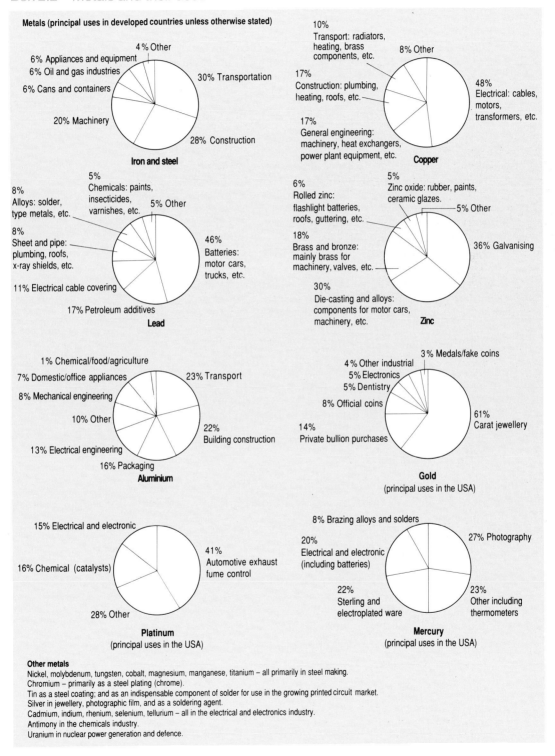

Metals (principal uses in developed countries unless otherwise stated)

**Iron and steel**
- 4% Other
- 6% Appliances and equipment
- 6% Oil and gas industries
- 6% Cans and containers
- 20% Machinery
- 30% Transportation
- 28% Construction

**Copper**
- 10% Transport: radiators, heating, brass components, etc.
- 8% Other
- 17% Construction: plumbing, heating, roofs, etc.
- 17% General engineering: machinery, heat exchangers, power plant equipment, etc.
- 48% Electrical: cables, motors, transformers, etc.

**Lead**
- 5% Chemicals: paints, insecticides, varnishes, etc.
- 5% Other
- 8% Alloys: solder, type metals, etc.
- 8% Sheet and pipe: plumbing, roofs, x-ray shields, etc.
- 11% Electrical cable covering
- 17% Petroleum additives
- 46% Batteries: motor cars, trucks, etc.

**Zinc**
- 6% Rolled zinc: flashlight batteries, roofs, guttering, etc.
- 5% Zinc oxide: rubber, paints, ceramic glazes.
- 5% Other
- 18% Brass and bronze: mainly brass for machinery, valves, etc.
- 30% Die-casting and alloys: components for motor cars, machinery, etc.
- 36% Galvanising

**Aluminium**
- 1% Chemical/food/agriculture
- 7% Domestic/office appliances
- 8% Mechanical engineering
- 10% Other
- 13% Electrical engineering
- 16% Packaging
- 23% Transport
- 22% Building construction

**Gold** (principal uses in the USA)
- 3% Medals/fake coins
- 4% Other industrial
- 5% Electronics
- 5% Dentistry
- 8% Official coins
- 14% Private bullion purchases
- 61% Carat jewellery

**Platinum** (principal uses in the USA)
- 15% Electrical and electronic
- 16% Chemical (catalysts)
- 28% Other
- 41% Automotive exhaust fume control

**Mercury** (principal uses in the USA)
- 8% Brazing alloys and solders
- 20% Electrical and electronic (including batteries)
- 22% Sterling and electroplated ware
- 23% Other including thermometers
- 27% Photography

**Other metals**
Nickel, molybdenum, tungsten, cobalt, magnesium, manganese, titanium – all primarily in steel making.
Chromium – primarily as a steel plating (chrome).
Tin as a steel coating; and as an indispensable component of solder for use in the growing printed circuit market.
Silver in jewellery, photographic film, and as a soldering agent.
Cadmium, indium, rhenium, selenium, tellurium – all in the electrical and electronics industry.
Antimony in the chemicals industry.
Uranium in nuclear power generation and defence.

The metallic oxides, such as those of iron, zinc and tin, can then be reduced to a metal in a smelting furnace. The charge of the smelter consists of the metallic oxide, fuel and a flux. The fuel, which is usually coal or coke, serves a dual purpose. Its combustion provides the necessary heat to promote the chemical reactions required and it supplies the reducing agents needed to abstract the oxygen from the metallic oxide to set free the metal. Although the ore has been concentrated prior to smelting, waste material still remains. The **flux** is a material added to the furnace charge that combines with the waste to form a solid called **slag**.

The smelting processes, can of course, be considerably more complex and vary with the kind of ore under treatment. For example, from some sulphide ores, such as lead sulphide or mercuric sulphide, the metal may be liberated by smelting with a flux containing iron which combines with the sulphur, forming iron sulphide. Copper and nickel sulphide ores can undergo a multi-stage process in which the ores are smelted to form 'matte', which is a complex mixture of these sulphides with iron sulphide. This is blown with air under a siliceous flux, so that sulphur is given off as sulphur dioxide and the iron enters the slag.

There are a number of other means of separating out a metal from an ore, but electrolysis is by far the most important. This involves passing an electric current through a solution containing metal ions so that metal is deposited on the cathode. It is mainly used to produce aluminium. Pure aluminium oxide is separated from bauxite with a caustic soda solution. At the reduction plant, usually located to take advantage of cheap and plentiful supplies of electricity, the aluminium oxide is dissolved in molten cryolite and electrolysed to give pure aluminium. The production of aluminium therefore involves processes which not only have their power requirements far greater than those for other metals (between 15 000 and 25 000 kWh for every tonne of ingot aluminium, or as much as 20 times the energy equivalent needed to produce the same amount of iron), but in the production of the initial oxide leaves residues of caustic soda and fluorides in a red mud. Until recently, this waste was discharged into a tailings pond and created major environmental problems. However, as Chapter 3 makes clear, these have now been largely resolved.

The slag produced by the standard smelting techniques is tipped, but of all the environmental outcomes from smelting, the discharges of sulphur dioxide and small metal particles (particulates) from smelter stacks cause the most problems. Unless their venting to the atmosphere is controlled, they can severely damage ecosystems in a wide area around the mine, and the sulphur dioxide can contribute to the wider problem of 'acid rain', which will be discussed in later chapters. The environmental impacts of smelting are given further and more detailed attention in Chapter 3.

Q    From the discussion in Section 2, why is underground minerals mining likely to pose less of an environmental problem than open-pit extraction?

A    Underground working means that the excavation is not visible and large overburden tips will not be present. Underground working also offers opportunities for filled-stoping, thus reducing or largely removing the need for the surface disposal of tailings.

Q    What are the chief environmental impacts of the processing of metallic ores?

A   The output of the mill by way of tailings has a major impact if these are surface-dumped in a tailings pond. The smelting of metal ores, which employs the heating of oxides with the fuel acting as a reducing agent, will give off carbon dioxide, now known as an atmospheric pollutant. Roasting sulphide ores and processing matte produces sulphur dioxide which, when discharged to the atmosphere, may contribute to the problem of acid rain. The venting of metal particulates also has adverse effects on ecosystems. The production of aluminium oxide from bauxite uses process chemicals which may remain in the residues of red mud, which were until recently a major environmental hazard. The reduction process makes considerable demands on electric power, which in itself may have environmental impacts.

## 2.6   Healing the scars

What else does Daphne du Maurier state that is relevant? A striking feature of the author's vivid narrative not yet addressed is the idea that nature will take over to heal the scars of a defunct extractive enterprise, and to create a landscape of value, if only in its new-found beauty. Apart from the fact that her romantic view of this vast extractive area is not shared by all, the notion that such mineral workings can necessarily be abandoned to nature when their extractive life is over is hardly tenable; indeed, as has already been hinted, the aftermath of mining may not always be so benign.

In the late twentieth century many developed countries accept the idea that mining is a temporary affair and that land is a scarce resource. This is particularly true of the United Kingdom which has a large population compared with its size. This means that if minerals extraction is allowed to proceed, damage to the physical environment caused by extraction and minerals processing must not only be minimised during the working life of a mining operation, but totally rectified, insofar as this is possible, once it is all over. Indeed such a situation is one which companies winning the china clay now have to accept. Under the Town and Country Planning Act of 1971, they cannot legally walk away and leave a worked-out landscape to nature, even if relics remain of a time when this was possible, of which both our quotation and its accompanying photograph are a reminder.

## 2.7   Summary

In this section the extraction of kaolin has been used as a way into building up a broad picture of what is likely to be involved in the winning of a whole range of minerals, and some preliminary thought is given to what the environmental consequences of these activities might be. These likely effects, as they have been described, are largely of a local impact, but the secondary processing of minerals (for example, from ores into metals) indicates that these may have considerably wider effects, a matter to be considered in detail in the next chapter.

In Sections 3 and 4, consideration is given to those factors which determine the location and the circumstances under which minerals are exploited. Since the ultimate constraint upon where minerals are worked is that of geology, this aspect of the wider context for minerals extraction and their impact on the environment is examined first.

# 3    *Patterns of location and extraction*

## 3.1    *A geochemical lottery?*

Mineral resource analysts often use the idea of the average distribution or abundance (resources) of one particular group of minerals, the metallic ores, in the Earth's crust as a standard against which to evaluate the percentage of metal content that would constitute a resource of sufficient worth to win and process (reserves). Look at Table 2.1 which gives the average abundance of 20 metals, divided into percentages for the ocean and the continental crust. Any attempt to work a precious metal such as gold at 0.000 000 35% would plainly be absurd; indeed, economically workable deposits averaged 0.000 13% in the 1980s.

The reality of mineralisation, and the many different processes by which this has come about, is that many minerals have become concentrated in some places and not others, almost as if, at least to the non-geologist, it was the result of some great geochemical lottery. For a brief background insight into the processes involved, you should consult Box 2.3. What you need to understand as a result of your reading of this is that deposits of minerals (and this applies as much to metallic ores as any other kind of mineral) are only worked where geological circumstances

*Table 2.1    The average percentage abundance of metals in the Earth's crust*

| Ocean crust | | Continental crust | |
|---|---|---|---|
| aluminium | 8.4 | aluminium | 8.3 |
| iron | 7.5 | iron | 4.8 |
| titanium | 0.81 | titanium | 0.53 |
| manganese | 0.18 | manganese | 0.1 |
| vanadium | 0.017 | vanadium | 0.012 |
| chromium | 0.016 | zinc | 0.008 1 |
| nickel | 0.014 | chromium | 0.007 7 |
| zinc | 0.012 | nickel | 0.006 1 |
| copper | 0.008 5 | copper | 0.005 |
| cobalt | 0.003 7 | cobalt | 0.001 8 |
| lead | 0.001 | lead | 0.001 3 |
| tin | 0.001 9 | uranium | 0.000 22 |
| molybdenum | 0.001 5 | tin | 0.000 16 |
| uranium | 0.000 1 | tungsten | 0.000 12 |
| tungsten | 0.000 094 | molybdenum | 0.000 11 |
| antimony | 0.000 091 | antimony | 0.000 045 |
| mercury | 0.000 011 | mercury | 0.000 008 |
| silver | 0.000 009 1 | silver | 0.000 006 5 |
| platinum | 0.000 007 5 | platinum | 0.000 002 8 |
| gold | 0.000 000 35 | gold | 0.000 000 35 |

Source: *Atlas of Earth Resources* (1979), Mitchell Beazley, London, p. 149.

have concentrated them in sufficient quality and quantity to make their extraction viable. The corollary of this is that the environmental impacts caused by the extractive methods and processing techniques that we have already looked at are also spread *unevenly* across the surface of the Earth. Indeed, this in itself helps to account for the dramatic appearance of the Cornish china clay workings in an otherwise intimate landscape of green rolling hills.

That minerals are found and exploited with great spatial variation is something that now must be considered in a little more detail. In order to do this more effectively, it is useful to work within a classification which groups minerals together and takes account of their degree of availability and their physical attributes.

## 3.2   Non-metallic minerals

It is sensible to start with a group with which most people are familiar – the **non-metallic minerals**. As this name implies, they are not exploited as an economic source of metals, although they may contain metals in small amounts, and are sometimes referred to as industrial minerals. This group includes a collection of widely found materials, mainly used in the construction industry for building and roads. These are called **aggregates**, and include sand and gravel, igneous and metamorphic rocks, sandstone and limestone. All tend to be used according to local availability since they can often be substituted with one another. Aggregates thus serve local markets.

Their abundance, plus the relatively modest amount of processing they require (usually no more than crushing and grading) means that they are generally of low value. Sand and gravel, for example (Figure 2.3), may cost as little as £3.50 per tonne (ex-works 1987 UK prices). The only exceptions

◄   *Figure 2.3*
*A typical sand and gravel working seen through a gap in an amenity bank designed to screen extraction from public view. Compared with hard rock quarries, such operations are shallower, more extensive and yield much less material. However, they are more easily worked using earth-moving machinery.*

in the widespread non-metallics group are brick clays where they have been transformed into bricks, and limestone used for the production of cement. In both cases the application of much more sophisticated processing has led to the addition of substantial value to the basic raw material. It thus follows that for most construction materials transport costs are of particular significance, with the delivered price doubling at distances of 50 km from their points of production. The spatial distribution of such workings has therefore tended to reflect road transport costs. They remain operations of medium size and show a dispersed pattern related to major

## Box 2.3   Formation of mineral deposits

Human needs depend on relatively rare geological processes where the low amounts of metals in ordinary rock are concentrated to create a richer deposit which is economical to mine. There are two main types of processes, external and internal, that create a mineral deposit. Some of the external – those taking place near or at the Earth's surface – are shown in (a) to (c), together with examples of the minerals involved; those in (d) to (g) are internal taking place within the Earth, and have been responsible for the concentration of a wide range of metals in the form of oxides or sulphides. In practice many mineral deposits have been produced by more than one process, each taking place at a different stage in the deposit's formation. An ore deposit, for instance, may have been formed by hydrothermal processes but on reaching the surface it may have undergone further concentration by secondary enrichment. Internal processes are associated with earth movements and with molten rock (magma) welling up from the interior into the crust.

(a)   *Mineral salts form when the sun evaporates sea-waters trapped in a barred basin. Deposits tend to settle in layers; the more insoluble are deposited first, the most soluble last. Sodium chloride (common salt) has been formed in this way. However, many other mineral resources have been formed by deposition beneath continental shelf seas, including iron-ores, clays and limestones.*

(d)   *Main methods of magma separation: A, minerals crystallise and settle to the bottom of the magma chamber; B, the magma solidifies, forcing the molten minerals into fissures.*

(e)   *An ore deposit may result when gases and fluids, escaping from the magma, react with the rock face and alter the composition of the rocks by adding valuable elements.*

centres of population. This is in spite of a marked increase in quarry size over the past 20 years, with the costs of serving a wider market offset by economies of scale, improved transport and greater on-site processing to increase the value of the product. However, the movement of aggregates by ship from quarries located on a coast to areas of high demand can be economical, as research carried out for the Department of the Environment has indicated. The economies of scale achieved in superquarries producing up to 20 million tonnes a year, allied to low-cost shipping, enables materials to be moved many hundreds of miles, as exemplified by the

*(b)  Placer deposits occur where eroded particles of rock material pass into a water body. There, the heavier metal-bearing particles settle out early, leaving the lighter rock particles to be transported and deposited elsewhere. Gold placers were the objects of the Klondike gold rush in the nineteenth century.*

*(c)  Residual deposits occur where minerals, concentrated in a rock, are left behind when other material within the rock is removed by mechanical or chemical weathering. Weathering under humid tropical conditions causes the residual concentration of aluminium hydroxide (bauxite), the raw material for aluminium manufacture.*

*(f)  Dissolved minerals are carried into fissures by: A, hot fluids left when magma crystallises; B, surface water heated by magma; C, water from the hotter mantle.*

*(g)  In some cases mineral deposits are formed when an acidic water containing a metal reaches an alkaline environment, or where there are changes in oxygen content (A).*

1 km of motorway

15-storey office block
multi-storey car park
50 million gallon reservoir
1 km of roadway
3-bedroom detached house

◁ *Figure 2.4   Aggregate and construction.
Aggregates are the cheapest of all minerals
to exploit, and vast quantities are used in construction
work: 50 tonnes on average are needed for a
three-bedroom house and 62 500 tonnes for every
kilometre of a six-lane motorway.*

mammoth quarry near Oban on the west coast of Scotland which supplies granite aggregate to the Channel Tunnel operation. But the demand for hard rock aggregates has in some areas been such that much more modest operations in terms of size can export their output over long distances, provided transport is by sea. One coastal quarry near Penzance in Cornwall has developed substantial trade links with Belgium and Holland. Even so, such materials are generally not traded internationally. Construction materials also share one other characteristic – whether they are used in crushed form or as stone blocks, they are required in vast quantities. Figure 2.4 illustrates this point.

In contrast with the widespread non-metallic materials, *local* non-metallic materials are much more restricted in terms of the quantity available, and, as their name suggests, are less widely found. These factors, of course, lead to enhanced values and thus an ability to stand high transport charges to more distant markets. The minerals in this group are mostly raw materials for the chemical and fertiliser industries. Examples are shown in Box 2.4. Although not as widespread as the aggregates, production of these minerals is in many cases distributed across the continents and among the industrial powers. Thus, of the leading chemical materials such as sulphur and salt, some 30 countries have access to their own internal sources of each. Even barytes, the production of which is least widely distributed, is available in seven countries, the major suppliers being the USA and the USSR.

## 3.3   The metallic ores

### Activity 1

A consideration of metallic ores can usefully be started by comparing the prices per tonne for zinc, lead and copper with those quoted earlier for sand and gravel. You will be able to find these in the business section of many newspapers under 'commodities'.

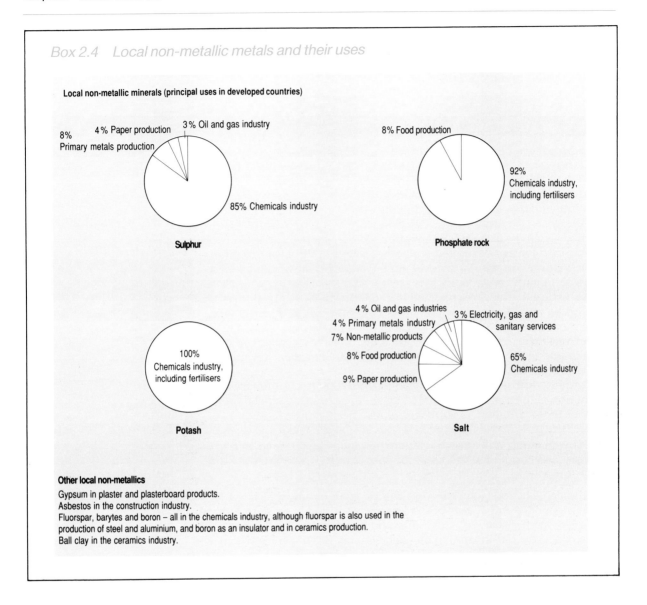

Box 2.4   Local non-metallic metals and their uses

Local non-metallic minerals (principal uses in developed countries)

**Sulphur**

8% Primary metals production
4% Paper production
3% Oil and gas industry
85% Chemicals industry

**Phosphate rock**

8% Food production
92% Chemicals industry, including fertilisers

**Potash**

100% Chemicals industry, including fertilisers

**Salt**

4% Oil and gas industries
4% Primary metals industry
7% Non-metallic products
8% Food production
9% Paper production
3% Electricity, gas and sanitary services
65% Chemicals industry

**Other local non-metallics**

Gypsum in plaster and plasterboard products.
Asbestos in the construction industry.
Fluorspar, barytes and boron – all in the chemicals industry, although fluorspar is also used in the production of steel and aluminium, and boron as an insulator and in ceramics production.
Ball clay in the ceramics industry.

Q   Why do you think metals are so much more costly per unit than aggregates?

A   Metallic materials are much less widely available than aggregate materials. This, together with the sophisticated processes involved in extracting the ore from the host rock, as mentioned in the previous section, makes them of relatively high value.

Although values are generally high for **metallic ores**, there is just one exception, that of **ferrous metal ores**, i.e. the iron-rich rocks known collectively as iron-ore. Once processed, iron-ore is without doubt the most indispensable of all metals and is the basis of modern industry. It has many uses, as you have already seen in Box 2.2. The much greater accessibility of iron-ore compared with other metal ores stems from the fact that it may be formed during a number of different geological circumstances.

Two of the chief iron-ores, haematite and magnetite, have been extracted on a large scale from massive deposits in the oldest of rock formations. Examples are Kiruna in Sweden, Krivoi Rog in the USSR (now the most important production areas in the world), Pilbara in Australia (now the world's largest exporter) and the Lake Superior area of North America. At these locations the iron content of the ores is in the range 50–60%. Elsewhere, residual or placer ores such as those mined in the Vermilion range of Minnesota (USA), Minas Gerais (Brazil) and Sishen (South Africa) can be as rich as 64–68% iron. Other sources of iron-ore are the extensive sedimentary deposits laid down between about 300 and 100 million years ago, but their iron content is only between 20% and 40%. The ore fields of western Europe associated with limestones are an example, and in England they are to be found in the extensive deposits of north Oxfordshire, Northamptonshire, Leicestershire and Lincolnshire. Open-pit operations in all these counties once supplied the steel-works at Corby. But their low iron content compared with other sources of iron-ore and the unavoidable environmental disturbance created by their working led to closure in the early 1970s.

The wide geographical spread of iron-ore production, involving some 40 countries, and its generally high metal content, contrast sharply with the far more scattered nature of the rest of the metallic ores, known as **non-ferrous metal ores**. These show great distributive inequality in their deposits among the nations of the world, and usually have a low metal content, frequently below 1%.

Figure 2.5 further illustrates this point since it offers a summary of the distribution of the major producers of the main non-ferrous metal ores and identifies those with high percentages of reserves.

Q   Of the minerals that are extracted in their own right, (a) which two enjoy the most widespread distribution; and (b) which three are the most restricted?

A   (a)  Lead and zinc, which are in any case geologically associated. Fourteen lead and 17 zinc producers are identified in western Europe, Africa, Australasia, Asia and North and South America. Although bauxite is the most common metallic mineral, it is in a form which is not open to exploitation as a source of aluminium – that is, in ubiquitous alumino-silicate rocks. Only when these are broken down by weathering to form deposits of bauxite are they in workable form from which aluminium can be extracted (see Table 2.1). Thus there is only one major supplier, Australia, along with three others of significance and five much smaller ones.

(b)  Uranium has only one moderately large producer (Canada) out of six, is among the least common metals and is worked in deposits that contain as little as 0.10–0.3% of the metal. Platinum is the commonest of a group of six precious metal ores, all of which are among the rarest metals in the world. Of the three producers of any significance only one is of major importance and that is the USSR. Manganese, a metal crucial to the production of steel, has seven ore producers, but has only one of prime significance, in the USSR – and supplies there could be close to exhaustion. Although South Africa has large reserves, the higher grades of ore are declining.

Although manganese is far from abundant at present, this could soon change, because it is estimated that there are around 1.5 trillion tonnes in

Figure 2.5
Non-ferrous metals –
production and reserve
potential by country.

| | manganese | chromite[a] | nickel | cobalt | molybdenum[b] | tungsten | vanadium[c] | bauxite | magnesium | titanium | copper | tin | lead | zinc | gold | platinum[d] | silver | antimony[c] | mercury | cadmium[e] | uranium |
|---|---|---|---|---|---|---|---|---|---|---|---|---|---|---|---|---|---|---|---|---|---|
| Albania | | ▨ | | | | | | | | | | | | | | | | | | | |
| Algeria | | | | | | | | | | | | | | | | | | | • | | |
| Argentina | | | | | | | | | | | | | | | | | | | | | |
| Australia | | | | • | | • | | R | | R | • | • | • | R | | | • | | | | R |
| Brazil | | • | | | | • | | | | • | | | | • | • | | | | | | |
| Bolivia | | | | | | • | | | | | | | | | | | | | | | |
| Canada | | R | • | R | | | | | • | | | | R | R | R | • | R | | | | R |
| Chile | | | | | | | | | | | R | | | | | | • | | | | |
| China | | | | • | R | ▨ | | • | • | • | • | • | • | • | • | | R | R | ▨ | • | |
| Cuba | | | • | • | | | | | | | | | | | | | | | | | |
| Finland | | • | | • | | | | | | • | | | | | | | | | | • | |
| France | | | | | | • | | • | • | | | | | | | | | | | • | |
| Gabon | | | | | | | | | | | | | | | | | | | | | |
| Germany (FR) | | | | | | | | | | | | | | • | | | | | | • | |
| Greece | | | • | | | | | • | | | | | | | | | | | | | |
| Guinea | | | | | | | | ▨ | | | | | | | | | | | | | |
| Hungary | | | | | | | | • | | | | | | | | | | | | | |
| Indonesia | | | • | | | | | | | R | | | | | | | | | | | |
| Ireland | | | | | | | | | | | | | | • | | | | | | | |
| Italy | | | | | | | | | • | | | | | | | | | | | • | |
| Jamaica | | | | | | | | ▨ | | | | | | | | | | | | | |
| Korea (DR) | | | | | | • | | | | | | | • | • | | | | | | | |
| Korea (Rep) | | | | | | • | | | | | | | | | | | | | | • | |
| Malaysia | | | | | | | | | • | | | ▨ | | | | | | | | | |
| Mexico | • | | | | • | | | | | | • | | • | • | | | • | • | • | | |
| Morocco | | | | | | | | | | | • | | | | | | | | | | |
| Namibia | | | | | | | | | | | | | | | | | | | | | |
| New Caledonia | | | ▨ | | | | | | | | | | | | | | | | | | |
| Niger | | | | | | | | | | | | | | | | | | | | | • |
| Norway | | | | | | | | | | ▨ | | | | | | | | | | | |
| Papua | | | | | | | | | | | • | | | | • | | | | | | |
| Peru | | | | • | • | | | | | | R | | • | | | | ▨ | | | • | |
| Poland | | | | | | | | | | | • | | | • | | | • | | | • | |
| Philippines | | | • | • | | | | | | | • | | | • | | • | | | | | |
| South Africa | R | R | • | | | | R | | | • | • | | • | • | • | ▤ | | R | • | | ▨ |
| Spain | | | | | | | | | | | | | • | • | | | | | R | | |
| Sweden | | | | | | | | | | | | | • | • | | | | | | | |
| Thailand | | | | | | | | | | | ▨ | | | | | | | | • | | |
| Yugoslavia | | | | | | | | • | | | • | | • | • | R | • | | | | | |
| USA | | | | | R | • | • | | ▤ | | | | | • | • | | • | R | ▨ | | ▨ |
| USSR | ▤ | ▨ | | | | ▨ | | | | ▨ | | | | R | R | R | ▨ | R | R | | |
| Zaïre | | | | R | | | | | | | | | | | | | | | | | |
| Zambia | | | | ▨ | | | | | | | | | | | | | | | | | |

**Percentage of total production**

| | • 2–6 | ▨ 12–21 | ▤ 32–41 |
| | ▨ 7–11 | ▨ 22–31 | ▤ 42–55 |

R   Major source of reserves

a   Chromite is always found with other metals (usually iron) as an oxide.

b   Molybdenum is sometimes produced as a by-product of copper.

c   Vanadium and antimony are produced only as by-products of other metals.

d   Only South Africa and the USSR mine platinum in its own right.

e   Cadmium is found with lead-zinc ores.

△   *Figure 2.6    Harvesting the sea-bed. One method may be to trawl the ocean floor with the aid of continuous buckets (above left). An alternative method may use a suction device similar to a vacuum cleaner, either a sled which is towed through heaps of nodules (above right) or an active head which can be swept from side to side (top right).*

the form of nodules lying on the floors of the major ocean basins. These nodules, which are to be found at depths of between 30 m and 3000 m, contain not only 24% manganese, but also 1.6% nickel, 1.2% copper, 0.21% cobalt and 0.05% molybdenum. The success of their recovery depends on two factors. First, international agreement is needed to determine the division of such a rich harvest between countries outside internationally accepted limits to territorial waters. Second, technological considerations require resolution. These involve the development of a reliable low-cost system capable of hoisting between 1 and 3 million tonnes of nodules from the sea-bed each year of the kind illustrated in Figure 2.6, and the development of efficient metallurgical processes for extracting the minerals from the nodules. Both are within sight of solution, but only then will it be possible to add substantially to the reserves of manganese and other minerals and exploit them in what will probably be a more environmentally friendly way compared with conventional mining techniques.

## 3.4   Carbon and hydrocarbons

These are the fossil fuels of Chapter 1 where the uneven distribution of present resources and the future reserve prospects were discussed. Two points need to be added here.

The first is that these minerals (especially oil and natural gas) are not merely used as a source of energy, but are also an important feedstock for the chemicals industry. A wide variety of industrial products depend on this source: for example, plastics such as polyethylene and polypropylene, together with artificial fibres, pharmaceuticals, resins, solvents, and a range of agricultural chemicals including ammonia and the fertilisers derived from it.

Secondly, the recent history of oil production deserves comment because of its strong political dimension and the considerable effect this has on the patterns of production. In the early 1970s, the Gulf States, Nigeria, Libya, Algeria and Venezuela had the lion's share of oil production (apart from the eastern European countries, the USSR and the USA). These countries founded the group known as the Oil Producing and Exporting Countries (OPEC). This was in effect an oil cartel, i.e. a producers' union aimed at managing the market for the product. Acting in concert through OPEC they proceeded to control output and to raise the price of oil in two major steps in 1973 and 1979. These policies, however, had other impacts, for the major consumers sought sources of supply outside OPEC control. Once other sources were discovered and their long-term capacity calculated, their productive capacity was developed as quickly as possible. Located in the USA, Canada, the United Kingdom and Norway, these are largely sites that prior to the rise in prices would have been uneconomic to exploit. This clearly illustrates the significance of a situation where major sources of the supply of minerals are not in the hands of the chief consumers, and not least the use of this situation as an economic or even political weapon against the short-term interests of consumers.

## 3.5   Summary

This section has briefly offered a geological rationale for the occurrence of minerals, and has provided further evidence of their global distribution by an examination of the major sources of supply by country in the late 1980s, together with some indication of the amount and location of reserves. You should begin to understand the environmental disruption created by the demand for new mineral supplies, especially after reading the more detailed account in the next chapter of the environmental impact that such minerals may have as a result of their extraction and processing. However, the patterns of production which might be expected to emerge as a result of any analysis of reserves are considerably modified by other factors. These are discussed in the next section, starting with a consideration of the attitudes of the companies whose business it is to extract and process minerals.

# 4   Constraints on points of supply

## 4.1   Transnational corporations and investment

Until the early 1970s any general comment regarding the structure of the minerals industry could not have failed to underline the significant control of minerals production by large international companies, mostly American based but operating in more than one country, often in the third world. Indeed, despite the rise of OPEC, seven major transnational oil companies dominated the world petroleum industry. Six large producers of aluminium set the terms under which most of the world's bauxite was extracted. Three companies controlled the uranium industry. Two companies overshadowed the production of much of the world's nickel. Many of them had extended their control through their ownership not only of the mineral rights and extraction and processing facilities, but also smelting and primary fabrication. Such a command of output exercised over mines in more than one country, allied with their market intelligence, ensured for them a strong voice in dealing with consumers.

However, the rapid extension of territorial independence to former colonial countries, and the desire of these new states for national management of their resources, has led to a considerable reduction in the foreign control of mining enterprises. Sometimes this has occurred through sudden expropriation by newly independent governments, as happened in Latin America and Africa during the late 1960s. In the case of the central African countries alone, 1969 saw the Zambian government take a 50% controlling interest in the two giant transnational copper mining groups, Anglo-American Corporation and Roan Selection Trust, later rising to more than 60% of the share capital. In Zaïre the government took over the interests of Union Minière. In Botswana the state acquired an interest in De Beers Consolidated Mines' diamond venture and in the copper-nickel mines run by a consortium of foreign companies led by the transnational company AMAX.

Such actions by host governments certainly caused the transnationals, partly or wholly dispossessed of their mineral holdings, to question their future patterns of mining investment. There was considerable reluctance on their part to invest further in territories where their capital would so readily be lost, especially when development costs for new mining ventures were escalating at a rate well in advance of general inflation. This was largely due to the greater sophistication of the minerals processing plant which was necessary to cope with the lower grades of ore generally being worked worldwide. At that time, an integrated copper mine, smelter and refinery could involve an outlay of around $US1 billion. But even where attempts were made to enter into profit-sharing schemes with less developed countries, the going was also not easy in what might be called the post-colonial environment. A case study illustrates this point well enough.

The setting up of the Cuajone copper project in southern Peru (Figure 2.7) involved reaching an agreement between the mining company and the government over the division of profits. This took several years to negotiate and was finalised in 1969. A further six years was needed to set up the complex financing of the operation (which thereafter included several metal mining companies, the World Bank and 29 commercial banks) before construction, planned to take seven years to complete, was begun. In the end the cost of development was $US726 million. But shortly after operations commenced, the Peruvian government, quite unexpectedly, imposed a range of export taxes on the output of the mine which lowered the return to capital investors. For potential mining investors this was but one example from many which graphically illustrated the point that hard-pressed governments in less developed countries may attempt to finance their social and other programmes by extracting the revenue they need from mining companies. Mining companies cannot resist such measures and have no means of redress.

This particular message was certainly taken to heart by the transnationals and those from whom they raised capital, causing by the early 1980s a dearth of mining development in the less developed countries. As the World Bank has shown, even by the mid-1970s the amount of exploration expenditure outside the centrally controlled economies had for the less developed countries fallen to 15%, while 80% was spent in just four countries of the developed world (Australia, Canada, South Africa and the USA). A study by the Group of Europe mining companies shortly afterwards produced an even lower figure of 13.4% for mining development in less developed countries, down from the 34% of 20 years earlier.

These changes in the location of new mining development could in the long term have serious repercussions, not only because of a failure of the developed countries to generate economic growth in the less developed countries, but because they could ultimately lead to a severe shortage of supplies of those minerals on which the industrial world depends – given the way the minerals market now operates. If the European Community alone is considered, it is apparent that its dependence on raw material imports is running at 95–100% for nickel, manganese, antimony, chromium, molybdenum, platinum, titanium, tungsten, vanadium and phosphate. For aluminium, copper, cobalt, lead, tin, zinc, iron-ore and uranium the level of import dependence is between 50% and 80%. Although sources of some of these materials are spread widely across the world, and supplies of many are forthcoming as a result of more recent developed world investments, the important point is that the less developed countries have 55% of total reserves (Plate 2). This highlights the ultimate interdependence between the present developed and less developed countries and, indeed, the transnational companies. Moreover, in spite of recent experience, it underlines the need to stimulate mining development in the less developed countries if future demand levels are to be met by the conventional operation of the market.

Such an approach to the solution of ensuring the continuing availability of minerals is nevertheless founded on two assumptions. First, it assumes that less developed countries will continue to have low levels of minerals consumption themselves. A rise in internal demand in these

▲   *Figure 2.7*
*Cuajone copper mine,*
*southern Peru. The mine,*
*which was difficult to*
*negotiate with the state*
*and to finance in the world*
*capital markets, took much*
*longer than average to*
*develop and construct,*
*and is ultimately dubious*
*as a commercial*
*investment.*

countries could have other consequences, as will become apparent in Section 5.2. Secondly, it takes for granted that the level of the consumption of newly won minerals in the developed world is really necessary. It may well be that real needs can be met by much lower levels of minerals exploitation and that recycling and substitution can play a much larger part than is the case at present in meeting world demand. Again, these are matters addressed in Chapter 3.

If the pushing of minerals investment back into the developed world has had a clear impact on the location of sources of exploitation, this has come at a time of increasing concern in those countries regarding the impact of extractive operations on the environment. It is to the framework of environmental controls that have been built up in these countries over recent years that attention must now be given, not only to look at how these have developed, but also to illustrate the kind of constraints these offer on the extractive process, and therefore upon their propensity to affect the environment.

## 4.2   *Statutory production constraints*

That mining companies are now rarely allowed to pursue activities with completely unbridled freedom and without regard for any other interests was made apparent in Section 2.6 of this chapter. Apart from being constrained by regulations which in developed countries concern the safe working of pits and underground mines, the extractive industries have found themselves increasingly operating within a framework of controls not only relating to rehabilitation of land but also to the use of land and its air and water environs. These are legally enforced and administered by one or more government departments operating nationally or regionally.

The reason for the growth of such controls in most developed countries lies in the view that in highly populated and complex societies land is increasingly seen as a scarce resource for which at any one time there may be competing uses, and that the market place cannot be relied upon in terms of equity to decide what activity is carried out where, when, and to whose benefit (though, of course, in the case of minerals, they can only be extracted where they exist and where conditions allow extraction at a cost that will enable them to be marketed). At the same time, in the wider general interest, the costs of visual damage and pollution (which will be examined in detail in Chapter 3) cannot reasonably be borne by the public at large. They must be dealt with at source by those who create them, although such costs will almost certainly be reflected by an additional charge upon the products of the company concerned. Nor can it be appropriate, it has been argued, for mineral operators, once the material has been extracted, to abandon land, leaving it to other public agencies to undertake and to pay for its rehabilitation.

The development of the framework of controls to deal with these concerns began after the First World War. In the USA, federal legislation was passed in 1922 to regulate land use by a system of zoning ordinances – a set of rules which govern the location of factories, educational institutions, shops, hospitals, housing, etc. and prevent the close juxapositioning of incompatible forms of land use such as heavy industry and housing. At the time, mineral working was outside its scope, but the zoning of other forms of development was a major factor in ensuring that the production of, say, aggregates, did not occur in urban or semi-urban environments, even though benefits might have accrued to the operator

from the close proximity of suitable markets. Similar development controls
spread in the inter-war years to Europe, but it was mainly after 1945 that
the closely defined regulation of such matters occurred in Sweden, Italy,
France, Denmark and the United Kingdom.

In the case of the United Kingdom, a rather more sophisticated
approach was adopted and set out in the Town and Country Planning Act
of 1947. By the beginning of the 1970s many developed countries had a
similar system of development control. This system involved the
preparation of broad general plans relating to future land-use needs, which
were usually formulated at the provincial or county level with much more
detailed programmes set out at the level of the municipality or district.
Such arrangements also offered a means by which the desirability of
specific development proposals could be considered as and when they
were put before the relevant authorities for adjudication (Figure 2.8).
A means of appeal by the unsuccessful applicant for a particular land-use
change was usually incorporated in the system. Within such broad
generalisations there remain, of course, wide variations. Although a
number of countries (including the Scandinavian countries and the Federal
Republic of Germany but not the United Kingdom) have a comprehensive
approach covering all land, it remains the exception rather than the rule.
Even in the United Kingdom agricultural activities and forestry remain
outside the remit of the 1947 Act (discussed by Blunden in *Sarre, 1991*,
Chapter 5).

In the USA in the meantime, although such a system of development
control had not emerged by the 1970s, more rigorously applied land-use
zoning put minerals exploration and development off-limits in ever larger
areas of government land. Although this was done in the interests of

▲   *Figure 2.8    Merehead, the largest limestone quarry in the Mendips, UK.
Somerset County Council were one of the few counties to use their powers under the
1947 Town and Country Planning Act to draw up a coherent plan to meet the future
needs for Mendip stone in a way which would prove to have some degree of
environmental acceptability.*

environmental protection and wildlife conservation, it has not been
without protest from the mining industry, unions, local government, and
regional economic development groups. But claims that these withdrawals
were excessive have largely been ignored. Indeed, constraints on other
lands have been increased, as the next section makes clear.

## 4.3   Acts and agencies

The system of national controlling agencies is also variable, and although
in most countries minerals come within the purview of ministries of mines,
minerals, energy and/or natural resources, in some countries departments
of environment, planning, construction and even agriculture may be
concerned. For a number of nations the responsibility for looking after
minerals may vary according to the mineral in question, particularly if
strategic considerations are involved. Belgium and some Australian states
have such an approach.

In the case of the United Kingdom, although all minerals are handled
together, there is little centralised control at national or provincial level;
responsibility is almost completely devolved to counties or, as in Scotland,
the regions. Only where mineral development proposals are likely to be of
a particularly contentious nature are they 'called in' by the Secretary of
State for the Environment, who, after receiving the evidence of a local
public inquiry through an inspector's report, will then make a judgement
on the issue. The relevant Secretaries of State for Wales and Scotland
perform this task for those countries.

The growing environment debate of the late 1960s and early 1970s in
the USA introduced a new element into minerals development which was
embodied in the Federal National Environmental Policy Act of 1969. This
attempts to address the issues of resource conservation and pollution
control *together* whenever a new major official land-use development is
proposed. These issues are reviewed in each case through the preparation
of an **Environmental Impact Statement** which sets out the ways in which
the proposed development will affect the environment. In practice it
usually also incorporates a cost-benefit analysis of that development. This
has offered the opportunity to supplement existing legislation, whether its
aim is land-use control or the maintenance of public health, and to provide
a means of analysing all the factors for and against the proposal. It is an
approach which has been copied by many US states, by many Canadian
provinces, by Australia at national and state level, and by the Federal
Republic of Germany, Denmark, France and Ireland, and is under
consideration by others, including Norway and the European Community
as a whole.

Although a wide range of other considerations is addressed by
Environmental Impact Statements, it should not be supposed that land-use
planning controls, by contrast, can perform that role alone. In the United
Kingdom context the submission of an application to extract minerals will
cause the recipient local authority's planning department to address
considerations which cover its interaction with other forms of land use,
and therefore, human activity. If the potential extractor wishes to open up
new ground not already designated for mineral working, the proposal will
be referred to other government departments such as the ministries of
agriculture and transport, the National Rivers Authority and to agencies
such as the Nature Conservancy Council, the Countryside Commission
and the Health and Safety Executive. Their respective views as to the

desirability of the proposed operation will be made available, as will any conditions they feel should be applied to the working, if it is permitted to go ahead. For example, the National Rivers Authority, using the Rivers (Prevention of Pollution) Acts of 1951 and 1962, might demand that the disposal of mine or quarry waters should not alter the mineral content of streams or rivers, while the Health and Safety Executive may wish to control dust or other emissions from secondary processing activities under the Clean Air Acts of 1956 and 1968.

Agencies controlling mineral development, in whatever ways they exercise their role in the developed industrial countries, are increasingly seeking to apply conditions to consents which demand a degree of site rehabilitation either as a mining operation progresses or upon its completion. In the United Kingdom such a requirement was first demanded under legislation dating from 1951, but it took another 20 years for this to be upgraded into a demand for a much more sophisticated scheme of aftercare.

Such rehabilitation considerations were first invoked in the USA just before the Second World War in connection with the strip mining of coal in West Virginia (Plate 3), but they have chiefly been embraced by other countries only since the early 1970s. Apart from the United Kingdom, these include the Federal Republic of Germany, France and other states or provinces of the USA, Australia and Canada. In some instances the government authority has insisted on the deposition of a cash bond before extraction commences, which may be drawn on for rehabilitation purposes. British Columbia in Canada, for example, operates such a scheme. Since its development as an important source of minerals did not begin until the late 1960s, the province was able to impose it on most mines. The virtue of the scheme plainly lies in ensuring that rehabilitation is not at the public expense should the extractor become bankrupt or otherwise cease operations prematurely.

## 4.4   Cost of environmental controls

Chapter 3 discusses the impact on mining enterprises of legislation to control dust, noise, effluent discharges to air and to natural drainage systems, and the disposal of solid wastes, as well as to ensure landscape rehabilitation. Here it is only necessary to note the particular importance of such legislation for mines in the developed countries and that the significance of such measures of control can be seen as an additional cost factor. What were once environmental costs borne by the wider community before the days of control have now become part of the internal cost structure of mining companies. But just how important can this additional financial burden be?

Unfortunately, little analytical work has been carried out into answering such an important question outside that undertaken by the Centre of Resource Studies in Canada. However, that country is one of the world's key mining provinces and the results of the Centre's research are clearly applicable elsewhere, so it is worth citing what their answer would be. In general terms, it would appear that the costs of such controls can indeed be critical in the case of workings operating at the economic margins, whether they are metalliferous mines, aggregate undertakings or those otherwise connected with the construction industry. In a case study reported by the Centre in 1981, for example, an evaluation was made of the effects of water pollution control on the economics of 131 metal deposits discovered in Canada over the previous three decades, as well as all other potential mining developments in that country. The deposits were mainly copper, zinc, lead and molybdenum. It found that the total capital and operating costs (at 1979 prices) of the necessary pollution controls were $Can1200 million. The figure was 3–10% of total mine investment and 2–5% of operating costs. But it rose to $Can2100 million if it was assumed that the best possible water treatment schemes (given known technology) were employed. In the latter case water pollution controls would be 13% of total investment and 8% of operating costs.

As the Centre's study points out, while the impact of these controls varies according to mine size, deposit type and region, the incidence of expenditure to combat pollution is greatest for smaller sulphide deposits because of the need for more sophisticated means of treatment, the costs of which cannot be spread across a large output of ore. However, given the prevailing market conditions for copper and the other main metals at the time of the study and the rate of taxation, five deposits would have been rendered uneconomic by the levels of water pollution control then required. This would have meant forgoing a potential net value to society (defined as the increase in society's real wealth by investing in minerals as opposed to some other activity) of around $Can700 million.

Another study from the Centre for Resource Studies, dating from 1980 and using a sample of 57 Canadian metal mining and processing operations, considered the impact of air pollution in the form of sulphur dioxide resulting from local smelting activities. Although this study was less detailed in its approach compared with that for water pollution, it showed that control costs only marginally diminished the number of economic deposits. This is perhaps because of the location of the sample entirely on the Canadian Shield where deposits with reasonably high metal content can be profitably exploited. However, assumed sulphur dioxide control costs (based on legal requirements at the time of the study) did have a significant effect on the potential value to society of the base metals mining sector. When all other costs except taxation were taken into account, the amount by which pollution controls of this kind diminished their potential value was around $Can271 million.

There are specific tax advantages to be gained, however (especially in Quebec and Ontario), from the use of integrated processing systems in which smelters are presumed to be part of the total operation (as opposed to the use of an entirely separate smelter facility). This arrangement further favours the larger mines which have richer ore bodies to exploit. Overall these controls can be regarded as a disincentive to the development of smaller deposits of poorer quality while bringing extant medium and larger mines working ores of lower metal content closer to the margins of profitability. Clearly, either through reduced mining profits or tax reliefs on integrated smelters, the end result of air pollution controls for governments is a substantial reduction in their revenues from the minerals industry.

While some presumption of satisfaction must be supposed among provincial ministries of environment in Canada, this would plainly not be shared by mining companies. Moreover, Ontario's Ministry of Natural Resources recently agreed in a report that changes in the standards of environmental control had a distinct impact on mining investments in Ontario (which is Canada's leading minerals province and one of the most important in the world), but it also argued cogently that a similar disincentive existed where tax changes were concerned. When these were combined with additional environmental burdens they led to 'investment substantially lower than it would have been had the pre-1972 tax and environmental regimes prevailed'. Indeed, in a study published subsequent to this government report which used a computerised simulation model, research workers were able to show that 'the combined effect of changes (in taxation and environmental regulations) was a reduction in mineral investment of at least 20%' over that which would have occurred in the province had these changes not been introduced.

Although the environmental implications of this reduction in the number of places at which exploitation occurs are obvious, it is equally apparent that additional costs incurred as a result of environmental controls have not been sufficient to overcome the resistance of resource developers, usually in the guise of transnational companies, to the less developed countries where on the whole the concept of environmental protection is not well developed. This assumes, of course, that there is a choice to be made – that is, that the desired minerals are available from both the developed and the less developed world.

Frequently, a less developed country will effectively trade off environmental protection against the benefits of incomes and jobs, by giving the former a much lower priority. But if many less developed countries appear to offer lower marginal costs in this way, some do not. Indeed there is evidence to show where a less developed country has created its own state-run mining company, transnationals which remain operating there are called upon to take much stronger environmental protection measures than the native company. Moreover, it is worth remembering that the price for a transnational being allowed to *develop* the mineral in such a country may be much higher anyway. Exploitation agreements between mining companies and governments in these areas often require that the former invests in schools, roads, better sanitation, water purification and other forms of local infrastructural investment.

## 4.5    Summary

This section has set out to show that minerals extraction does not occur in a situation dominated by the free interplay of supply and demand, but that constraints are imposed on production which go well beyond the limits of geological circumstance. These additional constraints, which may result in decisions to mine at one location rather than another, may be imposed by the mining companies themselves or by governments. Either way, the geographical incidence of environmental disturbance created by mining activity will be affected.

Even where extractive operations do occur, governments may further impose restrictive covenants detailing the circumstances under which mining and preliminary processing may take place and the treatment of the site once such activities are ended.

### Activity 2

To close Section 4, go back through it and list the constraints, other than geological, which influence the *location* of mining activities under the headings of those specifically aimed at limiting environmental damage, and those which may be termed economic or political.

# 5    *Patterns of consumption*

## 5.1    *Consumer groupings*

If the supply of minerals is significant in environmental terms, so, too, is their consumption. Here again there are considerable geographic variations. The major industrialised nations consume the greatest quantities. As already noted, iron-ore lies at the heart of an industrialised economy because it is used in so many products. If the way this is consumed around the world in the form of steel is examined, the differences between the industrialised and non-industrialised nations immediately become apparent.

Consider Figure 2.9 which shows changes in the apparent per capita consumption in selected countries for 1938, 1978 and 1988. Between 1938 and 1978 world steel consumption (excluding the USSR) rose by more than four times. The figure indicates for this period that the highest increases were achieved by the developing countries such as China where consumption increased 15 times and in the South American countries of Colombia and Venezuela where the increases were around nine and six times respectively.

*Activity 3*

Let's work out from Figure 2.9 just how the developed nations have fared over the period 1938 to 1978.

First, the countries of Europe which had the greatest amount of ground to make up, compared with their northern neighbours, were those of the Mediterranean. If Yugoslavia managed a 14-fold increase in consumption per head and Turkey an 8-fold increase, work out what the European Community countries of Spain, Greece, Italy and Portugal managed to achieve. If consumption doubled in the other industrial countries, how did Japan fare over the period?

USA consumption per head between 1938 and 1978 in absolute terms remained far and away the greatest over the period, with the United Kingdom approaching it only at the beginning of the period. Identify other countries that have caught up with US per capita consumption or even overhauled it by 1978.

In the decade since 1978, as Figure 2.9 makes clear, the world economic recession has affected steel consumption in most of the western industrialised countries, which now have modest to nil growth and, in some cases, falls in per capita consumption. Latin American utilisation of steel has similarly fallen. Only countries such as China, Taiwan, Korea and Singapore have continued to achieve quite remarkable increases in per capita consumption. By using the 1988 data it is possible to divide the world into four main groups of steel consumers. The first group consists of about 860 million people living in 24 industrialised countries who in 1988 consumed steel at an average rate of 418 kg per head. The second group

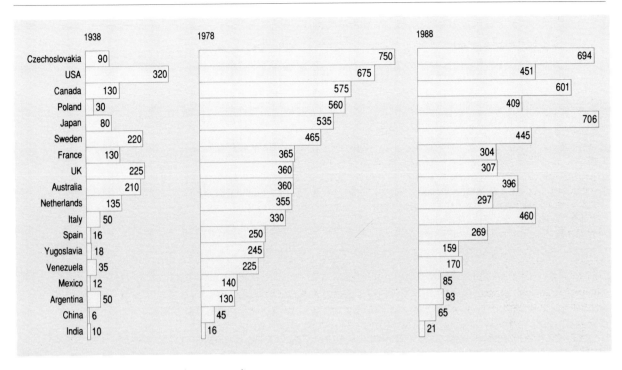

▲   Figure 2.9   Steel consumption per capita.

consists of around 369 million people living in 12 countries including some
of the developed countries peripheral to the western European industrial
heartland and the larger developing nations of Latin America. In 1988 the
countries in this group had a per capita consumption averaging 109 kg of
steel. The third group consists of 7 developing nations with a per capita
consumption averaging 44 kg and a total population of 1282 millions of
which the people of China made up over 90%. Of the rest of the world's
steel users, the 751 million inhabitants of India consuming more than 20 kg
of steel per head in 1988 stand out from the remaining 1435 million people
not accounted for so far and whose steel consumption is even lower.

## 5.2   Less developed countries and minerals consumption

The key question to ask here is what would happen if attempts were made
by less developed countries to meet the per capita levels of steel
consumption existing in the USA or Sweden in 1988, let alone rivals with
higher per capita consumption such as Canada, Japan and Czechoslovakia.
If the countries in the second and third groupings only were involved, it
seems likely that steel output would need to rise at once by around 600
million tonnes to meet average per capita consumption in the 24
industrialised countries. As for those in the fourth group, a rise of more
than 570 million tonnes would be required, even assuming that per capita
consumption across the group proved to be close to that of India. In all,
steel production would need to be increased more than three times.
Whatever the practicability of such a situation for iron-ore in terms of
mining and primary processing including smelting, much more serious
problems of supply would soon arise for a number of other metallic

Table 2.2    Estimated life of selected minerals (years)

|  | Current consumption rates | | 2030 rates | |
|---|---|---|---|---|
|  | Reserves | Resources | Reserves | Resources |
| aluminium | 256 | 805 | 124 | 407 |
| copper | 41 | 277 | 4 | 26 |
| cobalt | 109 | 429 | 10 | 40 |
| molybdenum | 67 | 256 | 8 | 33 |
| nickel | 66 | 163 | 7 | 16 |
| platinum group | 225 | 413 | 21 | 39 |
| coal | 206 | 3226 | 29 | 457 |
| petroleum | 35 | 83 | 3 | 7 |

Source: *Scientific American*, September, 1989, p. 96.

minerals, as well as hydrocarbons, although not aggregates. It would be a situation exacerbated by a rising world population. Table 2.2 compares the levels of reserve and resource existing for these in 1989 with those postulated for 2030. World stocks will drop perilously low if less developed countries increase their consumption to match the USA. Reserves show quantities that can be profitably extracted using current technology, and resources show the total quantities thought to exist. Estimates of years left to depletion are based on current world consumption, or those for 2030 on the assumption that 10 000 million people will consume at current US rates. Assumptions are made regarding the future population but they also need to be made about technological change (including improved extraction techniques), and the ability of shortages to move some minerals from the status of resources to those of reserves because, as prices rise, it becomes profitable to work formerly uneconomic grades. Nevertheless, by 2030, supplies of copper, cobalt, molybdenum, nickel and petroleum could all reach critical levels.

   Attempts to resolve such a situation by extracting grades of ore even an order of magnitude less rich than those worked at present could only give rise to substantial environmental problems. For example, although the largest copper mines in the world (at Bougainville in the Solomon Islands and Bingham, Colorado) are enormous, they are only one-tenth of the size required in the situation just outlined. Energy requirements would also be a dominant consideration. Look at Figure 2.10, which again uses copper as an example, and consider the energy requirements for the mining, crushing and milling of different grades of a copper sulphide bearing rock extracted by open-pit operations.

Q   What do you deduce about the power needed to recover copper moving away from the lower end of currently extracted grades to approach those of the average abundance of the Earth's crust?

A   About 80 $kW_{th}$ of energy is needed for the extraction of copper grades of about 0.2–0.3%. This would rise gradually until the copper content fell to around 0.1%. Thereafter the energy requirement would rise steeply as copper content dropped to the average abundance figure of 0.005%. By then it would be around 3000 $kW_{th}$ – an increase by a factor of 37.5 on current requirements.

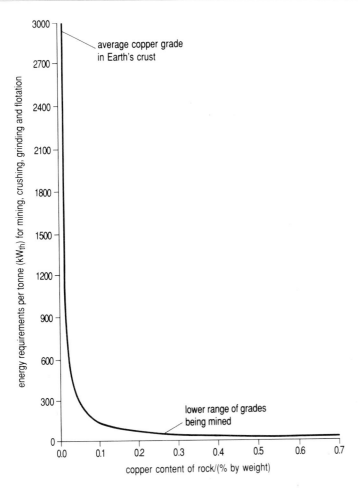

▲   *Figure 2.10   Energy requirements for mining and milling of a copper sulphide bearing rock from an open pit. The fact that lower grades of rock could entail finer grinding is not considered. Also excluded are the likely increases in energy needed to support efforts to dispose of the very large quantities of waste rock.*

These increases in both land consumption and energy requirement for copper extraction may appear formidable but they pale into insignificance compared with the gigantic requirements for the extraction of mercury or similar such metals at or near their level of average abundance. In the early 1990s mercury comes from a few deposits with a grade of 0.2–0.5%, whereas the average abundance of mercury is 0.000 04% – four orders of magnitude below the present cut-off grade at which the ore is no longer mined. Thus the working of most ores near their cut-off grades seems most unlikely, given that there is a geometric increase in the tonnage of waste rock to be disposed of for every arithmetic decrease in grade. It also has to be remembered that the volume of every tonne of waste rock removed from the ground will increase by between 20% and 40% after processing, thus further aggravating the waste disposal problem.

   Failing the identification of any new reserves (an increasingly less likely situation given the sophisticated state of exploration techniques), solutions to such supply problems can only be met in a limited number of ways. These include substitution between minerals in order to reduce the pressure on those in shortest supply, and the recycling of metals already in fabricated products. More will be said about these two possibilities in Chapter 3. For the moment it is enough to remind you that these spectacular readjustments in the relationship between demand for minerals and possible sources of supply are suggested to point up a particular set of possible environmental implications, even though they represent an extreme in the dynamic of supply/demand relationships unlikely to be realised except in the longer term.

# 6   *Conclusion*

This chapter began close to home, using the extraction of china clay in Cornwall as a base from which to examine the processes involved in extracting minerals from the Earth's crust and processing them. It was shown that the environmental impact they have when they are worked must be determined spatially, not only by geological circumstances which dictate where they occur, but also by the propensity of those who invest in mining (largely transnational companies) to choose among possible locations. In meeting a minerals demand that mainly stems from the industrial countries, the location for investment, if one is available, has increasingly been chosen in the developed countries. This is in spite of the stricter environmental controls exercised in those countries compared with the less developed countries.

The hypothesis that the levels of demand for minerals made now by industrialised countries might be made in the future by the less developed countries raises questions not only about the availability of some minerals in sufficient quantities, but also about the undesirable levels of environmental damage that could accrue. While these are questions to which further attention is given in Chapter 3, the next chapter also looks more closely, and in much more detail, at the impact of minerals extraction on the environment and the extent to which these questions affect it at the mine, in the territory immediately beyond, or even across national boundaries. Because this introduction also briefly identifies the consequences of further industrial utilisation of minerals, it should be seen as an essential background to the rest of the discussion on minerals and environment that takes place in this book.

As a concluding activity you may find it useful to glance at Figure 2.11. It is not possible in this to show the political and economic constraints on the location of mining activities or the constraints that may apply to the subsequent processing of minerals, their consumption by industry, or their ultimate disposal. However, the diagram does attempt to summarise the environmental impacts that may occur at all these stages. Although you may not find it totally understandable at this stage in your reading, it will do two things. First, it will give you a clear picture of where you are in the unfolding analysis of the environmental impact of minerals. Secondly, you should find it useful to remind you of the key issues relating to the discussion of minerals and the environment in this book.

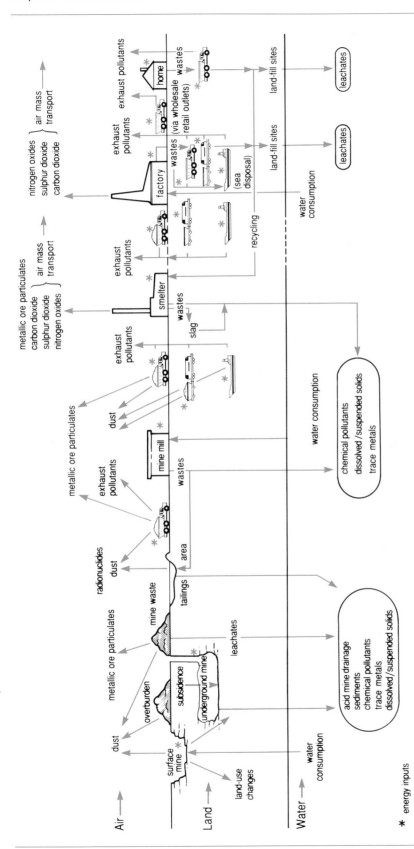

▲   Figure 2.11   Minerals extraction and use; a summary of environmental linkages.

## References

DU MAURIER, D. (1972) *Vanishing Cornwall*, Penguin Books, Harmondsworth.

SARRE, P. (ed.) (1991) *Environment, Population and Development*, Hodder & Stoughton/The Open University, London (Book Two).

## Answer to Activity

### Activity 1

Prices on the London Metal Exchange are quoted in sterling and US dollars per tonne. At the time of writing (1990) zinc was at $1364; lead £445 and copper £1332. You will see that rare metals such as platinum, silver and gold are given in $ per ounce.

# 1 Introduction

Bingham Canyon open pit to the south-west of Salt Lake City in Utah, USA (Figure 3.1) is roughly 4 km across and 1 km deep. Into it you could comfortably fit the cities of Bath or Winchester. From it 110 000 tonnes of copper ore are extracted every working day, making it one of the largest open-pit mineral workings in the world. Consider too, the metals smelter at Copper Cliff near Sudbury in Ontario, Canada (Figure 3.2). The substantial quantities of gases and minute metal particles (particulates) which come out of its 387-m chimney stack each year (685 000 tonnes in 1986) can affect environments many hundreds of kilometres away.

These are extreme examples of two different kinds of environmental impact caused by minerals extraction, and by minerals processing, one physical and one chemical. Whether minerals are won from the land's surface by open pit or quarry or by underground mine, and however they are subsequently processed, there will be environmental effects. This chapter sets out to examine these first of all, showing that they are both

◄ Figure 3.1
Bingham Canyon Copper Mine, Utah, which is 48 km south-west of Salt Lake City and reputedly the largest excavation produced by human activity in the world.

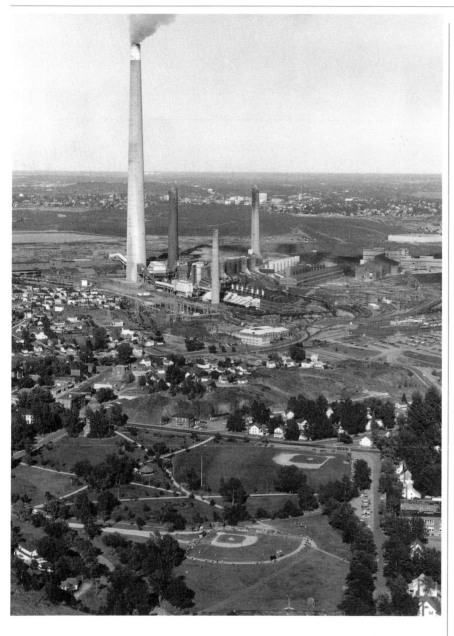

◀ Figure 3.2
Inco's giant 387-metre
smelter stack. Opened in
1972, it was designed to
reduce levels of effluent
in the city of Sudbury.

physical and chemical and have the ability to affect both amenity and
ecosystems. The effects are examined at a local or micro level, where
problems of visual disturbance will prevail (although air and water
environments may also be affected), at regional or meso level, where
effluent gases from smelters can have a major impact on finely balanced
ecosystems, and at inter-state or macro level, where air and water
environments may be affected by smelter contributions to ambient levels
of sulphur dioxide in air masses which may travel over considerable
distances. The chapter concludes by considering the means by which
environmental damage associated with mineral mining and processing
may be ameliorated, as well as ways in which the primary extraction and
processing of minerals may be reduced in the first place.

# 2   Micro environmental aspects of mining – visual intrusion

## 2.1   Topographical determinants

Mines, pits and quarries can make an environmental impact simply by their appearance. Bingham Canyon is a spectacular example of this. But the extent to which a mineral working intrudes on a landscape is generally local, to be appreciated at close range, and not necessarily related to the area of the working or the volume of material produced by it. Self-evidently, in an underground mine this must be so, since what is visible on the surface is related only to the various aspects of minerals processing (such as the mill or the smelter) and the areas given over to the disposal of waste rock, especially the tailings. But even in the case of surface workings, the operation can be large yet not obtrusive.

One of the biggest limestone quarries in Britain is at Merehead in a designated Area of Outstanding Natural Beauty in the Mendip Hills on the borders of Somerset. It produces four million tonnes of limestone a year, but is almost wholly invisible from points of public access. This is because the Merehead operation involves extraction from a deep pit located on a broad and gently sloping rock surface of considerable size. An operation which extracted minerals from a valley side or an exposed rock face would be far more obtrusive.

The nature of the topography and the spatial relationships between the excavation and the surrounding land forms are usually the prime factors that determine whether or not an excavation will be visible from public vantage points. This assumes, of course, that there has been no addition to the site of any artificial earthworks (usually known as amenity banks) or specially planted tree screens, so often insisted upon by planning authorities as a condition for consent to operate the extractive enterprise.

Nevertheless, the sheer size of a minerals working can still determine its visual impact. As Chapter 2 of this book indicated, the large-scale china clay workings of the St Austell area of Cornwall in England are a major visual intrusion in a rural landscape otherwise largely exploited by agriculture and tourism. Travellers approaching the area from the north-east along the A30 road can catch their first glimpse of them at least 12 km away. The same is true of the smaller Lee Moor china clay workings abutting the Dartmoor National Park in Devon – these can be seen from Plymouth 16 km away as well as from a number of tors (hills) inside its south-western boundary.

Of considerable size by British standards, the open pits at St Austell are roughly circular and can be as large as 40 ha (hectares), or about eight times the size of Wembley football stadium. The deepest is around 85 m deep, about the width of the grassed area in the same arena. In addition to the open pits there are the extensive ponds in which the fine waste materials from the processing of kaolin are placed. Of the material extracted, seven out of every eight tonnes are waste, which is piled up in immense white tips – this is why the workings are such a landmark. Not surprisingly, the land requirements for the industry in the St Austell area alone are of gigantic proportions, as Table 3.1 demonstrates.

Table 3.1    Land requirement (in hectares) for the china clay industry in the St Austell area

|  | Land occupied by industry 1969 | Land occupied by industry 1984 | Anticipated land occupied by industry 1991 |
|---|---|---|---|
| For pits | 645 | 992 | 1107 |
| For tips (quartz sand, overburden) | 830 | 1318 | 1434 |
| For micaceous residue disposal | 77 | 301 | 291 |
| For plant | 310 | 378 | 376 |
| Total | 1862 | 2989 | 3208 |

The problems of waste disposal for the china clay industry are particularly problematic. The four-fold increase in land used for the dumping of micaceous residues between 1969 and 1984 reflects the phasing out of marine disposal in favour of tailings ponds (see Chapter 2, Section 2). In the 10 years since 1977 when a reclamation scheme was instituted, 11% of the land taken for tipping and 23% of that given to tailings has been reclaimed, mainly for amenity purposes (see Section 8). Open pits remain unreclaimed. The relatively static requirements for plant over a period of increasing product output are an indicator of improved processing efficiency.

Source: English China Clays (personal communication).

## 2.2    The impact of aggregates

It is neither industrial mineral workings of the kind just discussed, nor metallic ore extractive enterprises that people are likely to be most aware of, or, for that matter, most environmentally concerned about. The widespread quarrying operations undertaken for the extraction of aggregate materials are far more important. As was noted in Chapter 2, their relative abundance is due to the wide range of rock types that can be used for aggregate, their low value, and in market economies, their inability to bear high transport costs. Moreover there has been a remarkable expansion of such enterprises in all industrialised countries to meet the rapid increase in building and road construction in the last 30 years. Production figures from the United Kingdom alone make this point clearly enough (Table 3.2). Such figures obscure a related feature – that of significantly enhanced output from a declining number of sites. From around 5000 in 1950 the United Kingdom total has fallen by 500 over a 30-year period.

From what has been said, it would be rightly concluded that the demands for aggregates from largely urban consumers will be met from the closest available sources. The most important of the aggregates group, sand and gravel, are usually to be found close to urban centres, simply because such settlements have tended to occur in lowland areas and frequently in river valleys where such materials are most likely to exist, so their ready availability ought not to be a problem. However, the appetite for sand and gravel has been particularly voracious. In London's green belt alone, in excess of 3300 ha has been actively worked for aggregates, almost wholly sand and gravel, with more than another 3000 ha approved by planning authorities for the same purpose. Nearly all of this is located in areas where there is significant pressure from other land uses which are not at all compatible with aggregate extraction. As sand and gravel workings are frequently unsightly, noisy and dusty, it is not surprising that they give rise to complaints about their environmental undesirability.

Public dissatisfaction is all the greater where the workings are associated with further processing. A survey carried out in Britain during

Table 3.2   *United Kingdom production of the main aggregate materials, 1969–89 (million tonnes)*

| Year | Crushed rock | | | Sand and gravel | Total crushed rock and sand and gravel |
|---|---|---|---|---|---|
| | Limestone | Igneous rock | Sandstone | | |
| 1957 | 13 | 13 | 4 | 60 | 90 |
| 1958 | 14 | 13 | 4 | 63 | 94 |
| 1959 | 17 | 14 | 3 | 68 | 102 |
| 1960 | 18 | 15 | 4 | 76 | 113 |
| 1961 | 20 | 16 | 4 | 85 | 125 |
| 1962 | 21 | 16 | 4 | 85 | 126 |
| 1963 | 23 | 17 | 4 | 89 | 133 |
| 1964 | 29 | 20 | 5 | 106 | 160 |
| 1965 | 34 | 20 | 5 | 102 | 161 |
| 1966 | 40 | 22 | 6 | 106 | 174 |
| 1967 | 48 | 25 | 7 | 112 | 192 |
| 1968 | 53 | 27 | 11 | 112 | 203 |
| 1969 | 55 | 28 | 14 | 109 | 206 |
| 1970 | 59 | 28 | 11 | 110 | 208 |
| 1971 | 62 | 29 | 9 | 112 | 212 |
| 1972 | 61 | 32 | 10 | 118 | 221 |
| 1973 | 74 | 38 | 14 | 130 | 256 |
| 1974 | 72 | 34 | 12 | 113 | 231 |
| 1975 | 67 | 32 | 10 | 117 | 227 |
| 1976 | 60 | 28 | 10 | 110 | 208 |
| 1977 | 59 | 26 | 9 | 99 | 193 |
| 1978 | 61 | 28 | 10 | 102 | 201 |
| 1979 | 65 | 29 | 10 | 103 | 207 |
| 1980 | 65 | 28 | 10 | 96 | 199 |
| 1981 | 57 | 25 | 10 | 89 | 182 |
| 1982 | 62 | 30 | 11 | 91 | 194 |
| 1983 | 70 | 31 | 11 | 101 | 213 |
| 1984 | 69 | 30 | 12 | 100 | 211 |
| 1985 | 72 | 32 | 11 | 102 | 217 |
| 1986 | 78 | 34 | 11 | 106 | 229 |

In spite of changing economic fortunes, for which aggregates consumption is a very sensitive indicator, demand for all aggregates has steadily increased over the period.

Source: British Geological Survey (1988) *UK Mineral Statistics 1986*, BGS, Keyworth, Nottingham.

the mid-1970s indicated that local authorities received more complaints about sand and gravel workings, even allowing for their greater prevalence, than any other extractive activity. Initially there were grounds for believing that the environmental problems might be reduced by increasing the output of sand and gravel extracted by dredging from the sea-bed (long a common practice off the coasts of south-east England and the eastern seaboard of the USA). However, claims have been made about the interference of such operations with navigation, submarine cables and pipelines. Even more importantly, it is alleged that they damage fishing grounds and cause coastal erosion.

To reduce the production of sand and gravel in areas close to urban centres, the working of hard rock aggregates at greater distances from them has increased; the higher transport costs are offset by bulk handling, specially advantageous transport contracts and by economies of scale at the point of production. In the United Kingdom this has led to greatly increased quarrying activities in places such as the Mendip region of Somerset, the Craven district of North Yorkshire, the Brecon Beacons of South Wales and the Charnwood Forest district of Leicestershire, all of which supply centres of consumption in the south-east of England. Unfortunately, these locations are in places of considerable scenic interest or are in or adjacent to National Parks or Areas of Outstanding Natural Beauty. Thus the amelioration of one problem has raised others, the only mitigating circumstances being that hard rock quarries are not as extensive in area, per tonne of product, as sand and gravel.

## 2.3   *Methods of mineral extraction*

Hard rock, like sand and gravel, is generally won by quarrying. There are few underground stone workings. In the United Kingdom only six mines are in operation producing under 0.5% of the total amount of stone each year. Nevertheless, there are environmental advantages to mining rather than quarrying. To begin with one major source of environmental impact is absent; that of the excavation itself. Its absence means that no overburden need be tipped and noise and dust nuisance are reduced, although some surface plant is likely to be in evidence. Because of the obvious advantages, the Department of the Environment in England has investigated whether damage to the limestone scenery of the Peak National Park, for example, might be reduced by the underground working of limestone for use by the chemicals industry. As it is, the ICI quarry at Tunstead, which produces over two million tonnes a year for this purpose, presents a scene of great visual disruption to the visitor entering the Park. However, the underground alternative would raise the cost per unit of saleable material by 50% compared with quarrying. Since neither ICI nor government are prepared to meet the additional cost, in spite of its environmental merits, nothing has been done.

In the USA a national committee was set up to study the underground working of stone and recommended a major research effort into trying to reduce its cost and sustain the rate of advance of underground excavation to the benefit of the environment. At present the main areas of progress in this field have been where major conurbations overlie horizontally bedded limestone strata. In such areas opportunities exist to extract this easily worked material and to sell the resulting space for underground car parks, shopping malls and even offices.

In spite of the undesirability of quarry and open-pit methods of minerals extraction, because of the likely damage done to the environment, the trend worldwide in this century has been away from underground production. This has been especially true in the USA where, until the mid-1960s, underground working predominated, with surface extraction being mainly confined to the aggregates industry. By 1980 though, over 80% of that country's minerals by weight was produced by open-pit methods.

Q   From what was said in Chapter 2, why has this change occurred?

A   This change is due to a widening gap between the respective productivity of open-pit methods and underground extraction. The former technique has been favoured by modern earth-moving equipment. In the 1960s it was estimated that the surface extraction of minerals could achieve a productivity rate of 500 tonnes per worker per shift compared with underground mining where 50 tonnes per worker per shift was common. This change also owes much to the fact that the extraction of metals, other than iron, demands ever greater emphasis on the use of lower grades of ore as the more concentrated veins of metallic ores have been worked out.

Although open-pit workings for metallic ores are much less common than quarry workings, where they do exist much larger extractive operations are needed. The leanness of the grades of ore will need to be offset by the massive scale of open-pit operations and by high levels of output per annum if companies are to minimise costs per tonne extracted and cope with increased demand. Such operations are not always going to be of the scale of Bingham Canyon open-pit copper mine; nevertheless, they could have considerable environmental impact.

The hypothetical proposals for an open-pit metal mine in the highland zone of Britain and its comparison with an underground mine illustrates this point (Figure 3.3). The proposed working area of 325 ha for the open pit within a site of 800 ha would have an extractive operation covering some 81 ha. This underlines the need in the case of open-pit metal mining for large areas to be given over for the disposal of overburden as well as tailings, and for the buildings required.

The usual arrangement is for most of the minerals processing plant to be housed within a single building or small group of buildings. Where metallic ores are concerned, this will be the mill. The crushing and grinding

▲   Figure 3.3   A hypothetical open-pit copper mine in a highland zone of Britain. Overburden is tipped to the left of the open pit. To the centre rear of the picture, the tailings area can be seen behind the dam wall. The processing plant is in the foreground.

of the rock and the removal from it of its metallic content is a complex
activity compared with the processing associated with aggregate materials,
so mills tend to be much larger than their quarry counterparts.

Regardless of the particular features of the fixed plant, whether
associated with quarrying or with ore processing, its visual impact will
depend upon location. In the past, plant sites were chosen only to fulfil
primary operating requirements; these inevitably involved minimising
haulage distances and avoiding sites beneath which valuable minerals
remained to be exploited. As operations proceed, it is of course possible to
move the processing plant inside the worked-out space, thereby
decreasing its obtrusiveness. However, where the plant has some years of
life remaining in it, or where the visual damage is not too great, then there
are few incentives for such action.

## 2.4    Wastes from minerals extractions

The main solid waste produced from the development of a quarry or an
open-pit operation is the overburden, which is usually dumped on the
surface adjacent to the working site. The amount of waste rock resulting
from the processing of aggregates is normally relatively small (compared,
for example, with the wastes produced from the processing of metallic
ores) and the ratio of excavated waste to saleable product does not usually
exceed 1:1 and may be zero. Other wastes, such as silts from stone washing
and dust, are generally small in volume and do not cause serious visual
impact when they are surface dumped.

The considerable problem of waste materials from china clay working
has already been fully described, but the quantities produced have been
exceeded at slate quarries in Britain. This industry, largely centred on
North Wales, has considerably reduced its output as a result of the
competition from substitute materials for roofing. Nevertheless, waste
from slate workings in the major producing area is thought to amount to a
total of 5000 million tonnes. The processes of splitting and dressing the
individual slates can result in the production of waste up to twenty times
that of the actual saleable product so that even modest production results
in large waste dumps. Even today large tips of broken slate and slate
chippings are frequently found disfiguring parts of the otherwise
outstandingly attractive scenery of Snowdonia (Figure 3.4). These are only
slowly eroded by the action of wind and rain so that natural vegetation
finds it difficult to establish itself on such dumps.

In the case of underground coal extraction such levels of waste
production are never reached. For deep mined coal in the United
Kingdom, the average waste to marketable fuel ratio was, in the early
1970s, 1:1.9. This meant that, by the end of that decade, about 67 million
tonnes of waste had to be disposed of annually. Three million tonnes of
this were retained underground; 61 million tonnes were dumped on the
surface in tips and the rest was disposed of into the sea. But whereas the
winning of coal has always involved the extraction of some worthless
shales along with the coal, increasing mechanisation has led to a waste to
coal ratio approaching 1:1 at fully automated coal faces.

National figures for waste produced by coal mining mask the
considerable geographical concentration of the disposal problem.
Calculations made in 1978–79 showed that the Yorkshire/Derbyshire/
Nottinghamshire coalfield accounted for 63% of waste output. The old coal
mining areas of South Wales and Scotland had 26% and 23% of all spoil

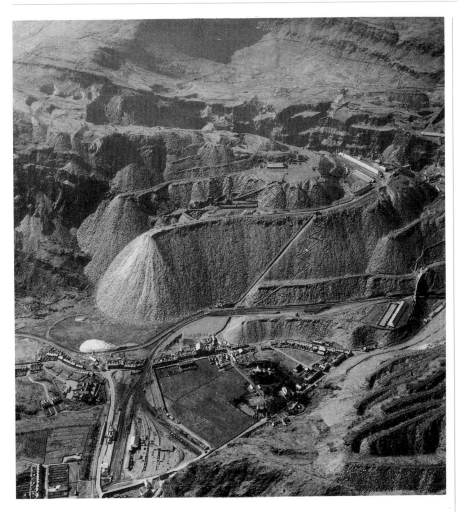

Figure 3.4
Slate waste at Blaenau
Ffestiniog. An area
understandably left
outside the Snowdonia
National Park at its
designation, but
surrounded by it.

tips in the United Kingdom but over 80% of these were no longer in use.
(**Spoil** refers to mining wastes tipped on the surface of the ground near
the mineral working.) This contrasted strongly with a county such as
Nottinghamshire, where the coalfields were and remain active. In this
county alone over 900 ha are already covered in spoil heaps (something like
the combined areas of Hampstead Heath and Hyde and Regent's Parks)
and the collieries produce about 13 million tonnes a year of spoil. The
county council has estimated that, by the year 2000, using present tipping
methods and assuming production constant at 1980 levels, 5000 ha of the
county will be covered by waste tips (something approaching the size of
the county town itself), with all that this means in terms of sterilised land
and severe visual disturbance. In the adjacent counties of Yorkshire and
Humberside, which have also seen increasing emphasis placed on coal
extraction, it was recently estimated that waste production during the
twenty years from 1980 may be as great as that which was tipped in those
counties in the previous 200 years.

As for the future for the underground extraction of coal in Britain,
British Coal have estimated that every 50 million tonnes of product will
require about 200 ha of new land for waste dumping and if this ratio
remains constant to the year 2000 then the land taken for this purpose will

be between 4500 and 4900 ha. This is not to imply that some waste cannot be suitably disposed of in an acceptable manner which could have some impact on such speculative calculations, or that in situ reclamation techniques that can improve the quality of local environments do not exist; these matters are explored in Section 8. Nevertheless, the environmental issue raised by the need to handle such large quantities of waste must give cause for concern. Indeed, underground operations strongly contrast with the winning of coal by open cast methods.

Although the adverse environmental impacts created by open-cast coal workings can last as long as 15 years, they are more usually short term because the area concerned is soon rehabilitated. However, given the present scale of operations worldwide, with 50% of all coal derived by such methods, the short-term environmental problems can be of considerable importance, especially in the more densely urbanised and populated zones of Europe. Productivity can be high. The bucket excavators of the Rhine lignite region, for example, handle up to 200 000 m$^3$ per day, but involve only five workers. However, such open-cast operations, in order to sustain the output levels of the early 1980s, have had to take over around 10 000 ha in Britain (Plate 4). In the Ruhr the figure is 19 000 ha and about 25 000 people have been temporarily displaced by these excavations. In the two to five years that an open-cast pit is in operation, apart from the displacement of people and other forms of human activity, the nuisances of noise, dust and traffic can be a problem. Visual disturbance is a considerable problem and is always difficult to deal with in the short term. The only exceptions are those workings which exist far from populated areas in countries such as Australia, the USA and Canada.

## 2.5   *Wastes from minerals processing*

The preparation of coal for sale, whether mined or produced by open-cast methods, inevitably gives rise to the need to dispose of the fine material into tailings ponds. These are not a significant element environmentally. Even at collieries which produce coking coal, where the largest quantities of fine waste materials are produced, tailings do not amount to more than 15–20% of total waste produced. This contrasts strongly with quantities of waste produced in the winning of metalliferous ores.

Although high-yielding veins of concentrated ore can be selectively extracted by underground mining techniques, thus considerably reducing the quantities of tailings produced in the milling process, the ore is frequently disseminated in the rock. Then, the valuable mineral content seldom exceeds a few per cent and may be a fraction of 1%. This means that the recovery of the metallic minerals in the milling process leaves tailings which are substantially the same mass as the ore treated, but which occupy a far greater volume than that material did when it was in the ground. Tailings ponds can be superficially similar in appearance to water reservoirs, but without their redeeming features of neatness and cleanliness. Both have a dam wall, but a tailings pond often consists of an extensive pool of discoloured water with a silt or sand beach which is usually dotted with the remains of dead trees and shrubs. The dimensions of a tailings pond inevitably relate to the output of the mill, in the case of metal mines, and the life of the mining operation. Self-evidently the disposal needs of a mine with a five-year life and a mill capacity of 2000 tonnes a day are quite different from one that has the same throughput but a life of 25 years. Operations which fall between these two examples would not be untypical for many non-ferrous metal mines, although a large enterprise could have a mill throughput of more than 9000 tonnes a day. In quite exceptional cases, such as the gigantic Bougainville copper mine in the Solomon Islands, 78 000 tonnes per day of tailings are disposed of, but in this instance into the sea. Such a means of tailings disposal, together with their discharge into lakes, has the advantage of getting rid of a visual problem, but they can and do create water pollution and damage to the aquatic ecology.

It is difficult to generalise about the surface area of tailings ponds. In Ontario most cover less than 245 ha, but some are over 1000 ha in extent (Figure 2.2). The problem is not just one of mill output, but the nature of the terrain. This may determine whether the mine operator opts for a shallow, but really extensive pond, or a deeper one of limited size. If there is any choice in the matter, the former has advantages since the larger surface area will allow greater opportunities for oxygenation, thus improving water quality. But the latter may be visually more acceptable, a matter of consequence where new operators may be required by government agencies to seek to diminish the impact of this environmentally disturbing aspect of their operation.

Without regulatory controls the operators would inevitably minimise costs by transferring wastes by pipelines to a site closest to the mill which fulfilled their disposal requirements. In areas of considerable scenic attraction where a mine has been allowed, it has been known for the regulatory agency to insist on the dumping of tailings many kilometres away in an area of less environmental significance. In Japan one mining operation is more than 70 km from the tailings pond. In Britain one planning authority was insistent that any further development of an underground fluorspar mine in the Peak National Park would have to depend on the dumping of tailings in such a way as to prevent any interference with the environment. A feasibility study was therefore undertaken into the possibility of transporting these by pipe to a site outside the boundaries of the Park.

Eventually, when the tailings area is full, there will probably be some attempt at site rehabilitation in order to stabilise it and improve its visual appearance. This frequently involves establishing some form of vegetation cover although this may not be easy. These are matters which will be discussed in Section 8. In the meantime, during the life of the tailings area, which may be a long one, it may be necessary in the interests of near-by communities to do as much as possible to improve the appearance of the site. This is usually achieved by maintaining a cover of water over as much of the tailings as possible.

## 2.6   Summary

This section, which has concentrated on the visual obtrusiveness of mineral extraction, began by showing that although sheer size can be determinant, topographical considerations are important. Aggregate production may also pose problems, but not because of size – rather, the frequency with which they occur. Indeed, all kinds of open-pit mining operations are gaining ground at the expense of the less obtrusive underground workings. The quantitative aspects of waste production were then considered as a visual hazard with particular reference to the winning of a number of specific minerals, and concluded with an analysis of the particular difficulties created by the disposal of tailings.

*Activity 1*

Go back over the discussion of tailings disposal, listing the advantages and disadvantages of tailings disposal in (a) the sea; (b) a narrow but deep valley; (c) a shallow broad land depression.

Although the brief section on subsidence which follows shows that it obviously has a strong visual outcome, its propensity to cause damage to the interests of other property owners and land users justifies its separate treatment and the exploration of the particular problems that can be caused by the extraction of coal, salt and oil and natural gas.

# 3   Micro environmental aspects of mining – subsidence

## 3.1   Subsidence and coal mining

**Subsidence** can occur as a result of the underground working of minerals, but its impact on the surface may be considerable and will undoubtedly affect more than just the eye. Perhaps the most frequent cause of subsidence is the working of coal. The removal of whole seams of material, frequently of considerable width and many metres thick, inevitably results in the collapse of the overlying strata. Mining a vein of metallic ore does not usually have this result. Coal mining subsidence mainly causes damage to buildings, roads, underground pipes, sewers and cables, and to agriculture through the disruption of drainage systems. In the USA, the Bureau of Mines reckon that over 32 000 km$^2$ have been affected by subsidence, nearly all of which can be attributed to the underground working of coal. This figure is expected to rise by another 10 000 km$^2$ by the end of this century. Of the areas especially affected, the Illinois Basin is outstanding with 10% of the nation's total subsidence problem, followed by western Pensylvania and northern West Virginia, where around 45 major subsidence incidents are reported each year, mostly involving abandoned mines.

In most other countries where underground mining is important, no overall estimates of subsidence are available, although there are individual case studies. One of the best documented is of a ten-year period in the English East Midlands and included the Nottinghamshire, Derbyshire and Leicestershire coalfields. This showed that one in three houses had to some extent been damaged by subsidence, although of the 62 500 properties involved, only in 4% was the problem appreciable. In the rural context about 728 ha were sufficiently affected for the National Farmers Union to seek compensation. This, however, represented less than 2% of the total agricultural land inside the area influenced by mining.

Another study in the Nord Pas-de-Calais coalfield of France has concentrated on measuring subsidence itself. Currently, over 16 000 ha of land, both urban and rural, are directly affected. In one district alone, around Lens, the ground has sunk about 5 m over an area of 20 km$^2$, but there have been changes in level in four of the basins which have formed within this zone of between 9 m and 14 m.

Although subsidence, along with waste disposal, has always been the major environmental impact of coal mining, its worst effects can still only be controlled rather than totally mitigated. Complete avoidance of subsidence would involve the leaving of unacceptably large quantities of coal in situ, destroying economic viability. However, there have been great advances in the understanding of subsidence since the late 1940s. These derive from work carried out in western Europe, Poland and the USSR. Although results do not relate to the prevention of subsidence, they enable predictions to be made of the degree of physical damage on the surface so that surface development and coal exploitation may be co-ordinated.

Three examples of co-operation between local authorities and the British coal industry to effect planned subsidence may be cited. When the plans for Peterlee, a new town in the county of Durham, were first prepared in 1947, about 30 million tonnes of coal remained under its 948 ha. After taking the precaution of carefully aligning surface constructions, it was found to be possible to build on land below which as many as three seams of coal remained to be worked. The phasing of coal extraction with motorway development took place when that section of the M1 which crosses the Nottinghamshire/Derbyshire coalfield was constructed. In places the motorway was built to allow for subsidence.

In a much more recent example, British Coal, when planning a new mining development at Selby in Yorkshire, acknowledged the need to prevent damage to buildings of historical importance and left coal in place in the seams both beneath and well beyond the area covered by such structures. Available evidence seemed to indicate that to protect a circular area on the surface with a diameter of 200 m, a 900-m diameter circle needed to be left intact in the coal deposits at 500 m, and a circle of over 1300 m diameter at 800 m. Estimates of the tonnages thus sterilised can be made; for example, if a seam one metre thick is abandoned at a depth of 500 m in a 900-m diameter circle, something of the order of 500 000 tonnes can be lost.

## 3.2   Other subsidence problems

The situation with regard to salt mining compares unfavourably with that of coal. A method is now in use which ensures the removal of salt in solution through the drilling of boreholes, the pumping in of water and the extraction of the resulting brine. This leaves behind large caves, but sufficient salt to support the overlying rock. This process, invented by ICI, is known as controlled brine pumping and largely eliminates subsidence. However, in the United Kingdom a great deal of salt has been won since the eighteenth century by the random pumping of salt dissolved in the groundwater from beneath the Earth's surface. This completely uncontrolled method of extraction has caused considerable subsidence, which has resulted in the permanent flooding of agricultural land in parts of Cheshire (Plate 5). In 1969 court action was needed to restrain further natural brine pumping activity. The problems created in the past, however, remain. In Cheshire the continuing unpredictability of subsidence is particularly serious since the areas of dissolved salt are not clearly established. A county council survey dating from the mid-1970s acknowledged just this problem. It suggested that at that time the total subsidence resulting from natural brine extraction was equivalent to a drop of 0.5 m over 119 ha in any one year. In reality, falls of greater magnitude, but varying widely, have been experienced over a much larger area.

The most notable cases of subsidence caused by the extraction of crude oil and natural gas are where they have occurred near sea-level. Flooding has been the highly unfortunate consequence. Evidence of this problem has come from an oil field on the shores of Lake Maracaibo (Venezuela), from coastal locations in Japan and the USA, and from the Po delta in Italy. Although they will have occurred elsewhere, the depression of the land surface will very likely have gone unnoticed.

Q   Why is the extraction of oil and gas less likely to create a surface problem than the underground extraction of coal and salt?

A   Subsidence resulting from oil and gas extraction does not derive from the subterranean *removal* of solid material such as with coal and salt, leaving cavities that can suddenly collapse, but from the reduction of fluid pressure in the underground oil and gas zones. This allows the strata above to settle slowly and evenly at a lower level.

The subsidence at Long Beach (Los Angeles), California, an industrial township lying 2–3 m above sea-level, provides a well-documented case study. As a result of the removal from 1936 onwards of oil from the Wilmington and Signal Hill fields, a substantial part of the central urban area of Long Beach began to sink. By the time the fall had reached 8 m, it was decided to take action to prevent the area being inundated by the sea. Retaining walls and levees were constructed and repairs to damaged oil well boreholes caused by earth movements were carried out. The cost of these projects was over $100 million. In the late 1950s attempts were made to repressure the oil zone by injecting water. This resulted in a 15% rise in the level of the land surface.

# 4   Micro environmental aspects of mining – aquatic damage

## 4.1   Water pollutants – the general background

One of the environmental hazards of mining that has received attention over recent years and is a local or micro problem is the contamination of surface waters with materials that can prove toxic. Such contamination may be by particulates of heavy metal (such as those of copper, lead, zinc, nickel and uranium) or by **sulphides**, or by other materials which may have been used to extract the ore. These problems are the direct result of the processes of mining and milling which break what was solid rock into fragments, so allowing air and water to react chemically with it. As these reactions depend on contact between air, water and rock surfaces, they are most prevalent where the material is finely crushed or ground. The finer the materials the greater the potential surface area is exposed within the body of material. Under the circumstances it is not surprising that tailings can offer the most serious problems, although waste tips or exposed stockpiles of untreated ore have been known to cause difficulties.

Even greater dangers of environmental pollution are likely to occur where the constituents of the rock fragments lead to an increase in acidity. Acid production, or **acidification**, is usually associated with the action of oxygen on sulphide minerals, most particularly pyrite and pyrrhotite, both iron sulphides, which often accompany the ores of lead, zinc, nickel and copper. In theory, this oxidation process can occur chemically or biologically. Although differences of opinion exist about the relative importance of the two pathways, evidence largely supports the latter. Initially, the reaction (whether chemical or biological) needs a supply of oxygen – that is, access to air. Then, the overall effect is to convert sulphide ions (electrically charged atoms) into sulphuric acid. This affects any waters that drain through the minerals by lowering their **pH** value, i.e. making them more acidic. (The pH scale is a logarithmic index of 1 (most acid) to 14 (most basic/alkaline); a neutral solution is 7 on the scale.) This is important because acidic solutions react with other metallic compounds present in the tailings, releasing metal ions (some of which may be toxic: for example, those of heavy metals) into solution and so into the groundwater. In waters where higher pH values prevail, most metals form insoluble oxides or hydroxides. Overall, then, acid generation can be considered as bad news – leading to enhanced levels of 'dissolved' metals and greater potential toxicity.

Where ores are not associated with these iron sulphides, acid drainage is less of a problem. It can also be counteracted by the presence of other rock materials. In the world's major lead mining area, that of south-eastern Missouri, for example, the ore is not associated with pyrites, but with dolomite, the base rock through which the natural drainage flows. Since dolomite is a limestone, the waters become alkaline and at alkaline pHs insoluble lead compounds are formed which precipitate out of solution. Thus, where it is necessary to engage in minor discharges of excess water (the situation at three of the five mines), a nine-day period of retention allows traces of lead, zinc and copper to settle out. This, plus some elementary sedimentation removal techniques, is all that is required before discharge into the drainage system. The pH levels in local streams are between 7.8 and 8.3, so the dissolved metal content in these is low.

A method of avoiding the problems that arise with pyrite discharges to the tailings area is to remove them in the milling process by flotation (as explained in Chapter 2). Unfortunately, this often reduces pyrite discharges by only 95%, their complete removal being impossible. Moreover, it would add other undesirable chemicals to the tailings, while still leaving 5% pyrite to form acid. At the same time, if the pyrite concentrate was to be dumped, careful isolation and monitoring would be essential.

Q   If the pyrite is not removed from the tailings, how could acid drainage be prevented?

A   Since acid formation involves the reaction of oxygen with pyrites, one approach would be to exclude air from the tailings. Another would be to use limestone to raise the pH of the drainage waters.

The exclusion of air from the tailings might be achieved through encapsulation, or inundation (i.e. keeping the tailings permanently under water), and, once the area is no longer in use, through the employment of physical covers, chemical 'fixation' or by creating a vegetation cover over the surface of the tailings, thus limiting the amount of oxygen that can enter them. Currently, vegetation offers the most practical long-term approach for reducing the problem when the tailings area is complete, a matter taken up in Section 8.

Once the abandoned areas of tailings have been flushed of process waters and vegetated, effluent treatment should no longer be needed. But while the operations continue, effluent waters may remain to be disposed of. A lead–zinc–copper mine at Sturgeon Lake in Ontario not untypically treats its contaminated water by adding lime slurry to bring the pH to 10. Large tanks with mixers are used to precipitate out the heavy metals as hydroxides, a practice which can be, and often is, pursued in the tailings pond itself at other mines. Flocculents (agents which encourage any remaining metallic compounds to settle out) are added before the fluid is passed to clarifiers. The settled-out sludge, once filtered and dried, is disposed of as a zinc concentrate.

The problems of working metallic ores that contain pyrites can also arise as the result of the mining of coal. The oxidation of the sulphur associated with the extraction of coal, particularly where local aquifers or streams are disrupted, leads to acid drainage problems. Areas of surface tipped waste can also be affected as rainwater drains through them (Plate 7). In regions where a considerable amount of land is given over to strip mining, such as Pennsylvania, Ohio and West Virginia in the USA, coal extracting companies have had to build drainage treatment plants to cope with acidic waters that can run as high as 5400 p.p.m. of acid. In compliance with the federal water pollution control standards, these plants use a relatively simple treatment of acid drainage water using hydrated lime. In the United Kingdom British Coal is similarly legally liable to control acid drainage from its mines and tips, even where these have been long abandoned.

Where metal mining is concerned, a report from Sturgeon Lake, Ontario, serves as a reminder that the water available from the active tailings area, and the water pumped from the mine or other parts of the processing plant, is not all disposed of. At this particular location, which is not untypical of lead–zinc–copper mining and processing undertakings, about half the water is reclaimed and retained to meet the requirements of the milling operation. Indeed, it provides a typical example of the substantial advances in recycling and in the standards of water treatment that have been achieved in base metal mines over the past 25 years.

Some water pollution can be generated by materials used in mining or processing. Mine drainage waters can contain both ammonia and nitrate, usually present as a result of the use of ammonium nitrate in explosives used for rock blasting. This chemical makes the explosives safe to handle, but because it is very soluble, excess quantities and spillage may be washed away. Ammonia in its molecular form is toxic and especially so in water where the pH is high. (In more acidic conditions, those of lower pH, the ammonia is converted to ammonium which is less toxic.) Discharges containing molecular ammonia into river water of pH 7 and above can cause severe problems for fish.

Q    What problems can arise from low pH values:
     (a)  in the waters of the tailings area of a metal mine;

     (b)  in the drainage waters of a mine site where ammonium nitrate explosives have been used?

A   (a)  These can lead to enhanced levels of 'dissolved' metals and a greater potential for toxicity. If these waters are discharged into the natural drainage system of the area problems can arise for aquatic life.

(b)  There should be none. Ammonia used in explosives for rock blasting only becomes toxic where pH values are high.

## 4.2   Radioactivity – a special problem

The operations at Elliot Lake, Ontario, raise the question of another pollutant primarily associated with uranium mining, that of radioactive waste. This arises from the presence of an isotope of radium which is a major waste product deriving from the milling operation and remaining undissolved in the process used to extract the valuable ore. Since 99% of this waste product passes through to the tailings, any disposal of surplus water from it into the drainage system can cause problems. Although a possible hazard of this kind was not recognised when uranium mining began in earnest in the 1940s, by the end of the 1950s it became clear that, for example, the ingestion of drinking water or the consumption of fish contaminated by the radium isotope could cause bone cancer. The first attempts at abatement procedures involving tailings were tried at the Durango mill on the Animas River in the USA. Since these were unsuccessful, subsequent and exhaustive research concentrated on techniques which, at reasonable cost, might remove the radium isotope at the mineral processing stage, but again without result. However, one short-term remedy is to treat the effluent from the mill with barium chloride which reacts with sulphuric acid to form a precipitate of barium sulphate and this carries the radium out of the solution. The longer term answer must be the stabilisation of the tailings, their vegetation and the prevention of the passage of further water through them that might leach out into the drainage system, a matter to which further reference is made in Section 8.4.

An even safer alternative method to dispose of radium waste might be to backfill the mine or the open-pit excavation with tailings. This process, which has been strongly recommended by the Australian government as a preferred solution, would consist of mixing the wastes with water and pumping them into place. The fine material contained in the wastes would then need to be removed so that the wastes could dry out after placement. Unfortunately, this fine material, which makes up 50% of the total, would still have to be dumped. One company, Anaconda, working in New Mexico, USA, has found a means of disposing of its separated fine material by injecting it deep under the Earth's crust via boreholes. This approach is also practised in Texas, where some land owners have demanded it in order to restore the landscape following the termination of open-pit uranium mining.

Whatever long-term measures are currently recommended to contain this problem of radioactivity, evidence from Elliot Lake has shown that mining prior to the late 1970s was certainly less than environmentally considerate. Indeed, two or three branches of the Serpent River system had been much affected by uranium tailings. These had been dumped in all four lakes on the central arm of the system, which, together with three in the eastern arm, all showed high levels of an isotope of radium released by the milling process (Figure 3.5). In the late 1970s a scheme for the expansion of mining in the area was proposed, but a provincial inquiry into environmental issues received evidence that all of these water bodies were

▲    *Figure 3.5    Uranium tailings at Elliot Lake, Ontario. More than 100 million tonnes of these were deposited directly into the environment, including the Serpent River system, before the problems of radioactivity in uranium tailings were properly appreciated. Present day legislation imposes strict controls on the disposal and proper containment of such wastes.*

quite unsuited in their present state for fishing or swimming. Since the area was in demand for recreational purposes, the inquiry concluded that the complete district would have to conform to specific standards of water quality before further development could be contemplated. This would involve, amongst other things, reducing the dangerous radium isotope to levels of $1.11 \times 10^{-11}$ Bq/l (becquerels per litre) or below.

As a longer term aim, both the Atomic Energy Control Board and the Ontario Ministry of the Environment agreed that all radium exposures must be the minimum that it is possible to achieve in the light of prevailing social and economic factors. The ultimate objective for the district at large had to be 'the restoration of the aquatic habitat to support a viable self-sustaining healthy and wholesome fishery'.

## 4.3    *Water pollution beyond the mine*

In most circumstances it would appear that problems regarding water contamination no longer have a deleterious impact in drainage systems at any great distance from mine sites, particularly if treatment schemes are undertaken. Where minerals extraction other than for metals or coal is concerned, there are also many examples of water quality improvements away from the immediate neighbourhood of the extractive operation. In the china clay working area of St Austell, Cornwall, over 600 000 tonnes per annum of micaceous residues were being discharged into St Austell river in the early 1970s. At the same time a further 300 000 tonnes per annum were being poured into the Luxulyan river. This waste material was transported downstream and deposited as white slimes in St Austell Bay. The unpleasant appearance of the river and the beaches of the coastal area led the responsible company, English China Clays, to assess a wide range of disposal alternatives. These included carrying the material 800 m out to sea by pipeline, a solution not favoured by fishing interests because of its propensity to have an adverse effect on the habitat of shellfish. Eventually, technical progress in the better separation of kaolin from these fine residues, thus reducing the amount of micaceous material, was achieved. As a result, it was decided that this waste should be settled out behind land-based dams, or disposed of into used pits, a solution that has been practised since 1975.

In spite of such improvements, some sites with long histories of extractive activity still remain polluted. For example, the Rio Tinto mining district of Spain, north-west of Seville in the foothills of the Sierra de Aracena, has been a site of the working of copper ore for 3000 years. But it was not until 1873, when the rapid development of its ore body had made it one of the largest copper producers in the world, that water pollution reached major proportions. The ore body is pyritic and contains high levels of iron, so acidic waters, stained red by iron ions, drain from old waste tips as a result of natural leaching and from the foot of disused, as well as working, tailings areas. Because these waters are not contained, they continue to do much damage to local river ecosystems.

In Cornwall, the designation of some rivers as industrial has allowed their continued use for disposal of effluents from tin mining operations. Up to the collapse in tin prices (1986) from which the industry is now recovering, the South Crofty mine near Camborne, for example, discharged the bulk of its mill waste water in the Red River. Heavily discoloured with haematite, 32 million litres of water a week containing between 60 and 90 g/l of particulates were carried to the sea some 20 km away. In West Penwith, Cornwall, similar problems arose at the Geevor tin mine, but here the effluent of 62 000 tonnes a year of solids suspended in more than 700 million litres a year of process water, passed immediately into the sea, causing heavy haematitic discoloration over a wide section of the coastline of outstanding scenic value near Land's End.

## 4.4   *Summary*

This section has shown that mine sites offer considerable possibilities for the contamination of rain or groundwater, and steps need to be taken to ensure that these are treated before they pass into the natural drainage system. However, by far the greatest problems arise from tailings. In a more detailed consideration of the hazards to water environments imposed both by uranium tailings and those containing sulphides, which have a propensity to generate acids, methods of reducing or eliminating these have been discussed. It is shown that while substantial advances in the standards of water treatment have been made in the last 25 years, including the recycling of much of the water used in the mill and collected on site, it is still possible to find river systems in developed industrial countries which have largely been abandoned to the discharge of mining effluents.

# 5   Micro environmental aspects of mining – air pollution

## 5.1   Problems of dusts

Drilling, blasting, waste tips, stockpiles and the loading and transport of ores from the quarry or open-pit face can all create dust. The dust can be dealt with by spraying water over the working surfaces and the watering of on-site roads or sweeping them if they are surfaced. The first stages of crushing the extracted rock can also create a dust problem. But here enclosure of the working plant and the use of dust collectors can both play an important part in minimising the nuisance. Metal concentrates may be dried before shipment to the nearest smelter. Where this occurs, the concentrates are more likely to release particulates rich in heavy metals into the atmosphere during transport unless steps are taken to prevent it.

Tailings ponds, apart from the problems which can arise from their appearance and the waters that can drain from them, can also expose finely ground and easily blown materials to the wind. Although there are circumstances in which the tailings may be completely covered by water, more often than not they lie above water level forming a sizeable, gently sloping beach. Substantial areas of the pond may also dry out at certain times of the year, or on closure, and if the coarser fraction of the tailings has been used to help build the dam wall, the remaining finer material may be even more susceptible to wind action.

If in exceptional cases the tailings area is very large, as at the Bingham Canyon Copper mine in Utah, USA, where the pond is more than 2100 ha in extent, remoteness means that dust is not a problem. However, at the Elliot Lake uranium workings, where one of the four major tailings areas in use covers more than 280 ha, the situation is quite different because of nearby settlements. Here, two of the tailings areas no longer in use are located on predominantly flat, high surfaces where some natural barriers and a number of dams contain the deposited tailings. Efforts have been made to reduce dust blow from these through the use of vegetation.

The Environmental Assessment Board, investigating the expansion of uranium mining in the late 1970s, recognised the hazard caused by dust with a radionuclide content to adjacent townships, especially Elliot Lake and Nordic, but also Denison and Quirke town sites. Its findings were echoed in a series of radiation surveys undertaken in 1980 at 20 uranium processing areas in the western USA which emphasised the serious hazards posed by such dust, both because it delivered a dose of radiation to the lungs and other internal organs of humans and other animals, and because it contaminated grass and became concentrated in local milk supplies. The province of Ontario's criteria for suspended particles were certainly being exceeded in the Elliot Lake area and it would appear that levels at Nordic in particular were well above 153 $g/m^2$ identifiable as tailings with a radionuclide component.

Radioactive dust is not the only problem in the vicinity of uranium tailings ponds. These impoundments tend to give off radon gas as radioactive materials decay. The breathing in of this gas can result in radiation doses to the respiratory tract that can lead ultimately to deaths from cancer. Evidence seems to suggest that levels above the natural background level may be detected from uncovered tailings to distances of 2.5–3.3 km or more. A further hazard derives from the fact that radon can build up inside buildings near tailings to quite dangerous levels.

Although levels of radon and radioactive dust in the Elliot Lake area have not caused immediate alarm to the provincial environment authority or to the Atomic Energy Control Board, they have been perceived as both an inconvenience and a possible danger to people and crops.

## 5.2   Smelting and the local environment

The processing of metalliferous ores beyond the stage achieved in the mine mill to the point at which the refined metal becomes available is carried out at the smelter. This is often located at the mine itself, although smelters which handle a wide range of metals are sometimes to be found close to the industrial complexes that use their end products.

The processes involved in smelting give off considerable quantities of waste gases and metal particulates which are vented to the atmosphere via chimneys. In more recent years, as concern about possible environmental damage and health hazards have risen, the waste gases vented from primary iron and steel, aluminium and iron-alloy production have been subjected to some cleaning, using methods which involve electrostatic precipitation or bag filtration. The smelting of sulphide ores has also been controlled. Sulphur dioxide (by reaction with oxygen and water) is now largely converted to sulphuric acid within the plant rather than in the atmosphere. The effectiveness of these containment procedures is no longer a technical problem; instead, it depends on what smelter operators are forced to spend on them. As it is, gases and metal particulates are still vented via stacks to the atmosphere in a compromise which not only reflects wider community needs, but also the capacity of the smelter operator to bear the expense of improved 'house-keeping'.

Although the use of very tall stacks as a means of achieving high-level dispersal of effluents has moved the impact of air pollution well beyond the immediate vicinity of the smelting operation and the community in which it is situated, this technique is not universally used and in many instances the effects of smelter discharges mostly remain a local problem.

Recent evidence from Poland, for example, shows the highly local impact of excessive levels of heavy metals (copper, lead, zinc and cadmium) on soils adjacent to a smelter. This has resulted in morphological and metabolic changes in the crops which they support. All these metals are toxic to plants, and are recognised as a hazard for people, as Box 3.1 makes clear.

Itai-itai disease can result from the inhalation of dust containing cadmium but is more likely to be from the eating of foods which have at some stage been subject to air pollution from smelters that process ores associated with this metal. The disease (which leads to bone porosity, followed by skeletal deformation, fracture and ultimate collapse) was first recognised in the vicinity of some of the 25 smelters in Japan. To cite one example: in 1960 amounts of cadmium in the atmosphere around the Annaka city smelter in Japan were as high as 18 p.p.m. in plants at a distance of 0.4 km, falling to 10 p.p.m. at 1 km away. Soil analyses showed cadmium had built up to levels of 33.5 p.p.m. 0.5 km away from the plant and to 9 p.p.m. at 1.5 km. In fields in the Usui river basin immediately beyond, cadmium in rice crops averaged 0.39 p.p.m., but in samples taken from areas where there was no known pollution, cadmium levels averaged around 0.07 p.p.m. By the end of the decade average levels in rice crops had risen to 0.49 p.p.m. while in the soils it averaged 22.3 p.p.m. By then the wider spread of the problem had been acknowledged by the setting up in Japan of a Committee on Cadmium Poisoning and the Itai-Itai Disease. Its deliberations eventually led to the banning of the use of cadmium in that country.

There are several other studies of cadmium smelting operations in England, the USA, Canada and Australia. All show that where the levels of cadmium in soils and vegetation near smelter chimneys are high, this rapidly falls as distance from the plant increases, just as it did in the Japanese examples. Only at Avonmouth (England) and Belledune (Canada) is there evidence of high levels of cadmium uptake by crops within 0.8 km of the smelters. Fortunately, in neither case are the crops concerned a staple part of the diet in the way that rice is in Japan.

One other smelter effluent also has a relatively local impact on plants as well as people and animals. Fluoride can be vented into the atmosphere in the process of making aluminium, but it may also be given off as a result of the processing of clays in the manufacture of bricks and ceramics, and the production of iron and phosphate fertilisers. Gaseous fluorides can be taken into the human respiratory tract and ingested through the intestines. Fluorosis, a form of osteosclerosis, has been known to result, but only in those exposed to high levels of fluoride on a continuing basis, as happened

---

Box 3.1

In 1985 the Polish parliament recognised 27 districts as being under ecological threat. Within these, four parts of the country were declared ecological disaster areas: Upper Silesia, the Krakow area, Gdansk Bay and the Liegnitz/Glogow copper belt. The official definition of disaster areas was that they were not safe to live in. But since the disaster areas identified were inhabited by 11 million people (30% of the Polish population) evacuation was not a practical solution. One exception was made, however: the five villages surrounding the copper smelters at Glogow, where the inhabitants suffered chronic health problems, including eye and chest disorders, dizziness and fatigue. Apart from the direct impact of airborne pollution on people, emissions from this smelter complex have affected drinking water and agricultural products in the surrounding area. Analysis of these has shown excessive concentrations of copper, zinc, manganese, lead and other metals.

By 1990 most people had been evacuated from around Glogow, including all the children, although one village on the leeward side of the plant is still used as temporary accommodation for its workers. Some small farmers remain since they have been paid to switch their crops to those likely to be much less affected by airborne pollutants, such as wheat.

Without reducing production, the copper smelter has increased its environmental acceptability by

having created around it a sanitary zone of hardy deciduous trees (conifers would be too susceptible to sulphur dioxide emissions). By fitting British filters and scrubbers, it has cut its metallic particulate emissions by 90%. Nevertheless, the plant's ecological destructive power remains high, and its copper smelters, Glogow One and Glogow Two, typify a wider problem for Poland.

Glogow Two is a hermetically sealed furnace built under Finnish licence in 1978. It produces 40% of the plant's copper, but yields only 10% of its total particulate emissions and 4% of its gases. The Soviet-designed smelter Glogow One, built seven years earlier, is responsible for the rest, amounting to 1700 tonnes of airborne copper particulates a year, plus 35 000 tonnes of sulphur dioxide.

The world demand for copper means that it could prove crucial to Poland's economic survival. Glogow One produces 180 000 tonnes a year. However, such an outdated means of production is unsupportably expensive, too wasteful of energy and raw materials and too polluting to be tolerated. Not surprisingly, in January 1990 when a list of the country's worst polluting industrial plants was published, Glogow One was recorded on it. By June each industrial plant in Poland had to present plans to make itself economically viable and environmentally safe. In such circumstances it was clear that Glogow One could not survive.

in the early European aluminium smelter plants. A more notable problem has been the ingestion of forage containing fluoride concentrations in excess of 40 mg/kg by animals, especially dairy cattle. This has been known to damage teeth and cause bone degeneration and lameness. Tests on cattle at 43 farms close by a source of gaseous fluoride near Peterborough in England were carried out by the Ministry of Agriculture, Fisheries and Food in the 1970s and revealed fluorosis at 19 of them. As to plants themselves, fluorides are absorbed through the leaves and concentrated in the tops, causing a burnt appearance. Among the most sensitive species are apricots and gladioli and among the least is celery. The evidence is that a concentration of 0.5 $\mu g/m^3$ (ten times ambient levels) to 1.0 $\mu g/m^3$ for 30 days in air could give rise to the 40 mg/kg level in vegetation, at which problems occur. A variety of techniques for the control of the gaseous fluorides from a specific source exist and can be relatively easily exercised up to 95% effectiveness. These are usually brought into play once a problem has been identified or, in the case of new plant, to meet the relevant environmental protection standards.

> *Activity 2*
>
> Look back over material in Section 5.2 and comment on the most important differences in the attitudes of various governments towards smelter pollution.

## 5.3   Summary

Mining operations can create a series of problems at the local level, including dust from working surfaces, waste tips and stock piles, all of which may be rich in heavy metals unless control systems are used. The major problems have really arisen from the smelting of metal ores, where the discharge of particulates from smelter chimneys create a major health problem for the area in the immediate vicinity – so much so that the emission of cadmium (which is readily taken up by field crops) from Japanese smelters has been banned. As with water pollution, the story is one of increasing awareness of the damage that can be done by the discharge of effluents, combined with ever stricter controls.

# 6   Meso environmental impacts of mining

## 6.1   Sudbury – a classic case

Several studies from the 1970s have shown that following the expulsion of effluents from very tall stacks, under certain circumstances mineral particulates, and especially sulphur dioxide (if a sulphide ore has been smelted), can travel substantial distances from their sites of release. Only their removal from the air by rain is likely to hinder this process.

The history of Sudbury in Ontario, Canada, illustrates the main trends in air pollution that derive from such a source and its changing role, first as a polluter of Sudbury and then of the region around Sudbury, but later as a major contributor to transnational problems.

The early years of mining and smelting at Sudbury (summarised in Box 3.2) provide the background to the more recent developments of the 1970s and 80s.

The key to the spread of air pollution problems into the meso environment came in 1972 with the construction by Inco of a 387-m tall

---

### Box 3.2   The Sudbury story – mining and smelting from 1883 to 1978

It is said that it was a blacksmith, Tom Flanagan, who in 1883 first noticed a rusty stain on a rock near what is now Murray Mine. There was some disappointment when it was discovered that it was an ore which contained nickel as well as copper, since the market for nickel was poor, and inadequate technology existed for the separation of the two metals. In the 1880s, however, a separation process was discovered giving rise to a tremendous expansion in the mining industry in Sudbury.

In 1886, S. J. Ritchie, an American, started the Canadian Copper Company and mining began in earnest. At first the ore was sent for smelting to Britain and Bayonne, New Jersey, but in 1888 the first roast yard and production-oriented smelter were set up in Copper Cliff. In the roasting of copper-nickel ore, sulphur is removed mainly from its associated pyrrhotite by heating in the presence of air to a sufficient temperature to begin a process of self-maintaining oxidation. In the early days the crushed ore was piled on huge beds of cordwood several feet deep, covered to prevent open flames, and ignited. The beds of ore would burn for two or more months before being loaded into cars with steam shovels and smelted in the furnaces.

The discovery of nickel-steel for armourplate and the Spanish–American war of 1898 boosted the demand for nickel, and by 1901 there were 80 roast heaps and 9 furnaces in the area. In 1902 the International Nickel Company of New York (Inco) was organized through the merging of many existing companies, and in the years that followed it purchased a number of other companies, including Mond in 1928. The only company remaining independent of Inco to this day is Falconbridge Nickel Mines, which was incorporated in 1928.

In 1916 the Canadian public demanded that the assets of Inco be placed under Canadian control. Also, in 1916, its open air roasting activities were moved from Copper Cliff to O'Donnell, where the remains of its main roast bed can be seen today. This roast bed operated until 1929, when government insistence resulted in the building of a new Copper Cliff smelter which had roasting furnaces and a 510 foot stack, the highest in the British Empire at that time. Although a number of new stacks were built at the various smelters over the years, the 510 foot stack was only exceeded in height by the 637 foot stack at the Copper Cliff Iron Ore Plant (1956) and the Inco 'superstack', which became operational as an anti-pollution measure in 1972.

In many ways, from an environmental improvement point of view, 1972 was a 'red letter' year, since it was also the year in which the Coniston smelter and a pyrrhotite roasting plant at Falconbridge were closed, the Inco iron ore plant cut back on emissions and both a strike and a holiday shut-down occurred. Probably the period most damaging to the environment, with the exception of the early roast bed days, was in the early years of the second world war, when production of copper and nickel were doubled in response to wartime demands, and pollution control had to take second place in company priorities.

A pleasing aspect of pollution control which has developed over the years, though not reaching the level hoped for by many environmentalists, has been the use of waste gases to manufacture sulphuric acid. The first acid plant was built at Coniston by Mond Nickel in 1925. Although Inco's first plant was built in 1930, its latest plant opened in 1967, producing 1400 tonnes of acid per day. In 1978, Falconbridge Nickel opened a sulphuric acid plant along with its new smelter. The cutback on sulphur dioxide emissions in 1972 (from more than 2 million to less than 1.3 million tonnes per annum for Inco, and from 344 000 to 244 000 tonnes per annum for Falconbridge), together with the better dispersion achieved by the 'superstack', have combined to give a noticeable improvement in plant growth in the Sudbury area and a marked reduction in what the Ministry of the Environment calls 'potentially injurious fumigations'.
(Keith Winterhalder, 1978)

chimney at Copper Cliff. This 'superstack' was designed to achieve a high level of effluent dilution, well away from the Sudbury area. Given that this was by then the largest single source of pollution in the world, such an approach seemed a reasonable one. In effect what happened was that Sudbury, through the superstack, managed to export most of its problems. These have been recognised in a belt extending some 60 km downwind of the plant in Sudbury, where not only some of the metal particulates in the plume, but also a good deal of its sulphur dioxide tends to fall back to ground level in this zone, having been converted by the action of the oxygen and moisture in the atmosphere to dilute sulphuric acid, popularly known as 'acid rain'.

Studies undertaken in the 1970s of some of the lakes in the affected area showed that in many instances the chemical balance of their waters had altered. The uncontaminated lakes were nearly neutral (neither acid nor alkaline) and, having a granite bedrock rather than a limestone or clay base layer, lacked resistance to acidification. So acid rain appears to have tipped the pH of a number of these lakes to values below 5.5, thus providing an environment in which fish and the organisms on which they feed could not survive.

Not unexpectedly, many of these water bodies also contained in solution abnormally high levels of heavy metal ions, particularly nickel and copper discharged from the plume. Although there was a lack of evidence from those lakes that had a low pH and were already biologically dead, it is known that metals of this sort can enter aquatic ecosystems and become concentrated in animal food chains with devastating effect. Not only are copper and nickel toxic, evidence shows that if both are taken into the food chain at the same time they enhance each other's toxicity.

Of the lakes closest to Sudbury, within 20 km of the major smelter, about 20 were part of a survey reported in the early 1980s. Because their bedrocks varied widely in chemical and physical characteristics, the degree of stress shown as a result of acid rain varied considerably, with about a quarter having unacceptedly low pH values. These lakes also varied in their metal content according to their pH but especially according to intensity of atmospheric input and thus distance from Sudbury. If the global mean value of 10 $\mu g/l$ of nickel is taken as a reference point, only four lakes at the outer edge of the 20-km radial were remotely close to or under this figure. Most were far above it, with one reaching the highest level recorded anywhere in the world – 512 $\mu g/l$. The highest levels of copper concentration in lake waters (102 $\mu g/l$) were to be found at this same location. Indeed, copper concentrations in the lakes in question followed a similar pattern to those for nickel.

Between 40 and 60 km from Sudbury, further studies concentrated on the presence of nickel and copper and the impact of sulphur dioxide upon lakes in the Killarney Provincial Park, relating these to the Inco stack at Copper Cliff. The Provincial Park is important for recreation, particularly fishing and canoeing. In the lakes largely located on granite, sulphur dioxide fall-out as dilute sulphuric acid has resulted in their waters falling below pH values of 5.5 (Figure 3.6) with a resulting loss of aquatic life. Although nickel concentrations at this distance (Figure 3.7) fell to levels which were acceptable in terms of the standards generally applied to domestic drinking water (at not more than about 25 $\mu g/l$), the presence of copper in many of the lakes remained above that level (Figure 3.8).

The effect of the situation created by the transport of effluents from Sudbury on a provincial park, once celebrated for its fishing, was not a matter of minor environmental significance. In the early 1980s water-based

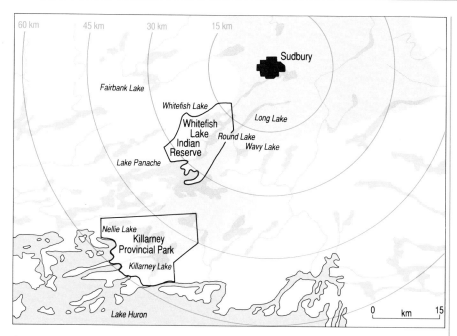

▲     *Figure 3.6     Sulphur dioxide emissions after the construction of the superstack at Sudbury. The shaded area may contain lakes with waters of pH 5.5 or less, depending on their bedrock.*

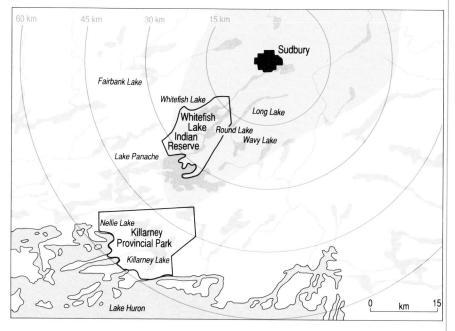

▲     *Figure 3.7     Nickel emissions after the construction of the superstack at Sudbury. Nickel can be used as a reasonable definer of metal emissions from the Sudbury area smelting complex since it is naturally low in lake waters. A global mean is 10 μg/l, while lakes in the shaded area can be as high as 300 μg/l, even where there are no direct discharges to these lakes of liquid effluents containing nickel.*

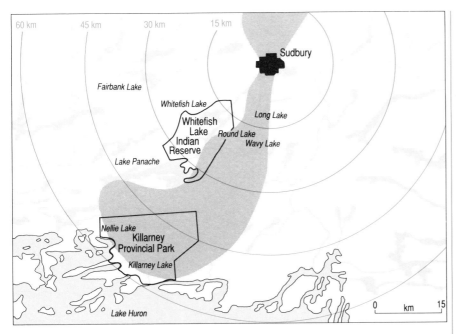

▲   Figure 3.8   *Copper emissions after the construction of the superstack at Sudbury. The shaded area may contain lakes with over 25 μg/l.*

recreational activities, such as those common in Killarney, directly generated annual expenditures of $900 million and indirectly a further $750 million in Canada. Because of their importance in terms of wealth creation it was perhaps not surprising that an attack was begun on the dual problems of low pH and elevated metals levels through the addition of lime to the lake waters. Such efforts to raise the level of the former and lower the level of the latter were seen as a prelude to restocking the lakes with fish. A similar programme has been applied to lakes less than the 20 km from Sudbury. The results coming from all these attempts at aquatic rehabilitation were far from entirely satisfactory. For example, Lohi Lake, some 6.5 km from Sudbury and one of the most adversely affected water bodies, had a first liming six years earlier, after which its pH rose from 4.3 to 4.8, whilst nickel concentrations dropped from 264 μg/l to 223 μg/l and copper concentration dropped from 84 μg/l to 61 μg/l.

## 6.2   *Regional improvements*

Notwithstanding such limited efforts to improve lake water quality, the situation with respect to the impact of Sudbury emissions on water bodies in the region has not remained static. Initial levels of discharge from the smelters were reduced by process improvements at Falconbridge in 1978 and Inco in 1980. The latter were also coupled with a regulatory control placed on the superstack in that same year limiting its sulphur dioxide emissions to an average of 2500 tonnes per day. At the same time, industrial problems, leading to an eight-month shutdown at Inco in 1978 and 1979 and the more recent world-wide industrial recession, resulted in a decline in the quantities of ore smelted and also, therefore, in stack discharges. Thus a comparison of data for the quality of 209 lakes collected in the period 1974 to 1976 with that for 1981 to 1983 shows signs of an improvement unrelated to any rehabilitation programme undertaken at individual lakes.

The key to a real and continued improvement in the water quality of these lakes has been the addressing of the problem at source. Following lengthy consultations with the industries concerned, in 1984 the Ontario Ministry of the Environment started a ten-year programme of sulphur dioxide reductions applied to all major sources of this gaseous effluent. This 'Countdown Acid Rain' scheme set for the Inco smelter a series of target falls in stack emissions, starting at 728 000 tonnes a year, reducing to 685 000 tonnes by 1986, and then to 265 000 tonnes by 1994. A further fall to 175 000 tonnes would then be negotiated.

## 6.3    Other meso studies

Although the Sudbury region remains an extreme case, other studies have been undertaken at a meso level of the impact of smelter discharges. In the case of copper smelting, for example, attention has been drawn to the propensity for not only the major components of smelter effluents to be transported long distances, but also trace elements as well. Indeed, in work carried out on five copper smelters in south-east Arizona, it has been shown by trace element analysis that each smelter has its own distinctive 'fingerprint' of metal particulates that may be identified at a considerable distance from a point source of pollution.

The world's largest lead smelter at Port Pirie on the Spencer Gulf in south Australia contributes not only lead particulates to the atmosphere but also those of silver, zinc and cadmium. Indeed, its impact on soils in the area can be traced up to 65 km from the operation, with the highest concentrations to the north and south in the direction of the prevailing winds. The overall spatial distribution patterns of contamination recognised in this initial study implied that stack out-fall would especially affect the Gulf area of the north-west and south-west quadrants. Further research in the early 1980s established just such a situation with over 600 km$^2$ of sea-bed sediments affected by these metal particulates. The probable ambient background levels of metallics in the region as a whole are for silver, cadmium, lead and zinc respectively: 0.3, <0.03 (less than 0.03), 2.9 and 10 $\mu$g/l. These may be compared with the sediment measurements shown in Figure 3.9. Analysis of the flora and fauna of the area has shown that almost all organisms contain elevated concentrations of cadmium, lead and zinc. Twenty common species of fish appear to have been eliminated or reduced in numbers by the presence of metals. Indeed, concentrations of 0.7 $\mu$g/g and above of cadmium and 92 $\mu$g/g of zinc seem to have a clear impact, though they cannot be assumed to be acutely toxic to all species. As far as the less mobile members of the fauna are concerned, the range of species could be observed to increase away from the most contaminated zones.

Of these other investigations, only the situation at Flin Flon, Manitoba, Canada, provides a strong parallel with Sudbury in that the discharge of sulphur dioxide and metal particulates from the smelting of sulphide ores containing zinc, copper and cadmium has also created environmental problems. Like the Sudbury area, Flin Flon lies on the granitic Precambrian Shield. But a few kilometres to the south of the city, this gives way to the limestones common in the central part of the American continent. A study dating from the mid-1970s not unexpectedly indicated that as a result of the discharges of its own 281-m superstack, many lakes in the area had become contaminated with airborne metals and had also been affected by sulphur dioxide fall-out.

Q   Given the two kinds of bedrock in the Flin Flon area and the knowledge you have gained in this section so far, what broad conclusions do you expect the study to show?

A   It will underline the potential for ecological disturbance in those lakes on the granitic Shield with their poor ability to neutralise acidity. This is important not least because of their use for tourism and sport. They may be contrasted with those water bodies located on limestone, albeit more distant from the smelter, which remain largely unaffected. This is because the limestone is chemically basic and so able to neutralise added acidity.

The most recent assessment of the impact of the smelter on its surrounding area is summarised in Table 3.3, which shows the annual deposition of metals at selected sites at different distances from the smelter. You can use Table 3.3 to compare deposition levels and their effects in two contrasting lakes, Nesootao and Hook. Both are considerably influenced by sulphur dioxide fall-out from the smelter (as acid rain). Although this has not been measured on a site-by-site basis, discharges from the chimney, at the time

▲   Figure 3.9   Sea-bed sediment measurements (in µg/l) of (a) lead and (b) zinc near the Port Pirie lead smelter, New South Wales, which contaminates areas with metallic particulates up to 65 km from its stack.

*Table 3.3   Deposition and distribution of smelter metals in six lakes near the smelter at Flin Flon, Manitoba*

| Lake | Distance from smelter/km | Deposition/($mg/m^2/yr$) | | | |
|------|------|------|------|------|------|
| | | Zinc | Copper | Cadmium | Lead |
| Cliff | 4.0 | 1400 | 62 | 3 | 32 |
| Hamell | 4.2 | 1287 | 58 | 3 | 31 |
| Lake 6 | 5.2 | 889 | 42 | 2 | 24 |
| Hook | 9.5 | 313 | 27 | 2 | 27 |
| Nesootao | 12.5 | 195 | 11 | 0.7 | 9 |
| Thompson | 20.2 | 87 | 5 | 0.4 | 5 |

Source: Franzin, W. G. (1984) Aquatic contaminants in the vicinity of the base metal smelter at Flin Flon, Manitoba, Canada, pp. 523–78 in *Environmental Impact of Smelters*, ed. J. O. Nriagu, Advances in Environmental Science and Technology, vol. 15, Wiley, New York.

the table was compiled, were in the range 232 000 to 306 000 tonnes per year, accounting for 4.5% of Canadian emissions. Because of the rapid decay factor for metal particulates with distance from a point source of emission, Nesootao is less contaminated than Hook. However, since Hook Lake is well to the south of Flin Flon and on a limestone bedrock which assists in the process of maintaining alkaline pH levels in its waters, its biota were found to contain relatively low metal concentrations. This contrasts with Nesootao to the north-west of the smelter. Its granitic base cannot modify the acidity of the lake waters arising from acid rain. This has led to the considerable bioaccumulation of metal particulates, especially by fish, in spite of the fact that the lake is less subject to metal particulate fall-out than Hook.

## 6.4   Pollution control problems

Although steps were taken in 1983 to reduce metal particulate emissions from the Flin Flon smelter, then running at 9600 tonnes a year, by 80–85%, no plans as yet exist to reduce levels of discharge of sulphur dioxide. What to do about such high levels of discharge inevitably creates a problem at most of the extremely remote smelter locations that process sulphide ores. Sulphur dioxide can be used in the manufacture of sulphuric acid, but if markets are distant and transport costs so high as to make it uneconomic as a saleable commodity, then this means of disposal cannot be used. This applies with particular force to the Mount Isa smelting complex in Queensland. There the processing of copper sulphide and silver–lead–zinc sulphide ores take place at a semi-arid location which is 960 km west of Townsville and 1560 km north-west of Brisbane, the nearest sizeable settlements.

Thus, in spite of the fact that Australia has the means to meet its own sulphuric acid needs, it is still cheaper to import the raw material for its manufacture, sulphur, even if the outlay in 1982 amounted to $A70 million. Only the nickel sulphide smelting plant at Kalgoorlie, which currently discharges some 330 000 tonnes per year of sulphur dioxide, offers a real opportunity to reduce this import bill. This is because of its location in the state of Western Australia, which is the nation's major user (at 31% of total consumption) of superphosphate, an agricultural fertiliser which is manufactured using sulphuric acid and phosphate.

If the only prospect open to such remote operations involved with sulphides is the release of sulphur dioxide to the atmosphere, at least the barren nature of the terrain for many hundreds of square kilometres around Mount Isa means that environmental damage is unlikely to be great. Nevertheless, such effluents still need to be vented away from the 27 000 inhabitants of Mount Isa township itself. These smelters produce between them nearly 400 000 tonnes per annum of sulphur dioxide, derived from the processing of 120 000 tonnes of copper and 120 000 tonnes per annum of lead. Certainly, readings taken around the settlement prior to 1977 and the implementation of the Queensland Clean Air Act were sufficiently unacceptable for the National Air Pollution Council to call for a programme of high-level sulphur dioxide dispersal from new chimneys (300 m and 270 m) for each of the smelters. More than this, discharges were only to be permitted when the prevailing wind blew stack emissions away from the community.

As for the particulates of copper, lead, arsenic, antimony, cadmium and mercury given off by the Mount Isa smelting operations, agreed pollution control standards after 1977 of a maximum total of 23 $\mu g/m^3$ effluent levels in the stacks were a substantial reduction on levels prior to that year. Formerly the lead smelter alone often discharged at values of 70 $\mu g/m^3$, and the copper smelter was putting out 530 $\mu g/m^3$ made up of lead, arsenic and copper. The improvements carried out at the behest of the National Air Pollution Council resulted from modifications or additions to existing gas-cleaning hardware and the installation of major new items of bag and filter equipment.

---

*Activity 3*

Describe the similarities and differences between the control measures imposed by governments on Mount Isa and Sudbury and the reasons for them. Your response will help you to summarise some of the key issues in this section of Chapter 3.

---

# 7   Macro environmental aspects of mining

## 7.1   Transfrontier air pollution

One definition of the macro impact of mining pollutants might be where these cross national frontiers. Such a definition could stretch credibility in the case of the Trail zinc smelting complex in British Columbia. The largest complex of its kind anywhere in the world, it has a long history in terms of air pollution.

Before the invention in 1929 of a practical method of producing sulphuric acid from the sulphur dioxide in the smelter effluent, emissions ran at around 300 tonnes a day of sulphur dioxide. The mountainous terrain in the vicinity of the smelter made it difficult for the gas to escape, and the area surrounding the operation had been denuded of vegetation. Today, however, 95% sulphur fixation is achieved, the spin-off product is used by the local agricultural industry, and the area has long been revegetated with acacia and conifers. Measurement of sulphur dioxide in the ambient air in a 7-km radius around the smelter indicates an average of 0.02 p.p.m. The air standards in the region beyond, because of the close proximity of the US border and the dispersal achieved from the release of effluents from the smelter stack, are controlled by an International Joint Commission, along with the provincial government. Critical emission levels are varied according to wind direction and the state of the vegetation growing season, but in all cases values fall within clearly defined limits.

Accepting that Trail must be a special case of transfrontier pollution, the smelter itself, like others discussed above and many more around the world, contribute their share of sulphur dioxide to the atmosphere. Depending on location and country they feed into the overall levels of atmospheric sulphur dioxide, along with power stations (especially those that are coal fired) and heavy industry. For example, in Canada, where emissions of sulphur dioxide in the mid-1980s amounted to around 6.5 million tonnes a year, smelters contributed two-thirds of the overall output. These Canadian figures compare with the US total for sulphur dioxide emissions of 3800 million tonnes per year, but the contribution to this by smelters is much lower at around one-third.

Nevertheless, the fact remains that sulphur dioxide from a wide range of sources, including smelters, can remain in the atmosphere and travel considerable distances across continents. Thus the out-wash of sulphur dioxide, which falls as dilute sulphuric acid, together with anthropogenically derived oxides of nitrogen, which are mostly created through the combustion of hydrocarbon fuels, can affect areas remote from their points of origin. The impact of these effluents can be adverse where the environment is one of peculiar sensitivity, in much the same way as they were in Killarney Provincial Park. Evidence now available shows that sensitive environments located on granite bedrocks such as those in eastern Canada, in the north-eastern USA, in the Federal Republic of Germany, in The Netherlands and in Scandinavia, are increasingly succumbing to damage from acid rain. These matters will be pursued further in Chapter 4.

## 7.2  Summary

In the discussion in this chapter so far, consideration has been given to the impact of minerals extraction and processing at micro, meso and macro levels. Throughout, some attention has been given to ameliorating the environmental effects that such activities may have on the environment during the operation of the mine or the smelter. These include the working of some minerals underground instead of by open pit, where visual damage can be a particularly sensitive issue; the extraction of minerals such as coal and salt in such a way as to avoid subsidence; the disposal of tailings away from areas of scenic quality and their placement underground if they are radioactive; the avoidance or reduction of acid drainage problems along with other attempts to diminish the exposure of tailings to the atmosphere during their operative stage; and the containment and reduction of smelter effluents.

In the next section the argument is taken a step further by considering ways to deal with those environmental problems which occur at the conclusion of minerals extraction and processing or at the end of a phase in such operations, for example, as the completion of a tailings pond.

# 8   Reclamation of mined areas

## 8.1   Some underlying principles

When mining operations at any site end, it becomes necessary to decide what is to be done to the area to mitigate the impacts of the operation on the environment. Several options are available.

- First of all, the site can be neglected, leaving natural processes to do what they will with it. In spite of legislation, this can still occur where sites are remote or where reclamation may be particularly difficult. However, the result is not always to be deplored. For example, disused chalk quarries on the downlands of southern England have been neglected because of the difficulties of rehabilitating vertical faces, but they have ultimately become valuable as nature reserves.

- More often than not, schemes will be undertaken for **reclamation** of the area as quickly as possible in order to improve its appearance, return it to some productive capacity or contain toxic materials that might otherwise damage adjacent habitats or, indeed, human beings. This may involve attempts to achieve **restoration** of the area by recreating the original topography and perhaps re-establishing the land use prior to mineral extraction. For all these purposes, a major aim is to establish soil and vegetation which will stabilise the surface, exclude air, reduce water penetration and so prevent acidification.

- **Rehabilitation** may also be considered in which the return of the land to some productive use involves the development of new land forms and/or ecosystems. In Kansas, for example, a grassland ecosystem that has been surface mined has been replaced with a lake because the area lacked standing surface waters. A well-managed lake might be regarded as more desirable than the original and certainly more desirable than the area in its unrehabilitated state.

- Other forms of 'enhancement' have involved such considerations as the rehabilitation of surface mined sites at slopes shallower than the original. In west Virginia, for example, the argument has been that reductions in the pre-existing slope of at least 20 degrees diminish the potential for surface erosion in an area prone to such problems.

Whatever the complex of the factors that may be involved in the decision-making process relating to how to treat worked-out mine sites, the fact remains that the characteristics of the waste materials and land surfaces after extractive operations are important factors affecting the ability of such sites to undergo effective reclamation or restoration. These may be considered under the key headings of physical and chemical.

## Physical properties

As was stated in Section 4.1, the physical and chemical properties of mining-derived materials are commonly associated with their particle size distribution, which may vary from the large person-sized blocks sometimes obtained from stone quarrying to the finest clay-sized particles resulting from the processing of metallic ores. As particle size decreases there is a corresponding increase in surface area per unit of volume. This determines moisture retention by particles, drainage and availability of nutrients to plants.

In the course of soil formation, physical processes tend to reduce particle size. Similarly, residual materials from mining activities may be reduced in size by environmental processes, although for tailings and hard resistant materials this may not be significant within a human generation.

## Chemical properties

Plants require a number of elements which they absorb mainly through their roots. Some plants specifically require more of one element than another, but in general those elements needed in fairly large quantities are nitrogen, phosphorus, potassium, calcium, magnesium and sulphur. Those required in only small quantities include chlorine, iron, manganese, boron, copper and molybdenum. The precise requirements of vegetation for each element are difficult to define and depend on a wide variety of factors such as type of vegetation and on the level of production required. Some elements may be available in such low concentrations in soils and waste materials that plants show deficiency symptoms and reduced size. On the other hand, some elements may be available in unnaturally high concentrations and produce toxic conditions. Spoil and tailings may contain elements which are directly toxic to plants even in quite low concentrations: cadmium and arsenic are examples.

The availability of a nutrient element is usually strongly influenced by pH conditions, as shown in Figure 3.10. In the favourable range 5.5 to 7.5, most plant nutrients are available, usually in the form of ions in the soil solution. These include both simple metal cations (like $K^+$, $Ca^{2+}$, $Mg^{2+}$ and $Fe^{2+}$) and polyatomic anions of non-metals (like sulphate, $SO_4^{2-}$, and nitrate, $NO_3^-$). Above pH 7.5 the availability of iron and manganese diminishes, because they begin to form insoluble hydroxides, and the same happens to copper and zinc above pH 8.

The original sources of nutrient input to the soil are rainfall, natural weathering and the fixation of atmospheric nitrogen by bacteria in the soil. Once a soil is established, nutrients are also available from decaying organic matter. Precipitation inputs may be significant but are usually insufficient for plant growth in most climatic regions. The natural weathering of rocks reduces average particle size and provides most of the plant nutrients with the exception of nitrogen. This can be taken through the leaves as well as the roots. Soil organic material accumulates large quantities of plant nutrients which on decomposition again become available for absorption by plants. A particular type of organic material, humus, also plays a key role, along with clay particles, in holding mineral elements in an available form.

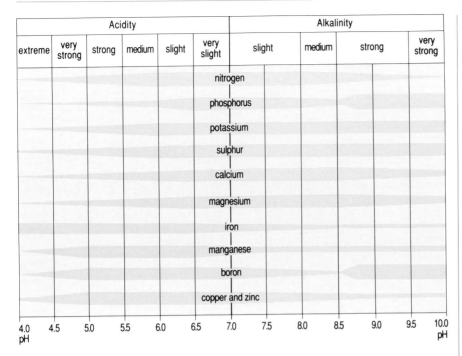

| Acidity | | | | | | Alkalinity | | | |
|---|---|---|---|---|---|---|---|---|---|
| extreme | very strong | strong | medium | slight | very slight | slight | medium | strong | very strong |

nitrogen

phosphorus

potassium

sulphur

calcium

magnesium

iron

manganese

boron

copper and zinc

| 4.0 | 4.5 | 5.0 | 5.5 | 6.0 | 6.5 | 7.0 | 7.5 | 8.0 | 8.5 | 9.0 | 9.5 | 10.0 |
| pH | | | | | | | | | | | | pH |

▲   *Figure 3.10   The relationship between the pH of the soil and the availability of mineral nutrients. The broader the horizontal bar representing mineral nutrients, the greater their availability.*

Against this background discussion of the key factors regarding the properties of materials that will play a major part in site reclamation, consideration can now be given to the processes involved. This may best be undertaken by grouping the sites into three: voids or open pits and quarries; overburden and waste tips; and tailings ponds.

## 8.2   The reclamation of voids

The commonest of all open-pit operations is that for sand and gravel. More often than not, workings have taken place below the water table. Even so, the voids concerned may be readily incorporated into a general reclamation plan. Any waste sand or gravel poses no threat to the environment and may be readily landscaped by using earth-moving machinery, often to grade gently into a central lake. In the United Kingdom the best known examples are along the River Thames, both in its lower reaches west of London and near its headwaters on the Wiltshire/ Gloucestershire border; near Olney in Buckinghamshire; and at Holme Pierrepoint in Nottinghamshire. Most of these areas have been reclaimed as recreational facilities in the form of water parks, catering primarily for watersports such as sailing, water skiing and fishing (Figure 3.11). Such pits have also long been considered as suitable fill sites for domestic, industrial and other wastes by many planning authorities. Several hundred hectares of wet sand and gravel pits have been filled in the Greater London area where the demand for building land has been strong. Where these wet pits are concerned, the main type of material used is rubble or inert waste,

▲   *Figure 3.11   (Left) The Cotswold Water Park, an area of nearly 600 ha on the Wiltshire/Gloucestershire border in the valley of the upper Thames, where local authorities have collaborated to rehabilitate worked-out sand and gravel pits as country parks. Alternatively, such sites can be given a new lease of life as a venue for water sports, as at Ringwood, Hampshire (right).*

for in spite of encouraging research into disposing of domestic refuse into wet pits, no satisfactory economic method of eliminating the risk of polluting groundwater supplies has been found.

Where open-pit operations have involved the extraction of rock aggregate, clays or metallic ores, considerable volumes of rock overburden may have been removed. Pits located in dense rocks or clays will likely fill with water and their fate will largely depend on their degree of isolation or the population density of the surrounding countryside. In the case of the large derelict brick clay pits of Bedfordshire and the Peterborough area, both in the highly populated south-east of England, their impermeability makes them ideal for the disposal of wastes such as garbage, low-toxic material and fly ash from coal-burning power stations. Indeed, research undertaken in Illinois on brick clay pits shows that toxic elements in wastes deposited in them have not migrated more than 0.5 m in more than 30 years. Nevertheless, waste containing a relatively high organic content can allow the formation of methane gas with the risk of explosion unless special precautions are taken. Deep pits of the dimensions which commonly remain after metal mining in most instances are too far from urban centres to be of use for waste disposal. Pits in limestone, or where there was some limestone overburden, may sometimes be useful as disposal sites for certain toxic wastes. The high pH of water percolating through the rocks around the site and into the pit, frequently around 8.4, will serve to hold many toxic elements out of solution. The soil and overburden removed from the pit will have been placed away from, but close to, the excavation. With the progress of time, forest vegetation will probably colonise these materials, as has happened, for example, at the iron mines near Star Lake in New York state.

Prior to excavation of the pit, however, sensible practice often dictates that the soil be carefully stored simply because it is an ideal medium for the establishment of the vegetation cover after mining. As soil consists of a number of distinctive layers called horizons, it is preferable to remove and retain the uppermost horizon on its own as this is the site of plant growth and organic activity such as that created by worms and microbes. This adds to the cost of rehabilitation so it is common practice to keep all the soil horizons together. There is evidence, though, to show that in soil which is stored for long periods of time the microbial and earthworm populations are reduced, soil structure deteriorates, and fertility declines.

In spite of efforts to restore voids to their original surface levels, this remains the exception rather than the rule, especially where hard rock quarries are concerned. In the United Kingdom, of the annual take of land for limestone, only 5% is completely restored. In such situations attempts at rehabilitation are confined to trying to mellow as rapidly as possible the disused vertical working bluffs. Here the natural or artificial regeneration of flora can be assisted by creating screes at their bases and by layering their faces with ledges on which plant life can take a hold.

## 8.3   Dealing with overburden and waste tips

Physically, these materials are usually very coarse but can consist of boulder-sized to clay-sized particles. The finer particles can fall into the voids between the larger fraction, leaving an uneven surface. Their physical nature makes them an unsympathetic site for plant growth, since they can be prone to drought. But of even greater concern in land reclamation is the increase in volume of the overburden once extracted. This poses certain problems when attempts are made to backfill the material into the original void. Where this is practicable it can often result in the creation of a surface higher than the original one.

Overburden and waste materials may range from relatively chemically inert rocks, such as quarzites, to soluble limestone and gypsum. Others may contain amounts of sulphide ores. The main indirect effect of these materials on the environment will be their influence on the quality of water draining through and from them. As was made clear earlier, calcareous materials such as limestone generally improve the quality of drainage waters. Sulphides, on the other hand, lead to acid generation. The best known example of the problems caused by this comes from Appalachia in the USA where acid drainage following the strip mining of coal has also caused the chemical release of heavy metals. Since no attempts have been made to rehabilitate these areas, great environmental damage has resulted along with much human suffering. At sites where fine quartz particles accumulate, these will provide sandy and infertile sites for plant growth, whereas accumulations of silt contain more clay and are generally more fertile. There are exceptions, however. Overburden consisting of heavy clay particles impregnated with salt overlying coal deposits near Edmonton, Alberta, has made restoration of the area very difficult.

The disposition of the overburden has a considerable influence on the logistics of land reclamation since its final resting place may vary from steeply inclined mountain slopes to reasonably flat surfaces. Among the most straightforward reclamation exercises are those where coal has been extracted from gently sloping or flat-lying sedimentary rocks. Here the overburden may simply be backfilled and its surface contoured to that of the original land surface as the operation progresses. Soils are first removed and stored in their separate horizons for ultimate replacement in the correct order. This makes the revegetation of the surface a relatively simple task once ditches, fencing and walls, etc. have been put in place.

Perhaps one of the most spectacular as well as successful examples of restoration from open-cast coal operations is that at Westfalen in Germany. In the United Kingdom restoration has been equally effective, with the Ministry of Agriculture, the Agricultural Land Service and the Agricultural Development and Advisory Service supervising a five-year course of treatment once the land surface has been restored (Plate 6). Only then is a permanent drainage system installed. However, the re-establishment of something like the pre-existing ecology takes considerably longer and may never be achieved.

In some instances in the process of open-cast coal working, land restoration has been attempted without separating the soil from the rest of the overburden. In southern Illinois the re-established surface materials contain metals such as iron, aluminium and manganese and are deficient in potash and phosphorus. The restoration of the land to agriculture has only been possible by the offsetting of these difficulties with high and continuing applications of fertilisers.

Of all the wastes tipped as a result of mining, the spoil from coal extraction is among the most problematic. If the coal contains sulphides it will not only be toxic, but also liable to spontaneous combustion as a result of reactions between finely divided iron pyrites and oxygen. Even though such spoil heaps may lose much of their toxicity as a result of combustion, they can remain physically unaccommodating for plant growth. Nevertheless, most colliery spoils become colonised in time by local grass and tree species.

Apart from coal, as far as the United Kingdom is concerned, two other materials can pose a reclamation problem when tipped. As was noted earlier, the slate quarries of North Wales have produced waste on a gigantic scale following their rapid expansion of output in the nineteenth century. The reclamation of these tips is desirable because of their close proximity to a national park. It is, however, hampered by the long, broad fragments of variable size involved and the absence of fine material. Thus the only solution is to crush and compact the waste and cover the tips with imported topsoil, but this is rarely adopted because of the expense involved. Such tips remain, therefore, largely unvegetated.

In the case of china clay, it is the physical qualities of the huge tips of quartz waste that hamper reclamation. Quartz is geochemically resistant and weathers very slowly. As silicon has no value as nutrient material, these are utterly sterile growth sites. Plant life is further restricted by the steepness of the sides of the tips and their inability to hold water. The material itself is poorly consolidated so that if trees are eventually established there is a danger that they will be toppled in high winds. But before this can happen, attempts have to be made to produce a vegetational cover of grass by **hydroseeding**. This involves spraying onto their surface a mixture of seed, a rich mulch and fertiliser in a chemical binder. Once the grass takes root, the sites require sustained additions of fertiliser for up to ten years; by then the soil and plants will have accumulated sufficient nitrogen and the vegetational cover will be self-sustaining. Many quartz tips have now been treated but only after these conically shaped dumps have been recontoured into more acceptable land forms.

Undoubtedly, hydroseeding techniques of the kind used for quartz tips or the use of suitable fine materials (if not soils) on deposits of overburden and other waste materials are the best and quickest means of providing adequate growth sites for plants and thus of most readily achieving a good standard of reclamation.

## 8.4   The vegetating of tailings areas

It must be apparent from the discussion earlier in this chapter that the nature and composition of tailings can vary greatly. Although tailings can in many respects be regarded as a primitive form of soil, they may also have a much higher potential to develop toxicity and are more physically homogeneous than many soil parent materials. In recent years some tailings have been deposited into basins which have been lined with a clay or plastic material to prevent acids and dissolved heavy metals leaking into the outside environment. Where such liners are not used it will be necessary during the active life of the tailings area to ensure that all waters emerging from it are collected and treated with lime to reduce acidity and precipitate the dissolved toxic elements. As even the most efficient lining material will have a limited life, its greatest value will have been to check problems of leakage at least while the tailings area is in use. At the closure of the site, the establishment of vegetation on its surface not only diminishes acid generation by limiting the amount of oxygen entering the tailings, but also regulates the amount of water entering the tailings, most of which should be accounted for by evaporation and plant transpiration.

After a number of years of experimentation with the vegetation of tailings areas, a relatively simple approach to its establishment and maintenance has been established. The area in question will require dressing with amounts of agricultural lime according to the chemical nature of the tailings, as well as the addition of considerable quantities of fertiliser, i.e. a mixture of nitrate, phosphate and potash. However, other problems may occur. For example, coarse textured dark tailings are strongly warmed by the sun and tend to dry out and blow quite readily. Drought and wind action may also retard seed establishment. Sharp sand-sized grains will shear off emerging seedlings. Very fine materials such as the micaceous china clay residues rapidly become compacted and as a result are only slowly permeable and resist root penetration. But once limed and fertilised, even the most unpromising tailings, such as coarse-textured sulphide tailings of Inco's Sudbury nickel workings, will usually support a dense covering of vegetation.

Tailings from non-sulphide ores are much more sympathetic growth sites as they are not potential sources for acid production. Tailings derived from some igneous rocks such as granite may provide sufficient supplies of most of the chemical elements necessary for reasonable plant growth. In this case only nitrogen fertiliser would have to be added.

In some tailings areas, the limiting factor for plant establishment may be toxicity derived from the chemicals used in the milling process. The production of gold involves the use of cyanide in the milling process which then appears in the tailings. In due course even this may be washed out of the surface of the tailings and vegetation can be established. However, at a gold mining site near Long Lake, Sudbury, Canada, the unvegetated medium to coarse sand tailings remain sharply divided from the boreal forest even after 40 years.

A factor which complicates tailings reclamation in some areas is the spontaneous combustion of waste materials. Although this phenomenon is well known in coalfields where spoil may burn for many years, it is also found in metal mining. One example of this involves pyrrhotite which occurs with the nickel ores of Sudbury. Here, the fine particles of the mineral burn on contact with the atmosphere producing a crust-like material. One mining company, Inco, separates out the pyrrhotite and stores it under water in a pond in the expectation of smelting it as an iron-ore. In the same area another mining company does not remove the pyrrhotite and disposes of it with the rest of the tailings. As the pyrrhotite comes into contact with the atmosphere, it hardens to a concrete-like mass so that all areas of the tailings pond above water resemble an uneven tarmac surface. In rehabilitating such areas, that company has covered the ponds with layers of gravel and fine sands available from glacial deposits on their property. These have been successfully sown with a grass/legume mixture.

The ultimate fate of a tailings body will mainly depend on the population density of its associated region, the climate of that region, the chemical nature of the body itself, and the existence of reclamation legislation imposed by the state. In order to provide some picture of the range of possible circumstances which can prevail three examples can be considered.

1   *Tailings close to an urban area*, e.g. those belonging to Inco at Sudbury – the company which separates out its pyrrhotite. Because their tailings lie adjacent to a city of 100 000 people, legislation was invoked for their reclamation. Completed ponds were first treated in the 1960s. In the initial years following the establishment of a range of grasses, regular fertilisation and liming was needed, but after ten years a substantial organic horizon developed, forming an embryo soil, and treatment is now no longer required (Figure 3.12). Originally, the grazing of animals was considered and in the first years the grass was mown and sold as hay. However, with the discovery of slightly elevated levels of nickel in the fodder, this practice was dropped. Although there are considerable areas of native forest and

◀   *Figure 3.12
Tailings at Copper Cliff, Sudbury, first rehabilitated in the early 1960s. After the successful planting with a mixture of grasses, eventually the voluntary invasion of indigenous deciduous trees occurred. The conifers were subsequently added as part of the management plan for the area.*

lakes in the region, the area presents a convenient domain near an urban area for recreational purposes, and the ultimate use of the area will be for a public park.

2   *Uranium tailings close to urban areas*, e.g. at Elliot Lake in Ontario. The need to contain radioactive dust and reduce radon emissions to safe levels has meant that completed ponds have had to be drained and covered with imported earth. This can be successfully achieved if the soil is added to a depth of between 2.4 and 3.7 m, the thickness depending on its characteristics.

3   *Tailings in isolated areas.* These are by far the most common with the major extractive complexes to be found in the North West Territories of Canada, the Scandinavian Shield, the western United States and Australia. In all these places stringent reclamation demands are placed on mining companies before mining permits are issued. Once the tailings body has been vegetated, the area is allowed to revert to variations of the natural surrounding ecosystem. Most commonly, both boreal and mixed forest will invade the area, which in a relatively short time will be recognised only by its unusually flat aspect. However, the oil crisis of the 1970s precipitated a search for new sources of oil supply that has, for a remote area of north-west Canada, resulted in a reclamation problem that is not only of enormous proportions but virtually intractable. The techniques used to remove petroliferous tar from the extensive deposits of tar sands in Alberta employ hot caustic soda, which results in a fine quartz residue waste suspended in a liquid. This has to be deposited in huge tailing ponds in which the settlement of this sand can occur. Estimates of the time this may take vary from hundreds to thousands of years, thus making any attempts at reclamation a very long-term goal indeed. In the meantime, these great lakes, consisting of a mixture of sticky bitumen, oil, caustic soda and sand, present a serious hazard to wildlife, especially birds.

4   *Tailings in arid environments.* Problems may occur over water availability, influencing both seed germination and the maintenance of vegetation. Indeed, there are many examples of newly seeded areas that have been abandoned for lack of enough water to establish a plant cover. However, in the semi-arid regions of Arizona in the USA, immediately south of Tucson, tailings from copper mining have been reclaimed. With judicious selection of plant species and seeding to exploit times of maximum available soil moisture, the tailings have been successfully stabilised. This was done by using barley as an initial crop in order to establish organic matter in the tailings and then by planting local shrubs, trees and perennial grasses. No additional irrigation was used and evidence suggests that the natural beauty of the desert was maintained. This example emphasises the need to use local vegetation species, particularly in stressful environments.

## 8.5   *The positive utilisation of mining wastes*

So far in this chapter it has been shown that waste materials produced by mineral extraction and processing may be used in the reclamation of voids, or cosmetically treated on site to blend as far as possible with the existing local landscape. Indeed, they may also form the basis of screens (amenity banks) designed to obscure from general view the least attractive aspects of the extractive activities. However, another possibility exists and that is to treat wastes as saleable products.

The opportunities for making use of wastes in this way are closely related to the quantities of waste available. Depending on the mineral being worked, these quantities at any one extractive site tend to be either very large in relation to the valuable product, or very small. Look at Table 3.4, briefly refer to Section 2.4, and then answer the following question.

Q   Which minerals wastes come into which category: (a) large or (b) small producers of waste in relation to the valuable product?

A   (a)   Coal mining is a large producer of waste wherever it is worked. In the United Kingdom kaolin and (in the past) slate quarrying are notable contributors. Copper accounts for 50% of wastes in the USA. Other large quantities of waste, taken in a world context, arise from the working of iron-ore and taconite (a low-grade form of iron-ore), uranium, phosphate, gold, gypsum, lead and zinc.

(b)   The small producers of waste include hard rock aggregate enterprises and those of sand and gravel, although here, as Table 3.4 indicates, remarkably little is known about exact quantities.

Table 3.4 also provides a picture of the purposes for which wastes are positively used, sometimes in their raw state and in others upgraded as major inputs to the production of bricks, artificial aggregates or cement. Although the range of uses may appear impressive, it remains a fact that there are few alternative uses of upgraded wastes that are economically viable in competition with natural products, particularly if significant transport costs are incurred in reaching markets. This is even more the case with respect to the use of wastes as a form of fill away from their sources of production. Over short distances (a radius of 15 to 25 km) it is quite possible that abandoned excavations may be advantageously filled with wastes from mines or quarries in production. This course of action has the environmental advantage of eliminating the need to take virgin land for tipping and, if the land surface of the abandoned excavation can be restored by filling with waste, of producing useful new land. If the distances are short, transport costs can be offset by the avoidance of land purchase for tipping and the value of the reclaimed land.

Computer data banks listing voids and wastes have been produced and programmes which associate one with the other, according to suitability and least cost, have been run successfully in at least one region in the United Kingdom (the West Yorkshire conurbation), as well as in Canada. However, the problem of moving waste materials to some more remote location for use in a major project remains a problem.

Feasibility studies have certainly looked at the possibility of transporting colliery wastes to reclaim sites on the Firth of Forth in Scotland and Humberside in England, in spite of objections that such actions destroy local marshland habitats. In the 1970s when a third London airport plan involved the reclamation of a coastal site at Maplin in Essex, the notion was also examined of moving 400 million tonnes of fill from the china clay wastes of Devon and Cornwall, the slate wastes of North Wales, or the colliery wastes from the Yorkshire/Nottinghamshire coalfields as well as those in the north-east of England and South Wales. In the case of coal spoil alone, about 12 000 ha of serious dereliction could have been removed, but all the schemes failed to be adopted because of transport costs.

Table 3.4   Production and utilisation of mines and quarry wastes

| | Production/ (Mt per annum) | | | Stockpiles/ Mt | Utilisation |
|---|---|---|---|---|---|
| | Waste rock (inc. overburden) | Waste rock and tailings | Tailings | | |
| **Australia** | | | | | |
| Lowgrade ilmenite | 0.2 | | – | ? | – |
| Lead/zinc ore | – | | 0.5 | 4.75 | – |
| Coal | | c.60 | | 3000 | Small quantities for road construction and fill material (burnt spoil). |
| **Belgium** | | | | | |
| Coal | | 4 | | – | Lightweight aggregate manufacture.[a] |
| **Canada** | | | | | |
| Iron ore | | 45 | | – | Aggregate fill; roofing granules. |
| Coal | | 5 | | ? | – |
| **Finland** | | | | | |
| Misc. operations | 3.1 | | 5.1 | 94.8 | Road construction; aggregate for concrete. |
| **France** | | | | | |
| Coal | | 20 | | 700 | Approx. 35% production used for: (i) road construction – fill material; (ii) lightweight aggregate manufacture; (iii) brick making. |
| **Germany** | | | | | |
| Coal | | 63 | | 100s? | Approx. 35% production used for: (i) road construction – fill and embankments; (ii) land fill. |
| **Holland** | | | | | |
| Coal | | 0.3 | | – | 40% production used for block making (from fired mixture of colliery waste, flyash and sawdust). |
| **India** | | | | | |
| Laterite | | ? | | – | Clay pozzolana;[b] lime substitute in mortar. |
| Gypsum | 2 | | – | – | Building plaster. |
| China clay | 0.2 | | – | – | Clay pozzolana; brick making. |
| Mica | – | | 0.005 | – | Mica insulation bricks. |
| Coal | | 8–10 | | – | Mine backfilling (large %); road construction; fill. |
| **New Zealand** | | | | | |
| Coal | ? | | ? | ? | Small quantities used for land reclamation and fill. |
| **South Africa** | | | | | |
| Gold ore | 4 | | c.40 | – | 50% waste rock used for road construction and aggregate (for concrete); silicate bricks (minor usage). |
| Misc. quarrying | | | | | Waste rock used for road construction and fill; tailings in silicate bricks. |
| Coal | | 9 | | 150 | Very little used. |
| **Sweden** | | | | | |
| Iron ore | 25 | | 9.6 | 289 | Land fill (limited use); road construction and brick making (small quantities). |
| Sulphite ore | – | | 11.7 | 57 | |
| **UK** | | | | | |
| China clay | | 26 | | 400 | Less than 5% production used in: (i) aggregate for concrete; (ii) silicate bricks; (iii) road construction; (iv) fill; (v) amenity banks. |
| Slate | | 1.2 | | 300–500 | Inert fillers and roofing felt (small % of total used). |
| Tin ore | | 0.5 | | c.0.30 | Aggregate for concrete (minor usage). |
| Fluorspar | | 0.23 | | – | Road construction and aggregate for concrete (minor usage). |
| Misc. quarrying | | ? | | – | Road construction; silicate bricks; amenity banks. |
| Coal | | 50–60 | | 3000 | 11–13% production used in: (i) road construction (fill and building); (ii) brick making; (iii) cement manufacture; (iv) lightweight aggregate manufacture. |
| **USA** | | | | | |
| Copper | 624 | | 234 | 7700[c] | Road construction; bitumen filler. |
| Taconite | 100 | | 109 | 3600[c] | Aggregate-skid resistant. |
| Phosphate ore | 230 | | 54 | 907[c] | – |
| Iron ore | 27 | | 27 | 730[c] | Road construction. |
| Gold ore | 15 | | 5 | 450[c] | Road construction; aggregate for concrete. |
| Uranium ore | 15.6 | | 5.8 | 110[c] | Aggregate for bituminous concrete. |
| Lead ore | 0.5 | | 8 | 180[c] | – |
| Zinc ore | 0.9 | | 7.2 | 180[c] | – |
| Misc. quarrying | 68 | | – | ? | Amenity banks. |
| Gypsum | 14.2 | | 2.7 | ? | – |
| Asbestos | 0.6 | | 2 | 14[c] | – |
| Barite | 1.9 | | 3.1 | 25[c] | – |
| Fluorspar | 0.1 | | 0.4 | ? | – |
| Feldspar | 0.2 | | 0.8 | ? | – |
| Coal (bituminous) | | 100+ | | 2000 | Small quantities used in: (i) road construction – base and subbase materials; surfacing aggregates; (ii) cement manufacture; (iii) mineral wool manufacture. |
| Coal (anthracite) | | 1 | | 700 | Anthracite waste used in: (i) concrete block making; (ii) brick making; (iii) manufacture of lightweight aggregates. |

[a]Lightweight aggregate is used for building purposes where structural strength needs to be combined with lightness of construction material.

[b]A form of hydraulic cement.

[c]Stockpiles for USA are tailings only.

Source: Blunden, J. (1985) *Mineral Resources and their Management*, Longman, London.

Also in the 1970s a major study was undertaken by Devon County Council into the disposal of 28 million tonnes of waste quartz from the Lee Moor china clay works on the boundary of Dartmoor National Park, since only about 8% of each year's production of waste was used locally. The idea was to use it in the manufacture of an artificial aggregate and sell it in south-east England where demand was high. Not only did the costs of this run out at four times those for natural aggregate available in the south-east, but it was also unable to compete on transport costs compared with its nearest rival, the Mendips, some 140 km closer to the market.

When considered in conventional economic terms, the long-distance transport of large quantities of waste is seldom likely to be attractive. For this reason it is unlikely that mineral operators will ever voluntarily undertake such movements. Nor is the market for upgraded wastes a particularly viable one, given the competition from natural products and the fact that these also have to be despatched to centres of demand. Conventional economics does not take account of unquantifiable benefits such as visual improvement, the lessening of nuisance or the removal of danger to the public. But it is when these factors appear important that there is scope for government intervention on the basis of a policy that could decide whether the benefits of waste removal are worth the apparent financial 'loss' in doing so.

It seems, therefore, that in the case of small-scale waste production (as at quarries) and because many opportunities for environmental improvement work at extraction sites still exist, current and future waste production will largely be devoted to on-site amenity works. Certainly, for major schemes of waste transport and utilisation, government support would have to be forthcoming.

The formulation by individual countries of any policy for the positive utilisation of mineral waste is hampered by the lack of quantification of existing waste stocks, and of current and future production, as well as insufficient information on the properties of the wastes and their suitability for different purposes. Nor does any national picture exist within those countries of the relative locations of waste heaps and the excavations to which they might be returned. The task of making such studies in a country such as the United Kingdom is feasible because of its small size and is important because of the shortage of land arising from a population density of 227 persons per square kilometre, as compared with 22 persons/km$^2$ in the USA. Even so, within North America and elsewhere there are areas that may be considered to be heavily urbanised where such studies could be equally valid. Until they are undertaken so that the relevant data may be obtained, proper planning for waste utilisation will not be possible.

## 8.6   Summary

In order to approach the question of the reclamation of mined areas, this section has tackled the subject under three main headings according to type of site. In a consideration of excavations both the problems and the opportunities have been explored, especially the use of such voids for the disposal of waste materials already occupying otherwise valuable land. Overburden is, of course, material which can be returned to an excavated area. However, conflation, the size or the size range of the materials in question, their chemical composition and their location may be difficulties that require to be circumvented in any successful attempt to rehabilitate the overburden. Many of the same considerations can also apply to waste tips and to tailings. If tailings have the advantage of being level and having a uniform relatively fine texture, they often offer a hostile environment for plants. Adjustment may need to be made to pH values and plant nutrients added before anything resembling a medium conducive to plant growth can be created.

This section concludes by taking a more positive attitude to wastes from mining by considering them not just as a problem requiring on-site treatment, but as materials to be used positively, even if this may require initiatives which are not forthcoming from the workings of the market-place.

While it is self-evident that any positive use of mining wastes must be beneficial to the environment, the need to undertake such a task at all is based on the assumption that the market demand for minerals is satisfied largely by the winning of fresh supplies from the ground. But need this necessarily be the case? An answer to this question is attempted in the following section.

# 9   Recycling and substitution

## 9.1   Technical problems and policy needs

Any review of mineral **recycling**, especially for the metals, would show that in the industrial nations between 25% and 30% of output is now made up from materials previously fabricated into consumer goods, industrial plant, etc., or wastes from their manufacture. This falls far short of what *might* be accomplished, in spite of what may seem the relatively high percentages of re-use already being achieved, especially for some of the precious metals (Box 3.3).

Steel, however, has gone somewhat against the trend, and the use of scrap, which had been rising in the 1960s and 1970s, actually fell during the 1980s. There were corresponding increases in scrap availability: in the USA alone this rose from 610 million tonnes in 1980 to more than 700 million tonnes by the end of the decade. This failure has to be seen, however, against the background of changes in production methods designed to reduce the amount of environmental pollution caused by the old open hearth technique. In this method, pig iron, steel scrap and limestone were melted in a furnace to allow the oxygen in the air to combine with carbon impurities, while the limestone formed a basic slag to remove phosphorus and silicon in the iron. Unfortunately, the new basic oxygen method, in which air is replaced by pure oxygen, can utilise only 15–30 tonnes of scrap steel mixed with every 100 tonnes of pig iron, as opposed to a nearly equal mix for the open hearth approach – hence the decline in scrap utilisation.

Some compensation for this state of affairs has been achieved by the development of a new low-volume production process. The minimill, as it is called, relies on an electric arc furnace and consumes almost entirely scrap steel. Although minimills are increasing their share of steel production, especially in the USA, so far it has not been enough to compensate for the lost demand for scrap to feed open hearth furnaces.

## Box 3.3   Recycling precious metals

High value and relative ease of recovery in the practical sense make possible the recycling of most precious metals. For example, nearly all of the mercury in cells, boilers, instruments and electrical apparatus is retrieved when such items are scrapped. The same is true of gold and silver in jewellery, optical frames, photographic laboratories and chemicals.

However, with the platinum group of minerals, only in their use as metals and in the chemicals industry have they so far been retrieved in large quantities. And as the flow chart shows, little has been achieved for one major use, that of an agent in vehicle exhaust systems which controls the output of noxious gases, so nine-tenths of the mineral is currently being wasted. Such a situation could be resolved by the imposition of a sales tax on vehicles, returnable when the customer's redundant exhaust unit containing platinum is returned to a collecting centre for recycling.

Moreover, the range of steels that may be produced from minimills is limited and these can only be made from scrap having low levels of impurity. This is a distinct problem when it comes to recycling special purpose steel scrap which will contain a high percentage of chromium, cobalt, molybdenum, nickel, tungsten and vanadium. At present these have to be remelted without the desirable removal of the alloy metals, if they are to be re-used at all.

A somewhat similar overriding constraint can be found in the recycling of aluminium. Scrap is only suitable for use in castings because this sector requires lower metallurgical standards than, for example, rolling and extrusion processes. For this reason, as matters stand at present, any growth in the use of recycled materials must come either from greater penetration of the castings market, or a faster rate of growth in the castings market itself. Indications are that although average annual growth in this sector has been healthy, it has not kept pace with the increasing use of aluminium as a whole. It would therefore seem that the extent to which increased recycling may be achieved is constrained by the demand side of the market. If there is no upsurge in the use of castings, increases in the use of recycled aluminium, as with special scrap steel, must therefore await new technological developments which will enable it to be upgraded to compete with the primary material.

Another recycling difficulty lies in the metallurgical complexity of many pieces of redundant household and business equipment. For example, separate copper and high silica steel components are frequently in close association in items such as motor armatures, field cores and transformers. The United States Bureau of Mines is now working on methods of disassociating these, using preferential melting in molten salt baths, a technique which may also assist in the separation of the constituent metallics of ferro-alloys.

Technological developments fostered by the same organisation may also lead to the recovery of lead and zinc, which are known to be given off as oxide effluents in steel-making furnaces. It considers that 100 000 tonnes of zinc and 10 000 tonnes of lead could be retrieved annually in the USA from furnace dusts, once an appropriate methodology is found.

Whatever technical solutions may be produced to assist in recycling, it is also clear that governments can play a much greater part in the conservation of minerals and therefore the environment. For example, the tipping of wastes containing metallic materials at domestic waste sites might be forbidden, while the mandatory sorting of waste at the household or factory end of the disposal chain could assist in the reduction of recycling costs. Moreover, there are a number of practical steps that they might take to lower the consumption of new minerals and to encourage recycling. These include the levying of a tax on the use of 'virgin' minerals for certain manufacturing processes. A number of variants of such a scheme have been suggested but the common view is that the tax would be imposed according to the weight or value of new mineral resources used in manufacture and distribution. Others also favour the inclusion of a negative tax or subsidy, according to the proportion of recycled materials used in them. Proponents of this general approach, though, divide into two camps over the imposition of the tax, with some calling for a uniform rate across the range of exhaustible resources used from new, while others favour a system which penalises the users of the scarcest materials. Yet another proposal suggests the inclusion in the selling price of a consumer durable, such as a car or refrigerator, a sum which would be refundable when the product is no longer usable and is returned to a centralised collecting centre for recycling.

Whatever the merits of the schemes to encourage recycling, each would at least spread the social costs of environmental and natural resource use throughout the community. Indeed, recycling has the further advantage in that in general it may be regarded as involving a far lower level of energy consumption than that involved in the extraction, processing and smelting of newly won metallic ores. For example, the energy needed to melt down old aluminium is only one-twentieth of that required to produce virgin metal from the bauxite ore (Plate 8). Moreover, remelt furnaces are comparatively inexpensive to construct.

Other savings should also not be ignored. In the case of aluminium, for every tonne recycled, savings are made not only of 4 tonnes of bauxite, but also of more than 450 kg of soda and about 113 kg of lime which would be required to refine the bauxite, together with 680 kg of oil derivatives, 27 kg of cryolite and 36 kg of aluminium fluoride. The use of recycled aluminium also achieves a remarkable reduction in environmental impacts because a smaller quantity of new metal then needs to be produced through a process which, in its first stages of production of alumina from bauxite, presents problems. Gaseous emissions include large volumes of carbon monoxide and dioxide, smaller amounts of hydrogen fluoride, sulphur dioxide, carbon disulphide, silicon tetrafluoride, carbon tetrafluoride, hexafluorethane and water vapour. Of these, hydrogen fluoride emissions cause the greatest immediate concern. In addition, solid emissions of alumina, cryolite, aluminium, fluoride, calcium fluoride, carbon and iron oxide are generated. The environmental impacts of these when vented from a stack will have been ameliorated by the use of equipment called scrubbers, but this produces a highly toxic liquid which ultimately must be disposed of.

A significant problem for the environment is the residual material left over from processing the bauxite itself. As noted in Chapter 2, this takes the form of a red mud which contains in suspension caustic soda and sand and has to be discharged into a tailings pond. Between 0.3 and 1.4 tonnes of this is produced for every tonne of alumina and in the 1980s production averaged about 40 million tonnes a year. The problems ultimately created by the tailings used to derive from the capacity of the solid content not to settle out from the fluid except in the relatively long term. This made rehabilitation a problem. However, this was overcome recently by a new technique which removes the liquid which can then be evaporated. Although the solids remaining can then be contoured, covered with soil and vegetated, the problems of the old tailings areas remain, along with the other environmental hazards created by the processing of bauxite. Thus, the winning of new aluminium compares unfavourably with the quite minor environmental effects of recycling it.

However, the problems attendant on the recycling of aluminium and some other metals cannot be ignored. Besides which, recycling always involves some loss of material and there is uncertainty as to how far its potential may be pursued. In an examination of the immediate possibilities for copper recycling in the USA, recent evidence suggests that an additional 10% could be readily obtained. This is in line with research findings, which also suggest that a further 25% of the aluminium requirement in the USA could be obtained by recycling. While these findings are not optimistic about iron, it is considered that an additional 18% for zinc, and 3–4% for lead are easily achievable objectives, even without Draconian legislation.

## 9.2    Substitution – old and new materials

There are two forms of substitution. One involves the replacement of one metallic mineral by another in a given usage. The other involves the substitution of a metallic mineral with an entirely different material.

Most metals have one or more metal substitutes for a given end use, as the matrix in Figure 3.13 shows. It also indicates that there are occasions when a metal has no metal substitute at all. However, the matrix cannot indicate that substitution is often only to be made at the price of losing some unique characteristic in a specific application, or, if it were to occur, it could only be at additional cost because the substitute metal is scarcer, its processing more complex, or the amount of energy used in its fabrication much greater. Cobalt and vanadium are, for example, technically substitutable in the production of a number of specialised steels, but the former is six times more expensive than the latter, which makes interchangeability a one-way process. While aluminium is an excellent substitute for copper in its electrical applications, it is less conductive. Thus it can be used in overhead power cables, but not where they are housed in underground ducts; overheating then becomes a problem. Moreover, it should also be remembered that aluminium smelting requires a much heavier input of energy per tonne than that required for iron and many other metals.

If there were a scheme for the taxation of the use of newly won minerals, especially the scarcer minerals, the incentives would be strong to

|  | Iron | Manganese | Chromium | Nickel | Molybdenum | Tungsten | Vanadium | Cobalt | Aluminium | Magnesium | Titanium | Copper | Tin | Lead | Zinc | Gold | Silver | Platinum | Antimony | Mercury | Cadmium |
|---|---|---|---|---|---|---|---|---|---|---|---|---|---|---|---|---|---|---|---|---|---|
| Iron |  |  |  |  |  |  |  |  |  |  |  |  |  |  |  |  |  |  |  |  |  |
| Manganese |  |  |  |  |  |  |  |  |  |  |  |  |  |  |  |  |  |  |  |  |  |  |
| Chromium |  |  |  |  |  |  |  |  |  |  |  |  |  |  |  |  |  |  |  |  |  |  |
| Nickel |  |  |  |  |  |  |  |  |  |  |  |  |  |  |  |  |  |  |  |  |  |  |
| Molybdenum |  |  |  |  |  |  |  |  |  |  |  |  |  |  |  |  |  |  |  |  |  |  |
| Tungsten |  |  |  |  |  |  |  |  |  |  |  |  |  |  |  |  |  |  |  |  |  |  |
| Vanadium |  |  |  |  |  |  |  |  |  |  |  |  |  |  |  |  |  |  |  |  |  |  |
| Cobalt |  |  |  |  |  |  |  |  |  |  |  |  |  |  |  |  |  |  |  |  |  |  |
| Aluminium |  |  |  |  |  |  |  |  |  |  |  |  |  |  |  |  |  |  |  |  |  |  |
| Magnesium |  |  |  |  |  |  |  |  |  |  |  |  |  |  |  |  |  |  |  |  |  |  |
| Titanium |  |  |  |  |  |  |  |  |  |  |  |  |  |  |  |  |  |  |  |  |  |  |
| Copper |  |  |  |  |  |  |  |  |  |  |  |  |  |  |  |  |  |  |  |  |  |  |
| Tin |  |  |  |  |  |  |  |  |  |  |  |  |  |  |  |  |  |  |  |  |  |  |
| Lead |  |  |  |  |  |  |  |  |  |  |  |  |  |  |  |  |  |  |  |  |  |  |
| Zinc |  |  |  |  |  |  |  |  |  |  |  |  |  |  |  |  |  |  |  |  |  |  |
| Gold |  |  |  |  |  |  |  |  |  |  |  |  |  |  |  |  |  |  |  |  |  |  |
| Silver |  |  |  |  |  |  |  |  |  |  |  |  |  |  |  |  |  |  |  |  |  |  |
| Platinum |  |  |  |  |  |  |  |  |  |  |  |  |  |  |  |  |  |  |  |  |  |  |
| Antimony |  |  |  |  |  |  |  |  |  |  |  |  |  |  |  |  |  |  |  |  |  |  |
| Mercury |  |  |  |  |  |  |  |  |  |  |  |  |  |  |  |  |  |  |  |  |  |  |
| Cadmium |  |  |  |  |  |  |  |  |  |  |  |  |  |  |  |  |  |  |  |  |  |  |

▲   Figure 3.13   Metallic minerals substitution matrix.

speed up substitution wherever this was possible. But for metals, such as tungsten and molybdenum, which are rather imperfect substitutes for each other in some uses, the incentive might be rather to encourage their more sparing use in the short term, and in the longer run to encourage even more resource-saving technological innovation. Where there has already been a move to substitute a more plentiful for a scarcer metallic resource, such as aluminium for copper and zinc, this would probably be further increased, especially in the automobile industry where there are opportunities for using aluminium castings made from recycled metal.

Even without such a tax, technological advances have made it possible to supplant the use of metals with other materials. Much lead and copper piping has been replaced by plastic equivalents, not least because it is light, easy to handle and non-toxic. Also, in the manufacture of vehicles the substitution of a metal by plastic materials made from tough polymers is now increasingly making its mark. While it is difficult to quantify the exact impact of such a substitution, there is evidence from the automotive industry that in the period between 1975 and 1985 more stringent safety standards and the desire to produce a lighter vehicle to improve performance in relation to fuel consumption led to the replacement in each unit of 453 kg of metals by 204–217 kg of plastics. The possibilities here are by no means exhausted. It should be added that although plastics, wherever they replace metals, generally require less energy in their manufacture and are readily recycled, they do require hydrocarbons for their production.

Although new forms of substitution from time to time are introduced as part of technological change, such as the use of video-tape in movie cameras instead of photographic film, or the replacement of copper telecommunications cables with those containing glass fibre optics derived from common sands, even more advanced forms of technology could make many more conventional metallic minerals redundant. Much research is being undertaken into the possiblity of using common materials such as clay as a parent material for new products and as a source of aluminium. Indeed, several automobile manufacturing companies are investigating the possibilities of using clays for ceramic engines.

The advantage of using clay and similar minerals as source materials in industry is that they represent a virtually limitless resource and are readily available in all parts of the world to meet whatever demand that might emerge. The rehabilitation of the areas from which these materials are won should prove much less of an environmental problem than those posed by conventional metal-ore mining. But there are several development problems that have yet to be resolved here, not least the high energy demands required to process such materials.

*Activity 4*

Review the above section, especially Figure 3.13, and look back at Box 2.2 in the previous chapter. Then try to respond to the following questions.

Q  Which mineral of those listed in Figure 3.13 appears not to have a substitute?

A  Manganese, in its primary role in the manufacture of steel.

*Q*   Which metal is most frequently substituted for copper in electrical applications?

*A*   Aluminium.

*Q*   What disadvantages accrue to the use of aluminium in this context?

*A*   Aluminium is a much less efficient conductor of electricity than copper. Aluminium smelting requires a much heavier input of energy per tonne of metal than that required for copper. Nevertheless, in France, India and the USSR, the use of copper is forbidden where aluminium can act as an adequate substitute.

*Q*   What are the main uses of silver?

*A*   In the making of jewellery, as a soldering agent and in photographic film.

*Q*   Why do you think that its use in the last named context is beginning to decline?

*A*   Because of the increasing use of video-tape in the recording of moving images. Silver forms a vital part of the light-sensitive make-up of traditional film, but this is being replaced as the recording medium by plastic tape coated with iron and chromium oxide.

# 10   *In conclusion*

In Section 9 consideration has been given to the extent to which the recycling of key minerals (especially those that are scarcer and more expensive to work such as some of the metallic ores) may be re-used and what opportunities exist to substitute the more abundant minerals for the less abundant or for those that are more environmentally disruptive to extract. More environmentally friendly methods of winning minerals have been touched upon earlier, but here for the first time in the chapter full recognition is given to the fact that there may be alternative strategies for meeting societal needs for minerals.

Some tentative steps down this road may already have been taken because waste minimisation activities are now being practised to a limited extent. The banning in some Canadian provinces of the use of non-returnable containers, such as aluminium cans used for soft drinks and beer, is one example of positive action. Another is the cash incentives given for the return of beverage containers in some US states. In some countries initiatives have taken other directions at a national level. In Japan and Sweden centres already exist for the collection of spent items such as batteries which contain heavy metals and may create environmental problems if just dumped. Indeed, market forces are also playing some part. The problems of a throw-away society in the USA are at last showing themselves in the growing scarcity of land fill sites. This has led to increases in the costs of waste disposal, rising from less than $20 a tonne in the early 1980s to $200 a tonne in 1989. This has had the affect of making the re-use alternative to disposal more attractive to the point where some communities have initiated waste sorting and recycling programmes.

If in the short term the recycling of metals is to become an important alternative to the mining of virgin resources, it will undoubtedly require, apart from the need for further research, an effective infrastructure put in place by government and backed up by some of the initiatives mentioned in Section 9.2 above in order to subvert the conventional economic approach which takes into account only the immediate effects of production decisions. This revisionist approach to normal economic theory has been elaborated by Professor David Pearce in his report for the United Kingdom's Department of the Environment *Blueprint for a Green Economy* (1989). This is discussed briefly in Chapter 4 of this book in relation to energy and the environment, but is returned to as part of the broader environmental debate in the closing chapter of Book Four of this series (*Smith & Warr, 1991*).

A concerted move to what may be described as a sustainable industrial ecosystem aimed at reducing both unnecessary primary production and consumption wastes may ultimately only be driven by increasing populations and overall rises in living standards in the less developed countries. Clearly, in such a situation, if reliance continued to be made on the securing of mineral resources by conventional extractive methods alone, some shortages would begin to arise. Moreover, as this chapter has demonstrated, ways do exist to overcome many of the environmental impacts of mining and minerals processing, but whether they occur in the vicinity of the mine of smelter or well beyond, the costs of carrying through such schemes are not inconsiderable. Indeed, they will rise sharply as the need to work leaner ores become a greater imperative.

Whether or not such a situation does come to pass, the move to a sustainable industrial ecosystem must be considered as highly desirable from an environmental perspective. Its effect would mean a considerable reduction in environmental problems created by the winning of new materials, especially the non-aggregate materials, and a reduction in ameliorative arrangements that must follow both during minerals production and processing and when these activities cease. Meanwhile, government control of emissions and the regulation of land use must continue to play some small part in what many hope will be a transition to the industrial-ecosystem approach. Ultimately, probably most of us would agree that if people are to raise their living standards without incurring further penalties for the environment that will ultimately degrade the quality of life for all, it is a transition that should be accomplished.

Finally, you will recall that Chapter 2 was concluded with a diagram (Figure 2.11). Now is the time to look back at this since it will act as a reminder of much of the discussion that has taken place in this chapter, and, of course, that which precedes it. It will be apparent from this that although the emphasis so far has been upon minerals extraction and processing and the possibilities of their more effective re-use, the environmental impacts of the industries which employ these minerals in the manufacture of goods has yet to be considered more fully. This is the subject of Chapter 6.

The complete programme of industrial activity with regard to minerals which Figure 2.11 attempts to demonstrate also shows in all its stages the significance of energy inputs. In the next chapter the environmental effects of present energy policies are discussed before turning to alternative strategies based on energy conservation. The approach used there parallels the discussion of minerals which has taken place in this chapter.

# References

PEARCE, D. *et al.* (1989) *Blueprint for a Green Economy*, Earthscan, London.

SMITH, P. & WARR, K. (eds) (1991) *Global Environmental Issues*, Hodder & Stoughton/The Open University, London (Book Four).

WINTERHALDER, K. (1978) A historical perspective of mining and reclamation in Sudbury, pp. 1–13 in *Proceedings Third Annual Meeting of Canadian Land Reclamation Association*.

# Answers to Activities

## Activity 2

In your response you should certainly contrast the respective attitudes of governments in western industrial economies and Poland, until recently part of COMECON. In the former the recognition of pollution from smelters has meant the imposition of controls on effluents, almost certainly pushed by public opinion. In Poland the problem has been suppressed in the interests of production, and whatever the recognition of the damage to health from smelter discharge in villages like those around Glogow, these were not to be articulated; at least not until the era of *glasnost*!

## Activity 3

Emission control programmes were initiated at both locations in order to protect their communities from smelter pollutants. These included, first, the building of tall stacks to achieve the better dispersal of sulphur dioxide and metal particulates, followed by reductions in effluent discharges. Concern at Sudbury through the 1980s has, however, concentrated on the damage done regionally to water bodies by sulphur dioxide, particularly at the Killarney Provincial Park, which has followed the building of Inco's superstack.

The 'Countdown Acid Rain' programme, which runs to 1994, has been aimed at achieving substantial reductions in sulphur dioxide discharges and especially from the superstack.

Although local weather conditions which might bring superstack discharges down into Sudbury are monitored so that remedial action can be taken if required, programmes of effluent control are not essentially geared to this objective. At Mount Isa, however, the need to avoid polluting the local community remains the key objective and levels of emission and the circumstances under which these may be vented are entirely aimed at achieving this end. Since the area around Mount Isa is semi-desert with few and well-scattered small communities, the effects of pollutants in the region beyond the township are not seen to be of primary importance. This diminishes the need to convert sulphur dioxide discharges to sulphuric acid in a situation where it is likely to be unmarketable.

# 1    Introduction

The first chapter of this book introduced the idea of energy, the natural resources available, and the way these are used at present to provide for human needs. The growth of urban-industrial society over the last three centuries has been strongly dependent on an ever-increasing use of fossil fuels (coal, gas and oil), hydroelectric power and more recently nuclear power. In 'developed' countries they have virtually replaced the traditional wood and other biomass fuels, though these continue to be important in 'less developed' countries. Economic development and an improved quality of life are often believed to depend on a continued extension of this process, but it is clear that energy use worldwide in this way on the scale of the most profligate countries would, at the very least, severely stress the available resources, particularly of oil, gas and uranium. In the market system this is reflected in price fluctuations, with their complicated impact on the rest of the economy – we have already experienced the effects of the sharp rise in oil prices engineered in the 1970s by the Organisation of Petroleum Exporting Countries (OPEC), the cartel dominated by, but not limited to, the Middle East. This caused a reduction in oil use, the development of alternative sources and a price slump in the 1980s. A corresponding uranium price rise, followed by overproduction and a slump, reflected changing perceptions over the same period about the future role of nuclear power. These basic supply and demand effects on prices are not, however, the main concern of this chapter. Many powerful organisations in the energy industries will continue to manoeuvre, with results that we can hardly expect to predict in detail. Evidently, non-renewable resources can't last for ever, so their prices must rise eventually – but there will be many fluctuations on the way.

What *is* our concern here is the growing recognition over recent decades that our present energy policies also have many undesirable environmental effects (from smog, acid rain and oil spills to Chernobyl and global warming) which are not, at present, reflected in immediate economic costs. We shall come back to the question of whether an 'environmental economics' can be developed which takes better account of these problems, but first we need to be clearer about their nature, and this is considered in Section 2.

Section 3 consists of a more detailed study of the fossil fuel that has been longest used, coal, and the way the environmental effects of its combustion have been seen to widen from a local to a global scale.

The ways that other components of our present energy system (other fossil fuels, transport, nuclear hydroelectric power and biomass) impinge on these global problems are outlined in Section 4, showing a possible progression back to purely local impacts.

Finally the options for technical improvements, and better inclusion of environmental consequences in economic, and other, value systems are introduced in Section 5.

# 2    A framework for analysis

## 2.1    Introduction

There is a growing interest in environmental impact assessment, and indeed an increasing requirement that such an assessment be included in planning proposals for new projects. So let us examine now what we mean by environmental impact and try to establish a systematic procedure for assessing it.

During the 1980s, the OECD (Organisation for Economic Co-operation and Development, whose members include all the developed countries of Europe, North America, Japan, Australia and New Zealand) carried out the 'Compass' project for the *'comparative assessment* of the environmental implications of various energy systems'. Its first report in 1983 suggested a framework for analysis which is a suitable starting point. There are four stages:

1    specifying the processes which are the *origins* of environmental effects;

2    listing the *residuals* of these processes which affect the environment;

3    determining the environmental *impact* of these residuals;

4    assessing the *damage* caused by these impacts.

At first sight these four stages may not seem to be very clearly distinguished, and we shall need examples to clarify the way the terms are used. There are some implicit assumptions about the nature of the environment in the approach used, and the language is often revealing; doubts and argument will be found to increase as we progress through the four stages. The procedure is detailed and thorough, as the complexity of the subject demands, but it is also rather tedious and bureaucratic, as such international recommendations tend to be. Some of the implications will be discussed as we proceed, particularly by looking more closely at the word 'environment' itself, and at the more specialised way it is used in systems theory.

## 2.2    Origins of environmental effects

### The OECD approach

We can work our way from the general to the particular in three steps:

1    The fuel cycle – this is the usual term for what is in fact a one-way process turning natural resources in the ground into useful energy and unwanted by-products. In the case of fossil fuels, the time scale for completion of the cycle, turning plant material formed by photosynthesis from carbon dioxide back into coal, gas and oil would be geological, hundreds of millions of years, while that of nuclear fuels would be cosmological, unimaginably longer – so in neither case remotely available on a human time scale. Only biomass fuels can be truly 'cycled', if they are grown at the same rate as they are used.

The OECD (1983) study breaks down this cycle in turn into seven stages, each with its own complications; some stages may occur more than once in the route from energy source to final use:

- exploration: geological studies, prospecting, test drillings, etc.;
- harvesting: a rather quaint term for the variety of mining and drilling techniques used as well as its more normal use for biomass collection (perhaps it sounds more comfortable than 'exploitation'; 'cycle' and 'harvesting' are both 'loaded' words – look out for others);
- processing: crushing, cleaning, grading, extraction, refining, blending;
- transport: by sea, land, air, pipeline, transmission line, of raw and refined materials;
- storage: raw and refined materials, large and small scale; for electricity, in batteries or, indirectly, as pumped storage of raised water, to be converted back to electricity when needed;
- marketing: wholesale and retail, of bulk and consumer products;
- end use: fuels for heat, heat engines for motive power or electricity production, chemical feedstocks; as electricity for heat, power, light, electronics and electrochemistry.

### Activity 1

Check your understanding of this breakdown of the fuel cycle by listing the stages as you think they might be involved using uranium ore from Namibia ultimately to power an electric vehicle in England.

2    The second step involves identifying the phases associated with each of the above stages of the fuel cycle (a particular usage of the word 'phase', based on the fact that these activities occur in an approximate time sequence, though they obviously overlap to some extent):

- construction of facilities: mines, oil platforms, refineries, power stations, etc.;
- operation: supply of materials and energy, removal of products and effluents, employment;
- maintenance: scale and frequency;
- decommissioning of plant: restoration of amenity and safety at the end of useful life;
- management of long-lived residuals: spoil heaps, toxic residues, radioactive wastes.

So with 7 stages by 5 phases, potentially 35 phases in all, it's getting complicated. But this is not the end.

3    Finally we come to the specific processes associated with each of the above phases. Here there will be endless technical detail about the particular methods used in each operation, limited only by human ingenuity – mining methods and machines, surface and underground, for coal or uranium; oil and gas drilling and extraction methods; refinery operations to produce particular transport fuels, residual fuel oil, petrochemicals; types of combustion system and nuclear reactor; transport and distribution systems, and so on. No-one can expect to know all the details, which need to be collected for each case considered.

The particular part of the fuel cycle considered in the detailed study of Section 3 will be the combustion of high-sulphur coal, by the methods formerly common for domestic heating, and by those now used in electric power generation. Some other environmentally significant operations in the energy system will be looked at in Section 4.

As all the above processes in the energy system themselves use energy and materials which in turn involve environmental effects in their production, there is some difficulty in knowing where to draw the line – should you include the effluents from the steel works that made the material for the drill of the oil well, or the exhaust from its Managing Director's car, or from the lorries delivering to the supermarket which supplies food for its employees? This will not be taken any further than to say that 'energy analysis' to discover the energy costs of various materials and processes, including energy production itself, has been carried out, with suitable rules for 'cutting off' the chain of contributions where their effect becomes negligible; that the resulting environmental effects are one stage more complicated; and that putting money values on them one stage more complicated still – so it is not easy to disentangle 'environmental costs' in detail. But by working back from a particular end-use of energy to its primary source we can at least get a first-order idea of its environmental implications. Such a demand-based analysis is more fruitful in suggesting ways of reducing energy use and/or environmental damage than starting with the energy resource, as the supply industries have a natural financial interest in increasing energy use.

As usual with an international body like the OECD, it is able to produce a thorough analysis of all aspects of the existing energy system which it would be hard to fault – after all these are the Facts, and very complicated they are. As we get into the more uncertain territory of environmental effects, and the more active steps of doing something about them, we may feel the complexity of all the possible options eluding our grasp; this is where 'systems' thinking may help. The first stage is to rephrase this 'origins' analysis in system terms.

## A system model

So far we have used 'environment' in the current commonsense way, for the surroundings of human beings that provide various amenities, but can be modified or damaged by our activities. The same word 'environment' is used in a related, but more specialised, way in systems theory. This sets out to provide an orderly way of representing, or modelling, complicated systems of all kinds, whether for analysing existing systems, or for designing new ones. The main difficulty, as we have already seen, is in deciding how much to include in the description, since everything always affects everything else to some extent. The first step is very simple, only putting into a diagram what we often do in our minds without being aware of it. We draw a **system boundary** round the **components** of the system which undoubtedly interact with each other, and call everything outside the boundary the **system environment** (Figure 4.1). This boundary might be a physical one (the walls of a factory or frontier of a country), but more often it will be a conceptual one, only existing in a diagram. The significance of this step will become clearer as we move into the later stages.

We can take examples, on various scales, from the many operations described above. A small-scale end-use might be a domestic central heating

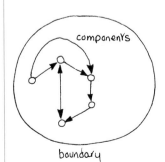

▲ *Figure 4.1*
*A system model.*

system, a larger installation might be a coal mine, larger still, the UK total energy system – or, going beyond human energy processes, we could consider the world's climate system. These are evidently related in various ways. Some systems are embedded in others to form a hierarchy: a system at one level of description can be a component of a larger one (up to the scale of the universe); and system components can themselves be analysed as smaller systems (down to the atoms, or beyond, of which they are made).

The OECD fuel cycle analysis is an example of this 'embedding' process, and also illustrates different kinds of components and interconnections. The steps 1 to 3 represent progressive breakdown of a particular fuel supply system into more detailed components each time (Figure 4.2). Let us take the final stage first, with one example of a familiar

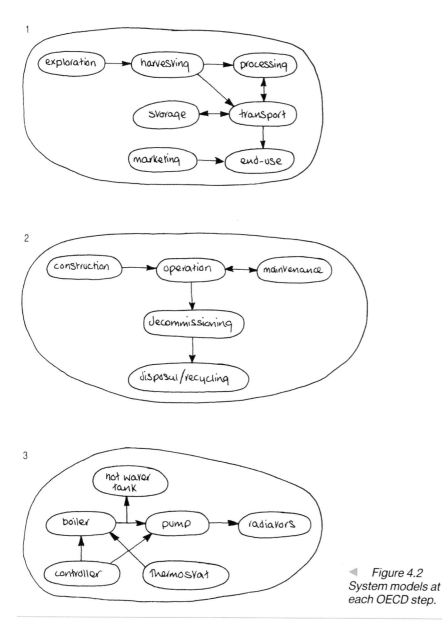

◄   Figure 4.2
System models at each OECD step.

end-use, a domestic central heating system. The components in this case are recognisable physical objects (boiler, pump, hot water tank, radiators, thermostat, time switch/controller) and the lines joining them stand for the pipes and wires connecting them together, the first stage of a practical design that could be turned into working drawings. But as we move back to steps 2 and 1, the components, and the connections between them, become more abstract. For example, if step 2 is concerned with the phases in the provision of central heating (in general), it will have as components one covering the construction of central heating equipment (in turn divided into the manufacture of separate parts, and the assembly of complete systems), others with operation (supply of fuel, control, safety), maintenance, decommissioning and disposal (which if not such difficult processes as for some parts of the energy system, nevertheless raise important questions about waste disposal and materials recycling). These system components are no longer physical objects, but each is a complex network of people and equipment; the lines joining them are not single physical connections, but represent all the interactions between them, varying with time. This abstract character is even more pronounced for the fuel cycle system of step 1, in which the final end-use component will include central heating as one of several competing applications, with economic factors determining their relative importance, and similar richness in each of the other components. The interconnections stand for a correspondingly complex pattern of information, energy and material exchange between the components.

At the same time, this cycle for a particular fuel (say, natural gas) is itself only one component of a larger fossil fuel system, in turn part of a larger national, or world, energy supply system, still only part of a total energy system (Figure 4.3), and so on.

You may well feel that drawing a system diagram in this way does not advance much beyond a description in words, and at this stage they are indeed fairly similar. However, in making a particular system diagram we

(a)

(b)

(c)

◀   Figure 4.3
Larger systems than
the single fuel cycle:
(a) fossil fuel system;
(b) (national) energy supply system;
(c) (national) energy system.

make two kinds of choice: first, we choose how to lump together the underlying complexities as 'components' which we won't analyse further at this stage; second, we choose the number of such components which interact together within a boundary to make up the system, with everything outside forming the system environment. It is important to emphasise that these are creative choices, useful to the extent that they provide a clear description of a complex situation. The consideration of effects across the system boundary is the next stage.

## 2.3    *The residuals from energy system processes*

### *The OECD approach*

Reverting to the OECD study, with its conventional use of 'environment': each of the above processes involved in the provision and use of energy has environmental by-products – not only the waste materials released *into* the environment which are the most obvious 'residuals', but also, stretching the meaning of the word somewhat, materials removed *from* the environment and structural *changes* to it. The environment may be understood to include not only the geophysical surroundings (air, land, water) and the biological (other living things) but also the socio-economic (employment, markets, welfare, amenity). The assessment process should try to determine the range and quantity of residuals produced over this very wide range.

The OECD study lists the following *Classes of Residuals*:

- Consumption or pre-emption of environmental resources (land, water, biomass, energy, inorganic materials) over and above the primary energy resource which is inevitably consumed at the 'harvesting' stage – a coal mine obviously removes coal, but it has a 'residual' demand for land for spoil heaps, and land pre-empted during the life of the mine for surface buildings, or, for a larger area but shorter time, for open-cast working; for water for coal washing, for biomass like wood for pitprops, for energy to drive the machines and pumps, for inorganic materials like constructional steel.

- Material effluents: solid, liquid, gaseous; inert, chemically active, radioactive.

- Non-material effluents: noise, heat, electromagnetic radiation.

- Other physical transformations: modification of surface or underwater topography (e.g. land filling or dredging), vegetation removal, erection of structures.

- Socio-political influences: changes in employment opportunities, in demands for social services, in population density and distribution.

Some of these last 'residuals' seems to be more like 'impacts' – this is the first sign of confusion, particularly in the 'socio-political' category, which will increase as we continue with the OECD approach, but which will be clarified by taking the systems view.

The residuals involved in the study of coal combustion in Section 3 are straightforward – solid and gaseous material effluents, like ash, dust, soot, sulphur dioxide and nitrogen oxides. Various other residuals will be mentioned in Section 4.

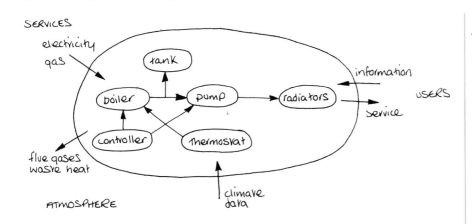

◄   Figure 4.4
A central heating system.

## Flows across the system boundary

Let us now relate this idea of residuals to our system by looking a little more at the domestic central heating system (Figure 4.4). Its components are undoubtedly connected together to form a system, and affect each other in ways we needn't go into any further, but which obviously had to be carefully considered in the design. A system boundary can naturally be drawn round these components, with an 'environment' outside. But the system is not isolated from this environment; many flows of material, energy and information pass across the boundary: gas, water and electricity supplies in, heat loss and exhaust flue gases out; information about the climate and the wishes of the users, a heating service to the users. These flows across the system boundary largely correspond to the residuals of the OECD method.

As there are these flows across the boundary, just as there are flows between the components within the boundary, how does the 'environment' differ from the system components? Why is it separated by the system boundary?

It can only be that, for the purpose of this system description, the environment is not affected by the flows in and out of it; it can provide whatever is needed and accept whatever is emitted without being changed – or rather, without being significantly changed, so there is some judgement involved about what counts as significant. This is a crucial idea. For example, the climate, the atmosphere, the national gas and electricity supplies are not significantly affected by the operation of one domestic heating system, though they obviously might be by the combined effect of all the country's heating systems. But in this case you're discussing a different system, with a different system boundary – a national energy or climate system, with the many domestic heating systems as separate components within a common boundary.

As well as these physical factors, let us think a bit more about the users of the central heating system. Their demands on the system may well depend on independent factors (their ages, working hours, say) which place them squarely in the system environment. But if the performance of the system affects their behaviour (their temperature preferences, the hours spent at home) then the boundary must be stretched to include them. More significantly, if we include economic factors like their ability to pay for the energy to run the system, the boundary must widen considerably, to embrace rival claims on their budget, employment opportunities, welfare payments and so on.

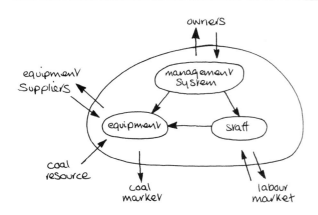

As a more complex energy system, consider a coal mine, which might be represented by the system diagram of Figure 4.5. This has clearly interacting 'components' inside the boundary – cutting machinery, transport and processing plant, pumps and other facilities, and the staff to run them, with now a significant planning and management system of some kind to be included. But what is outside the boundary as an independent 'environment'? There will no doubt be limited periods when further coal resources, energy, land and water, equipment suppliers, markets for the coal produced, a labour market able to provide or absorb staff, might be thought of as stable and unchanging for day-to-day purposes in running the individual mine. But there will equally obviously be time scales where this is not sensible, and the system boundary has to be enlarged to embrace wider relations between physical resources, people, economics and government. The individual mine can then be seen as one component of a variety of larger systems – political conflicts arise because different groups have different views about what these larger systems should include.

*Activity 2*

Use the format of Figures 4.1 to 4.5 and your general knowledge to propose your own diagrams for two such larger systems which include the coal mine (e.g. the UK coal industry, and the UK energy system), paying particular attention to the (relatively unchanging) factors which form the system environment, and the flows across the boundary, in each case.

Perhaps it is now clearer that there are two advantages to this component–boundary–environment approach to complex systems.

One the one hand it provides a basis for limiting the scale of a problem so you don't try to think of everything at once – either the endless detail about the way the components work, or the endless possible ramifications of external effects which might be important. There are plenty of cases where for all practical purposes the environment is effectively unchanging – it changes very slowly compared with the system processes of interest, or the effects of the system on it are very local, or very brief. One bonfire doesn't change the climate.

On the other hand we are obliged to remember that there are flows across the boundary and to consider when they would change the environment and what new, larger system boundary has to be drawn to take their effects into account. All bonfires maybe can affect the climate.

The 'residuals' are these flows, in and out, across the system boundary. These might be materials extracted or deposited, people employed or laid off, money flows, or more abstract influences like rights or regulations. They will necessarily change the environment in some degree, but the essential idea from the point of view of a particular system is that these changes are negligible: the environment is assumed to go on providing and accepting the flows as required. How to assess the effects when this is no longer true is the next stage.

## 2.4   *The impacts of these residuals*

### *The OECD approach*

The aim of this stage is to examine the way conditions and processes in the environment are modified by the residuals – the spread of pollutants downwind from a power station is a straightforward example, which we will return to in Section 3. In general, there will be pathways of cause and effect by which residuals alter the environment – transportation through air, water, soil/rock, living things, with physical, chemical or nuclear transformations on the way. Variation with time and space is an important issue – how long does a residual last, how far away from its source can it be detected?

Again, the OECD study suggests various *Classes of Impact* (which have been grouped to indicate some differences of emphasis):

● reduced availability of environmental resources

● altered chemical concentrations: in air, water, soil, biota
● altered circulation patterns: in the atmosphere, water bodies, ground water
● altered temperature, humidity, precipitation
● altered electromagnetic fields

● absorbed radiation dose
● perceived noise

(There is a change of emphasis in these last two from the four previous classes, as these two depend not only on alterations in the distribution of radioactive material and noise, but also on the extent to which humans are affected by them, which depends how the humans are distributed too. It might be better to preserve this distinction.)

● other alterations to, or loss of, habitat

(That is, the attributes of the environment making it suitable for particular species – with a human tendency to concentrate attention on those non-human species that we find more appealing: badgers rather than cockroaches, for example. 'Alterations to habitat' may be 'impact', but 'loss of habitat' sounds more like 'damage'.)

● socio-economic stresses

(This is a bit vague, with the distinctions from 'residuals' and 'damage' again not very clear.)

## Changing the system boundary

The 'impacts' of a system are arrived at by extending the system boundary, so that it now contains the previous system as one component, interacting with others via its residuals, the flows across the original boundary (Figure 4.6a). We have a choice as to how to do this, depending on the nature of the particular residuals. If they are gaseous effluents, we will want to consider their interaction with the atmosphere, or other parts of the geosphere (Figure 4.6b); if they are toxic we will need to consider the ecosystem effects (Figure 4.6c); if staff movements, we should consider effects on employment or population distributions; if money flows, effects on the economic system and so on. We are replacing the idea of a generalised impact on 'the' environment by a series of more specific studies of particular larger systems that we judge to be relevant. Each of these systems has its own boundary and flows to its environment which we can examine to see whether we have gone far enough. We might hope during this stage to determine the effects, in time and space, on the system we have chosen (e.g. the atmosphere) of the particular energy process we started with (e.g. a domestic heating system) – its 'sphere of influence', or perhaps better, its 'bubble of influence' (Figure 4.7). This will have a

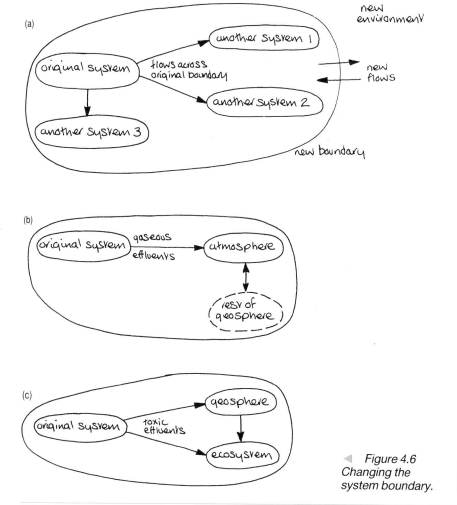

Figure 4.6
Changing the
system boundary.

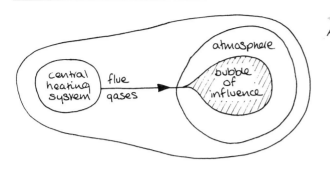

◁   Figure 4.7
A 'bubble of influence'.

straightforward physical meaning for gaseous pollutants in the atmosphere, but the same idea can be extended to other flows and other systems, including more abstract forms of influence.

Evidently, judgement is involved in deciding which larger system is to be looked at. Even if the resulting 'bubble of influence' can be determined (which may not be easy in larger cases), it is still possible that the effect on some other system has been overlooked. This may sound complicated – and indeed it is; the consequences of human actions can be very involved and difficult to predict. But at least this stage, of simply mapping the effects, shouldn't be too controversial, once we have agreed which larger system is being considered. This may be a more political decision than meets the eye: choosing the larger system for study is 'setting the agenda' – we may be looking at the atmosphere and neglecting rivers, or the ecosystem, or employment, welfare, economics, amenity, and so on.

## 2.5   The damage caused by these impacts

### The OECD approach

In considering 'damage' the study now makes human value judgements about the effects of these environmental impacts on us. While the 'origins' and 'residuals' can be defined quite precisely, and the 'impacts' can be traced, even if with difficulty, fairly clearly, the measure and characterisation of the resulting potential harm to human well-being, or to vulnerable parts of the environment, is more difficult and controversial. In Section 3 we shall consider the relatively straightforward example of coal combustion and its solid and gaseous effluents. The resulting impact of smoky, foggy atmospheres was evident, of acid rain somewhat less so, but a *measure* of the resulting damage, in increased respiratory disease, or in ecological effects in lakes and forests, has proved much more difficult to obtain conclusively. Similar difficulties have arisen in tracing the link between nuclear operations and childhood leukaemia, for example.

The OECD study lists the following *Classes of Damage*:

●   Direct, to human health and safety – resulting from accidents, sabotage, routine emissions and exposures harmful to humans, either short or long term.

●   Direct, to economic goods and services – accidents, sabotage, effluents and other environmental transformations.

●   Impairment of environmental goods and services – impaired visibility, dust, ugly structures, annoying noise and odours, reduced diversity.

- Disruption of socio-political conditions and processes – increased centralisation of political power, loss of civil liberties, excessive burdens on social services.

- Psychological distress – physical displacement or unemployment; fears of the above damages, whether or not they materialise (!).

This is a revealing list. As with the three previous ones, you may well feel it progresses from well-defined to increasingly fuzzy issues. There is also a new element, in the attitude it now shows to 'the environment' – one which may be a common human perception, but is surely worth looking at a bit more closely. In the first two items, human welfare and the economic system that provides goods and services seem to be seen as proceeding smoothly in a 'normal' environment; the routine or eccentric behaviour of energy systems may produce environmental impacts, as considered above, that can damage these 'normal' activities. And the last two items, though vaguer, can perhaps be linked with the first two – 'psychological distress' with 'health and safety' (personal), 'socio-political' with 'economic' (social), all providing a human-centred view of our own affairs, and only considering the environment explicitly when it is a potential source of trouble. However, it comes into its own in the middle item, as the source of 'environmental goods and services', which is very much an economist's description of the way we value our surroundings – apparently as a source of pleasant sights, sounds and smells which might be impaired, and, tucked into a corner (ecological?) diversity which might be reduced. Are these just human 'goods' or 'services', to which we might put a price in environmental economics, or do they have other values? What do you think?

Perhaps there are two separate issues. We have been trying to clarify this four-stage environmental assessment procedure by introducing the 'system' view of 'environment', and the choice of progressively wider system boundaries to examine the consequences of our activities. On this view we can hardly see 'environmental damage' as separable from 'normal' activities; it is a potential consequence of any of them. Various responses, using this system approach, are pursued below. But this still leaves the larger ethical question about the attitude of human beings to the world – do changes only matter to the extent that human welfare (which can include our aesthetic responses) is damaged, or are at least some 'environmental impacts' to be seen as unacceptable even if there is no 'damage' to human interests? These are questions which continue to arise throughout this series of books, and to which there will be no final answers; they are left here for continuing discussion.

In the OECD approach, it is argued that if environmental damage can be measured, and if the probability of its occurrence from a particular process can be determined (both considerable 'ifs') then the simplest way of characterising the process is by the 'average or expected harm'. This can be defined as the probability multiplied by the damage, summed over all forms of damage. (This might be seen as providing an illusion of mathematical precision for a very vague process.) Apart from the difficulty of carrying this out, it is not the only possibility. Other relevant attributes might be considered:

(a) the magnitude of the worst-case event, irrespective of probability;

(b) the distribution of damage over time and space – potential damage to future generations or remote communities;

(c) the degree of irreversibility of the damage.

All of these have been cited as arguments against continued and future use of nuclear power, for example, even where estimates of average or expected harm seem favourable.

## *Responses to 'damage' in the system model*

We have seen that by enlarging the system boundary we can interpret the effect of one system on another that we consider to be important as a 'bubble of influence', but to interpret that as 'damage' introduces difficult and controversial value judgements. In some cases the bubble of influence of human activities might not be called 'damage' at all: if the natural energy flows of the wilderness are disturbed to create an elegant garden, a well-run farm or a thriving city, many people would not call that damage – but note the human values embodied in all those adjectives. However, if we think we know what 'damage' is when we see it, we can still seek to assess it or contain it.

The last sentence contains an insidious 'we' that implies the existence of a rational human consensus about such controversial questions. It is only too obvious that this does not exist, either about the nature of the problems, or about the sacrifices of self-interest required to solve them. But if 'we' is understood to stand for some underlying trend of human understanding, which is only turned into action by agonising political processes where conflicts of power and interest are resolved with difficulty (if at all), it may still be a useful shorthand for the rest of this section. But always ask yourself: Who are 'we', making these decisions?

A natural question is 'How big, or long-lasting, is the bubble of influence?'

1    If it is small or brief enough (a puff of smoke) we will ignore it.

2    But suppose it were a speck of plutonium, or any other toxic waste? Obviously there is then another set of questions, about the extent of the overlap (in space and time) between the bubble and the components of the ecosystem (including humans), the flow of materials through the ecosystem, the sensitivity of human or other living 'systems' to toxic inputs. These are usually quite difficult to answer. If we conclude there is a hazard, we will try to put a fence around the rubbish dump where it arises, or find a remote enough place for it. We will then have to deal with all the questions this raises about interference with rights of access and the difficulties of satisfactory containment.

3    Or we will try to disperse effluents, which means making the bubble larger but of lower intensity, so that ecosystem effects are reduced to an acceptable level (again according to someone's value judgement).

4    Or we may conclude that the effects are too serious for the process to be allowed to continue, and we will abandon it.

Finally, and most important, when we have come to terms with the bubble of influence of one energy process, by ignoring it, containing it, modifying it, or rejecting it, we have to consider the overlapping effects of all energy processes. The difficulties encountered at present arise most of all from the continued growth in the use of processes which might be individually tolerable but are unacceptable when combined. In Section 3 for example we will see how the scale of problems associated with coal combustion has progressively expanded, now perhaps to a global scale, and in Section 4 how other parts of the energy system impinge on these global problems.

## 2.6   *Summary*

A procedure for assessing the environmental effects of energy systems has been suggested, involving four stages – identifying their origins in the innumerable processes of the fuel 'cycle', the residuals of these processes, their environmental impacts, and the resulting damage. We have recognised some progressive difficulties of definition and feasibility in carrying out this procedure, particularly over socio-economic and ethical issues, but it provides a useful initial framework. It has been clarified by introducing a 'systems' view of processes on all scales. Interacting components within a system boundary are distinguished from the 'environment', in a new narrower sense, outside it. The effect of flows across the boundary (residuals) can only be examined by studying a larger system with a new boundary. This idea sheds light on 'environmental impact' and 'damage'; there is no longer a single environment to consider, but a range of alternative larger systems affected by different residuals.

*Activity 3*

Before reading any further, use this framework to make your own notes of the 'environmental damage' you associate with the present use of coal. This will help to define the issues discussed below.

# 3   *Coal: from a local problem to a global one*

Let us now look in more detail at one of the simplest and most familiar sources of environmental effects, the burning of coal. The first stage of the assessment procedure is to understand something of the particular process involved.

## 3.1   *Coal composition and combustion*

Coal is a rather variable material produced from buried plant remains in swamps by geological effects (temperature and pressure) over very long periods of tens to hundreds of millions of years. Its use as a fuel depends on its mainly carbonaceous composition of modified organic compounds of carbon with oxygen and hydrogen in varying proportions. Initial bacterial breakdown of the plants ceases when they are buried under suitable conditions; the resulting peat is only about half carbon. In the process of coal formation the oxygen content is gradually reduced as the 'rank' of the coal changes, through soft brown lignite to hard black bituminous coal; the final changes involve the reduction of hydrogen content too, to anthracite and finally almost pure graphite (one form of crystalline carbon). The local geological history determines the rank that has been reached by the present time; different coal deposits worldwide represent all of these various stages. (There are of course no significant changes taking place on the human time scale.) The presence of volatile organic compounds (i.e. those driven off by heating) in the lower rank coals makes them easier to burn, but with a smokier flame. The volatile contents can be driven off to form coke, as used in the iron and steel industries, or to provide an artificial smokeless fuel alongside the natural anthracite.

Coal also contains varying amounts of inorganic impurities depending on its source – material that either accumulated along with the plant remains or was introduced during the geological modifications (Table 4.1). Clays and carbonates are the main contributors to the ash that remains after combustion, but small amounts of sulphur (mostly as iron sulphide, pyrite) and salt (sodium chloride) have a great effect on the ability of the ash to corrode boilers and thus on the practical use of particular coals.

Table 4.1    Principal constituents of typical European coals

| | |
|---|---|
| carbonaceous material | 70–90% |
| water | 0–7% |
| nitrogen | 1–2% |
| sulphur | 0.5–2.5% |
| other inorganic material | 5–20% |

During combustion the inevitable primary products are the heat released when carbon, hydrogen and their compounds react with the oxygen of the air, and the resulting carbon dioxide and water if the combustion is complete. This is the whole reason for using coal, for domestic or industrial heating or to drive heat engines (steam engines, steam turbines) in factories or power stations. We shall return later to the possible effects of these primary residuals – which would not usually be called pollutants. For the present we shall be more concerned with other products, obtained because the combustion is incomplete, and because of impurities in the coal. They depend on both the particular coal used and on the way it is burned. A domestic open fire produces much less complete combustion than an industrial furnace. There is much combustion engineering knowledge available; however, it will be sufficient here to recognise that in general visible smoke contains particulates, which are unburnt carbon (soot) and ash, contaminated with tarry unburnt hydrocarbons and other impurities, some of which might be carcinogenic or corrosive. The sulphur and nitrogen impurities burn to produce (invisible) sulphur dioxide ($SO_2$) and various nitrogen oxide gases, collectively known as $NO_x$, where x stands for varying proportions of oxygen (these can also be formed from the nitrogen in the air when the combustion temperature is high enough).

Let us now examine the impact of these residuals.

## 3.2    Air pollution: a local problem

As the earliest industrial society, Britain had an unenviable reputation for air pollution in its larger cities, which is still vivid for anyone whose memory of them goes back before the 1950s. It didn't require any systematic modelling or elaborate analysis of 'bubbles of influence' to observe the environmental impacts and damage inflicted by coal burning factories, and innumerable domestic open fires. The cities were the dirtiest in the world, with dark skies, acrid smoky air, blackened buildings, and an unhealthy urban population. Charles Dickens in the 1850s wrote in *Bleak House* of a foggy November in London, with 'smoke lowering down from chimney-pots, making a soft black drizzle, with flakes of soot in it as big as full-grown snow-flakes – gone into mourning, one might imagine, for the death of the sun.' He also wrote in *Hard Times* of Coketown, which 'was a town of red brick, or of brick that would have been red if the smoke and ashes had allowed it; but as matters stood it was a town of unnatural black and red like the painted face of a savage. It was a town of machinery and tall chimneys, out of which interminable serpents of smoke trailed themselves for ever and never got uncoiled.' (He acutely went on to use the fog and grime as symbols for the obfuscations of the law and the aridity of a Utilitarian fact-based education system, which perhaps goes some way to explaining why it took another century before the problems were tackled.)

Manchester in 1853 was described by a visiting Frenchman, de Tocqueville, as 'given over to industry's use . . . large palaces of industry . . . keep light and air out of human habitations which they dominate; they envelope them in perpetual fog . . . a sort of black smoke covers the city', while in Sheffield as late as the 1930s 'every square foot of exposed masonry was black and filthy. The sun rarely penetrated a vast umbrella of smoke and soot.' The effects in respiratory disease and stunted growth – of vegetation and humans – were plain to see, though the defiant 'Where there's muck there's brass' was as likely to be mouthed by its victims as its beneficiaries, as they too depended on the employment provided.

Concern grew through the twentieth century, and the turning point for pollution control is usually considered to be the 'Great Smog' of 5–9 December 1952 in London (characteristically, not in one of the industrial cities, where they were also commonplace). Sulphurous soot particles in moist air formed an acrid 'pea-soup' fog that persisted for several days under particular adverse weather conditions. It led to an estimated additional 4000 deaths in the following weeks, due to heart and lung diseases. The Beaver Committee was appointed to examine the problem and two years later estimated that pollution was costing the country (at 1954 prices) over £300 million a year (at last providing the facts to satisfy the Utilitarians?).

The problem, seen as a localised one around areas of dense population and heavy industry, was tackled through the Clean Air Acts of 1956 and 1968. They focused on visible air pollution, their major thrust being to cut soot emission from chimneys and prevent smog formation. The greatest proportion of this was from domestic fires, so local authorities were empowered to declare smoke control zones, within which emission of smoke from houses was banned. Emission from factories and power stations was tackled by removing larger particulates at source, and using taller stacks to dilute and disperse the smaller particulates and gaseous pollutants ($SO_2$, $NO_x$). The rules did not set out to stop or control the production of these gaseous pollutants, but only to disperse them over a wider area.

These controls, along with a transfer to cleaner fuels like natural gas and oil, have reduced smoke emissions by more than 85% since 1958. There have been corresponding great improvements in the visible quality of the air in industrial cities (Figure 4.8). There have also been reductions in invisible pollutants like $SO_2$, mainly from reduced domestic, industrial and transport output. The largest part now comes from power stations, whose

▲   Figure 4.8   Air pollution – before and after the Clean Air Acts: the Tees near
Middlesborough (above) in 1924; (below) in 1972.

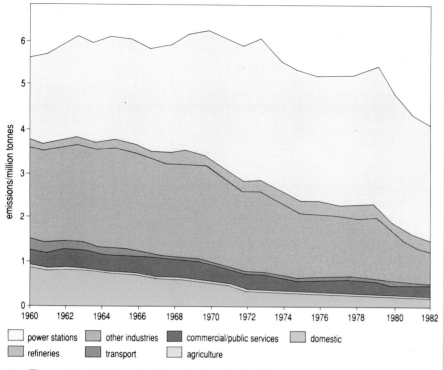

▲    Figure 4.9    Sulphur dioxide emissions in the United Kingdom, 1960–82.

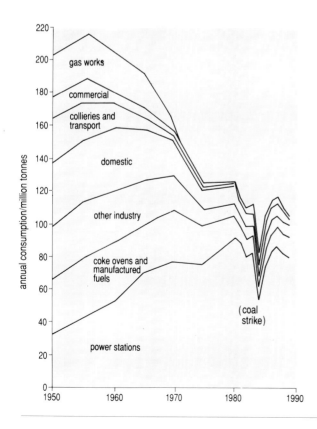

◀    Figure 4.10
Coal use in the UK
1950–89.

output of SO$_2$ has increased (Figure 4.9). This has been associated with a reduction in total coal use, from about 90% of UK energy in 1950 to just over 30% in 1990, and a reduction in its use for all purposes other than electricity generation (Figure 4.10). The industrial use could recover as a result of changing economic and technical circumstances (lower price relative to oil, less polluting 'fluidised bed' coal combustion methods), but at present (1990) UK coal is mainly used for electricity production, with large power stations sited near the major coalfields (Figure 4.11).

▲   *Figure 4.11   Coal fields and power stations.*

## 3.3   *Air pollution: a regional problem*

This national history, of industrial dependence on coal, concern about air
quality, clean air legislation and shifts in fuel use from coal, mainly to oil
and gas, could be matched with appropriate local modifications in each of
the industrial countries of Europe, North America and, increasingly, the
rest of the world. The different stages of this process in different countries,
and oil price increases, have in fact led to a steady increase in total coal use
through the 1980s both in Europe and the world as a whole, maintaining a
share of total energy use in these areas of about 20% and 30% respectively.

Following the continuing growth in total energy use, and the
recognition that pollutants do not necessarily stay in the country where
they were produced, the scene has been shifting during recent decades to
larger stages: Europe (as a result of developing European Community
controls), the developed world (responsible for 70% of energy use, with
agencies like the OECD, and its Compass project), and the world as a
whole (through various United Nations agencies). Let us concentrate next
on the European scale.

### *European concern*

Despite the local improvements in air quality and reduction of $SO_2$
described above, concern grew in the 1970s about adverse impacts and
damage in the UK and in Europe from $SO_2$ and $NO_x$ produced in various
ways (Figure 4.12).

Q   In these data, what is the main source of each of these effluents?

A   In both cases, power stations, which produce more than half of the $SO_2$
    and just under half of the $NO_x$.

Q   What is the next largest source of each?

A   This is markedly different in the two cases. For $SO_2$, it is other
    industrial processes, including smelting operations like those
    described in Chapter 3. For $NO_x$ it is transport.

Although this section is about the effects of coal combustion, some of them
are so interwoven with those of these other sources that they will have to
be considered at the same time.

In the case of power stations and other industrial sources, taller stacks
had dispersed these effluents and improved conditions locally, but where

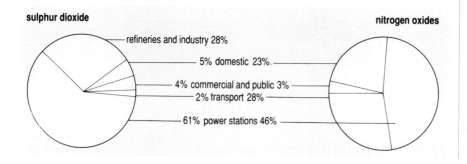

**sulphur dioxide**                                              **nitrogen oxides**

refineries and industry 28%

5% domestic 23%

4% commercial and public 3%

2% transport 28%

61% power stations 46%

*Figure 4.12
Main sources of $SO_2$
and $NO_x$ in Europe.*

had the dispersed gases gone? They had been exported to the countryside downwind of the source, carried maybe hundreds of kilometres, and falling as wet or dry acid deposition. This was the 'tall stacks paradox', the inadvertent replacement of the original visible local problem of soot by the invisible long-distance, even transnational, problem of acid precipitation. A study in 1982 by the (UK) Institute of Terrestrial Ecology showed increased rainfall acidity in parts of Scotland (pH up to one unit lower than normal background levels).

An earlier study from the OECD in 1977 had already suggested after a 5-year investigation that the consequences could be more international. The total quantity of $SO_2$ produced in Europe (about 9 million tonnes in 1973) was stretching the acceptability of dispersal; the UK, with 2.8 million, was the largest single contributor. Furthermore, some countries, with the UK again in the lead, were net $SO_2$ exporters with more of their emissions falling on other countries than they received from others, while countries downwind of them like Norway and Sweden were net importers, receiving more than they emitted to other countries. This imbalance was gradually shown to exist throughout Europe (and similarly in America), as a consequence of varying industrial activity and pollution control measures combined with prevailing winds.

It is evident that net importers have much more reason for interest in international regulation than net exporters, which no doubt goes some way to explaining controversy about control measures; costs and benefits are not equally shared.

## Acid rain: formation

We have seen that $SO_2$ and $NO_x$ are important residuals of coal combustion, and other processes. Now let us consider their physical transport and chemical transformation in the atmosphere to produce environmental impact from **acid rain**. The chemical processes are very complex and not fully understood, but the broad sequence of events is approximately:

1   Oxides of sulphur and nitrogen are released, from natural and human (anthropogenic) sources. In Europe the $SO_2$ is 90% anthropogenic (power stations etc.) and 10% natural (e.g. volcanoes, sea spray, rotting vegetation, plankton). $NO_x$ is 50% anthropogenic in rural areas, more in urban regions (with vehicles as important a source as stationary emitters).

2   As they are dispersed downwind there are various physical and chemical effects, shown in a simplified way in Figure 4.13.

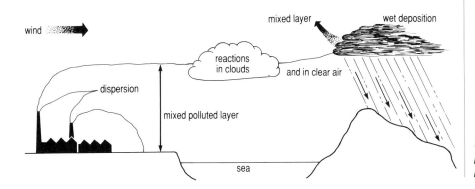

Figure 4.13
Dispersion of pollutants leading to acid rain.

3    Considering $SO_2$ first: there is some dry deposition, mostly near the source, as adsorption on surfaces or take-up by plants, but this is a comparatively slow process (even for low-level sources), so much $SO_2$ remains airborne for long distances, particularly in dry weather and if emitted from tall stacks when it can readily reach hundreds of kilometres from the source. While airborne it can be oxidised – that is, have its proportion of oxygen increased, forming the 'higher' oxide $SO_3$, but this is not straightforward. While it remains a gas the reaction with sources of this extra oxygen is very slow. But it is much faster if the $SO_2$ is incorporated in clouds or fog as water droplets. The $SO_3$ produced then reacts with water to form sulphuric acid $H_2SO_4$, ionised in solution as $H^+$ and $SO_4^{2-}$. The dilute acid can finally reach the ground as wet deposition.

4    For this oxidation to happen, there must be an oxidant: a source of extra oxygen. Even in wet reactions, atmospheric oxygen acts only slowly as an oxidant under normal conditions (though its effect can be speeded up by traces of metal ions such as $Mn^{2+}$ and $Fe^{3+}$); Usually the major oxidants are hydrogen peroxide ($H_2O_2$) and **ozone** ($O_3$). These are produced in the atmosphere by photochemical effects: sunlight stimulates their formation from oxygen and water vapour. But these processes are themselves sensitive to the presence of other gases (an effect that is returned to in more detail by Warr in *Smith & Warr, 1991*, Chapter 3). In particular, ozone production near ground level is much enhanced by the effect of sunlight on the mixture of $NO_x$ and unburnt and partially burnt hydrocarbons in vehicle exhausts. This is a pollution problem in its own right: the **photochemical smog** of such concern in sunny cities with many motor vehicles, such as Los Angeles. Its importance here is to emphasise the interrelated, synergistic, character of pollution studies: acid rain production from power station $SO_2$ is much affected by vehicle $NO_x$.

5    A further important influence is natural ammonia rising from land or sea and joining in the process; oxidation of $SO_2$ by ozone is slowed down as acidity increases, so would be self-limiting, but ammonia can neutralise the acid, keeping up the conversion rate.

6    The primary $NO_x$ emissions are transformed in a rather different way. There is little dry deposition of NO, and it is oxidised to $NO_2$ and $HNO_3$ as a gas, as neither NO nor $NO_2$ is very soluble in water. There can be dry deposition of nitrate particles, while incorporation of $HNO_3$ in clouds and raindrops leads again to wet deposition.

7    Thus, acid rain, containing sulphate $SO_4^{2-}$, nitrate $NO_3^-$, ammonium $NH_4^+$ and hydrogen $H^+$ ions (in addition to the natural bicarbonate $HCO_3^-$ from $CO_2$), falls to earth.

## Measured increases in rainfall acidity

Direct observations of this impact depend on the pH scale of acidity. Small numerical changes in pH have a significant effect on many processes, particularly biochemical ones.

'Normal' rainfall is already somewhat acidic, from the carbon dioxide in the atmosphere (dissolved to form carbonic acid) and naturally occurring sulphur compounds (from volcanic eruptions and biological processes). A standard pH figure for 'clean' rain is 5.6, though natural variability can lead to values as low as 4.5 (which confuses argument about anthropogenic change). Systematic comparisons of rainfall acidity show consistent evidence of deepening pH 'holes' below 4.1 (i.e. acidity peaks) over the regions affected by $SO_2$ and $NO_x$ emissions – see Figure 4.14 for studies of north-west Europe and eastern North America (for two time periods). More widespread global monitoring is now under way.

(a)

◀   Figure 4.14
Variation in the acidity of rain:
(a) Europe;
(b) eastern North America.

(b)

## Damage attributed to acid rain

A further complication is that the acidity of surface waters can be reduced from that of the rainfall by the natural neutralising capacity of the rocks over or through which they flow. Limestone in particular is alkaline, and such areas are less affected, whereas rocks like granite, quartz and sandstone are poor neutralisers. The soils that form and the vegetation grown on them, such as conifer plantations, can increase the acidity of surface water. Nutrient enrichment from sewage, fertilisers and forest fires can reduce it. Factors such as these provide reasons for uncertainty in the secure linkage between emissions, acid rain and ecological effects.

Nevertheless, international concern was first expressed at the UN Conference on the Environment in Stockholm in 1972, when the Swedish Ministry of Agriculture reported massive fish kills which were attributed to acid rain, particularly resulting from UK emissions. These original Scandinavian problems are now seen as part of a wider pattern, including forest decline, particularly in Germany and central Europe (*Waldsterben*, the death of the forest, is shown in Figure 4.15 and Plate 9), lake acidification, and declining fish populations, which have been reported in nearly every European country and related to industrial activity, though there is still not a consensus on their detailed origin. There is also structural damage to buildings – already a familiar observation at earlier times in UK industrial towns.

In the case of forest damage, it has been argued, particularly by the UK's Central Electricity Generating Board (CEGB), that this results not from acid rain but from the direct toxic effects of ozone in the lower atmosphere, which is derived from photochemical effects on vehicle exhausts, while other workers attach most importance to toxic minerals leached from the soil into surface waters by the changed acidity.

## Scientific complexities and political responses

Thus evidence of environmental damage has been emerging in many European countries. While many scientists and politicians, particularly in the countries most affected, attribute this directly or indirectly to acid rain, it is in fact difficult to establish the links beyond doubt. In the UK a Parliamentary Select Committee took evidence in 1984. It echoed these uncertainties, but it proposed action even though the evidence was incomplete:

> While a direct and proportional link between sulphur emissions and environmental damage is not scientifically proven, the case against $SO_2$ is telling enough and the damage severe enough that action must be taken before all the evidence is in.

A similar European Commission (EC) study in the same year stated:

> It has not been unequivocally established that environmental impacts are caused by acid pollutant emissions . . . nevertheless circumstantial evidence would suggest that acid emissions and their subsequent chemical transformation and precipitation are at least a partial contributory cause to the observed effects and may be giving rise to as yet unidentified impacts, some of which could be irreversible.

There has been some 15 years of controversy; the UK in particular has been intransigent over control measures, claiming that the inadequate evidence did not justify the increased cost to the electrical industry and the

◀   Figure 4.15
Damage to forests in Europe.

consumer. But action was agreed in November 1988 when an EC Directive to reduce $SO_2$ and $NO_x$ emissions from large combustion plants was adopted. A 3-stage reduction from 1980 levels of $SO_2$ from existing plant over 50 MW was accepted, with overall community targets of 23%, 42% and 57% reductions by 1993, 1995 and 2003, and a simultaneous 2-stage reduction in $NO_x$ of 10% by 1993 and 30% by 1998 (and corresponding national targets adjusted for local conditions). The implications for the UK are costs of perhaps £2 billion for the installation of expensive flue gas desulphurisation (FGD) measures in some large coal-burning power stations, as already adopted throughout West Germany, and of £200 million for combustion modification to reduce $NO_x$, though it seems that the timetable will only be met by also using imported lower sulphur coal and/or introducing gas turbines. It should also be noted that FGD requires the provision of large quantities of limestone and disposal of the resulting calcium sulphate – as so often, replacing one disposal problem by another.

In March 1990 the final report was issued of the joint £5 million UK–Scandinavian Surface Water Acidification Project (SWAP) funded 5 years previously by the CEGB and National Coal Board (NCB), when claiming research information was still inadequate. It broadly justifies earlier Scandinavian findings, while providing more detailed insight into the complexities outlined above.

These agreements to control emissions from coal-burning plant can be seen as part of the development of an international 'regime' (of the kind explored more generally by Greene in *Smith & Warr, 1991,* Chapter 4). This involves fossil fuels more widely, particularly including transport vehicles, which we have already seen to be significant sources of $NO_x$ and other pollutants (hydrocarbons and carbon monoxide). Apart from their intrinsic toxicity, they are implicated in the production of photochemical smog and particularly ozone, in turn intrinsically damaging and linked with acid rain production.

An outline chronology of the agreements negotiated by the UN Economic Commission for Europe (UNECE) and by the European Community (EC) is shown in Table 4.2, to indicate the interlocking nature of these political processes, and the way 'we' struggle forward when a 'damage' problem has been identified.

A similar pattern of observations, inter-state conflicts, resistance to action and final agreement to (some) emission reductions can be traced in North America. No doubt the coming decades will see similar processes developing in the industrial areas of eastern Europe and the Far East, and increasingly, with industrial development, worldwide.

*Table 4.2    Agreements on pollution controls*

|       | UNECE | EC |
|-------|-------|-----|
| 1970  | Vehicle exhaust emission standards (limits for $NO_x$, hydrocarbons, carbon monoxide) | Policy to implement UNECE regime |
| 1975  |       | Gas oil directive (max sulphur content) |
| 1979  | Geneva Convention on Long-range Transboundary Air Pollution (LRTAP) (general principles) | |
| 1980  |       | Air quality directive ($SO_2$ and particulates, 1983 target, 1993 compliance; 29 UK local authorities in breach) |
| 1982  |       | Air quality (lead) |
| 1984  | An informal Scandinavian agreement to reduce $SO_2$ emissions – the '30% club' | Industrial plant – 'framework directive' |
| 1985  | Helsinki Protocol (ratified 1987, but not by UK) (30% national $SO_2$ reductions by 1993 from 1980 base) | Air quality directive ($NO_x$ standards, 1987 target, 1994 compliance) |
| 1986  |       | Single European Act (legal and philosophical basis for environmental policy) |
| 1987  |       | Vehicle exhaust emission standards (1985 'Luxembourg' agreement; optional, to be applied by 1988–93, depending on category) |
| 1988  | Sofia Protocol (signatories include UK) on $NO_x$ standstill by 1994 from 1987 base (also further informal 12-country '30% club') | Large combustion plant directive ($SO_2$, $NO_x$ dust standards for new plant; national targets 1993, 1998, 2003 for existing plant; review 1995) |
| 1989  |       | Small cars exhaust emission standards (mandatory by 1990–92; catalytic converters). Amendment to $SO_2$/dust air quality standards; national monitoring; review 1992 |

## 3.4   Carbon dioxide and the greenhouse effect: a global problem?

Thus we are slowly coming to terms with these regional pollution effects caused by the combustion of impure coal (and oil, for transport). They can in principle be removed, though at a price, by better cleaning and combustion methods. At the same time the impact of the primary residual of fossil fuel burning, carbon dioxide, in modifying the 'greenhouse' effect on a global scale is beginning to be feared, with its implications for climate change and sea-level rise. This is discussed in more detail in Ross (in *Smith & Warr, 1991*, Chapter 2). It (almost certainly) cannot be dealt with by cleaning methods and is only modified, not eliminated, by changing to the cleanest fossil fuel, natural gas. The uncertainties and dependence on complex scientific models are even greater, and again it will be prudent to act before effects are certain, or they may by then be irreversible. The scale and nature of international agreement that will be needed to achieve this are unprecedented, and seem certain to dominate the international politics of the coming decades – see Greene (in *Smith & Warr, 1991*, Chapter 4).

## 3.5   Summary

The residuals of coal combustion have been shown to produce major environmental impacts and damage on widening scales. The earliest, most local impact was from visible smoke, soot and fog, which are contaminated particulate emissions in urban industrial areas; this was overcome by Clean Air legislation. The second, on the transboundary regional scale, arose from invisible emissions of sulphur and nitrogen oxides, believed to produce acid rain and ecological damage; this is being reduced by flue gas cleaning and improved combustion methods, along with related vehicle exhaust measures. The third is the modification of the global greenhouse effect, still controversial in its detailed implications; this is a problem common to all forms of fossil fuel use, and it seems will only be overcome by a reduced dependence on fossil fuels, and negotiations of an unprecedented nature in order to arrive at an international control regime.

# 4   Energy and environment – from global to local problems

## 4.1   A basis for considering the present energy system

We have seen how the environmental problems associated with coal burning have gradually widened from local to global scale issues. In surveying the rest of the present energy system we can order the consideration of the other components by the extent to which they contribute to these global effects.

Q   What other components are there in the present energy system?

*A*   Natural gas and oil; nuclear; hydroelectric and biomass.

*Q*   Which of these also contribute to 'greenhouse' $CO_2$ production?

*A*   The other fossil fuels: natural gas and oil.

It seems appropriate therefore to start with consideration of these other fossil fuels, and the transport system that is so firmly dependent on them at present. Nuclear power, though not a direct source of greenhouse gases, has its own environmental problems, and an indirect link with the greenhouse effect needs to be recognised. It should also be recognised that both fossil and nuclear energy release add to the total heat input to the Earth, implying a fundamental 'thermal pollution' limit to the use of either form – though this is rather theoretical at present.

Only the use of solar energy, directly or indirectly, avoids all these problems. At present this means hydroelectric power and the use of biomass; these still have local environmental effects, but in principle are free from the global ones.

It should also be recalled for completeness that we have only considered so far the effects of gaseous residuals of coal combustion. There are many others, but some have already been covered in Chapter 3: the direct impact of extraction methods, the disposal of (acidified) surplus water, the effects of subsidence and unsightly or hazardous spoil heaps, the radioactive products of coal-burning. To these might be added the level of accidents in a notoriously dangerous industry; constant efforts have been needed to contain them to the current (UK) figures of some 30 deaths and 800 serious injuries every year (about 1 and 20 per million shifts per person respectively). Any comparison of energy processes worldwide has to consider these, and relate them to the different hazards of off-shore oil and gas operations and of uranium mines – and to the massive transport accident figures (see below).

## 4.2   Petroleum

There is some variation of usage, but, conventionally, petroleum is the general term for the second broad type of fossil fuel, produced, like coal, by geological processes acting on buried plant remains. The fundamental difference in the end product is that coal is essentially solid carbon with other materials (including some inflammable hydrocarbons), while petroleum is a mixture of hydrocarbons, innumerable compounds of carbon and hydrogen ($C_xH_y$), many of which are gaseous or liquid, and other materials (particularly oxygen, nitrogen and sulphur compounds). The differences arise from their origins (coal largely from land plants and petroleum from marine sediments), from the detailed geological processes of formation, and particularly from the way gaseous and liquid products can migrate through favourable rock formations to accumulate in 'fields' away from their source. These natural accumulations can be gaseous (natural gas), liquid (crude oil) or solid (asphalt). A complication in this description is that gas fields can be associated with coal as well as with oil formation.

A more detailed classification of petroleum products, which reflects the separation processes used in oil refineries, is based on the carbon number: which is the number of carbon atoms in the hydrocarbon molecule, increasing as the components get denser (Table 4.3).

*Table 4.3*

| carbon numbers | term |
| --- | --- |
| 1–3 | gases (methane etc.) |
| 4–10 | gasoline ('petrol') |
| 11–13 | kerosine ('paraffin') |
| 14–18 | diesel fuel |
| 19–25 | heavy gas oil |
| 26–40 | lubricating oil |
| >40 | waxes |

The hydrogen content for each carbon number can vary: as many as 1200 different hydrocarbons have been identified in crude oil, but in general the proportion of hydrogen decreases with increasing carbon number. When hydrocarbons are burned in air the energy-producing reaction with oxygen produces water ($H_2O$) as well as carbon dioxide ($CO_2$), so there is less 'greenhouse' $CO_2$ production per joule of energy released than from coal. This difference is greatest for the lightest hydrocarbon, methane ($CH_4$), the main component of natural gas, with $CO_2$ production about 0.6 of that for coal for the same amount of energy. Fuel oil is intermediate between methane and coal.

## Natural gas

The cleanliness and convenience of natural gas have already led to its largely taking over from coal for domestic heating in the UK and in varying degrees elsewhere, and to similar arguments that it should be used for electricity generation, particularly in 'combined cycle' gas turbines, which are more efficient than, and can now be as economic as, steam turbines. This would also have the advantage of alleviating, though not removing, 'greenhouse' concerns for the reason just given. But two further problems have to be borne in mind.

The first is that methane is itself a 'greenhouse' gas, 30 times more effective per molecule than $CO_2$, though at present of so much lower (though rising) concentration in the atmosphere that its total contribution is less. Any leakage of unburnt methane from the natural gas system adds to this concentration, so leakage from an expanded system might outweigh any advantage of the change in fuel use.

The second is that the natural gas resource, which is limited like all non-renewables, is particularly under stress. The figures for 1989 for the time that proved reserves will last at current extraction rates were 13 years for the UK and 56 years for the world, the major reserves being in the Middle East and USSR. Of course the usual economic pressures will produce price changes and new assessments of reserves, but the limits are clearly in view. Synthetic natural gas (SNG) can be made from coal, for which reserves are greater. So, to the extent that economic dependence on fossil fuels will continue at least temporarily in face of greenhouse concerns, a route that would in principle overcome other pollution problems from coal would be large-scale conversion to SNG near the mine, with gas distribution and clean combustion at the points of use. (This of course assumes that the SNG plant is itself designed to be non-polluting and is economic, which is not the case at present. But this is a potential medium-term option for retaining the advantages of natural gas while taking advantage of the much greater coal reserves.)

## Oil

All stages of the exploration and extraction process produce residuals, impact and damage broadly similar to those of other mining operations: visual impact, noise and dirt, employment effects, accidents. The extreme conditions of off-shore operations make particular difficulties for the staff, though out of sight of most oil users. A major feature of the present industry is the development of ever-larger crude oil tankers, which have their own impacts and hazards, in order to satisfy the voracious demands of the industrial economies. Refineries, too, are large processing plant with obvious local effects, and which contribute significantly to long-range $SO_2$.

At the other end of the 'cycle', end-use combustion produces particulates and gaseous effluents, depending on the particular fuel and combustion conditions, which we have already seen being subjected to increasing controls along with those on coal combustion. Internal combustion engines are major contributors to $NO_x$ levels, highly toxic carbon monoxide (and the consequent photochemical smog) and tarry particulates (particularly from diesels) which newer designs seek to reduce:

- Lean-burn engines use a smaller proportion of fuel in the mixture entering the cylinder, and better control of ignition, so that less pollution is produced in the first place.
- Catalytic converters operate on the exhaust gases, effectively removing oxygen from the $NO_x$ and adding it to the hydrocarbons and $CO$ to produce $N_2$, $CO_2$ and $H_2O$ only.

The fundamental fossil-fuel effect of the production of the greenhouse gas, $CO_2$, remains, of course.

Perhaps the most distinctive environmental effect of the oil industry results from spillage at all stages of production and transport to the user, where the unwanted residual is oil itself, because of the direct impact and damage it produces.

Oil is in a sense part of the natural environment, but is normally buried; it enters the surface regions, on land and sea, by natural seepages. The Trinidad asphalts are an example of an enormous seep on land, and there are various oil sands and shales near the surface forming part of the oil resource. Marco Polo in the thirteenth century noted a natural seepage at Zorzania where 'there is a formation of oil which discharges so great a quantity of oils as to furnish loads for many camels.' Over the last 100 years there have been increasing unnatural spillages of oil into ecosystems which have evolved in its absence and are therefore damaged by it.

Oil wells can go out of control, releasing oil on land or in the sea; crude oil tankers have accidents, or release part of their cargo in tank washings, operational discharges or during loading and unloading; storage tanks on shore can leak; refineries discharge their effluents into rivers and the sea; oil or its products can escape from pipelines, tankers or road vehicles.

Off-shore exploration and extraction have increased drilling problems and the risk of contamination; the scale of spillage worldwide is thought to be about 100 000 tonnes per year (100 kilotonnes/year). This is to be compared to a natural seepage into the marine environment of about 600 kt/year, but damage is particularly associated with individual localised incidents: the EKOFISK blowout in 1977 released 30 kt of oil into the North Sea over 7 days; IXTOC-I in the Gulf of Mexico in 1979 released even more – 4 kt/day for 3 months, over 350 kt in all.

Individual tanker accidents likewise attract much attention, such as the *Torrey Canyon* off Cornwall in 1967 (100 kt spilt) and the *Amoco Cadiz* off Brittany in 1979 (220 kt). In 1989 12 accidents involved a total spillage of 162 kt, the two largest being *Kharg-5* off Morocco (76 kt) and the *Exxon Valdez* off Alaska (36 kt) – this last is generally considered to be an environmental disaster because of its particular location, though it spilt the smallest quantity of oil among those mentioned. These spectacular individual events are to be compared with routine discharges of oil from tankers before entering port, which are estimated to involve up to 1 million tonnes per year (1 Mt/year).

One estimate of the total flow of oil into the marine environment is about 5.3 Mt/year, of which nearly half (2.25 Mt) comes from run-off from the land from rivers, drains, municipal and industrial wastes, and a further 1.2 Mt from natural seeps and atmospheric fall-out. Against this background the 0.12 Mt or so from production and refining losses does not seem large, but the 1.76 Mt from all aspects of ocean transportation is significant (Figure 4.16; and a further discussion by Smith & Greene in *Smith & Warr, 1991*, Chapter 1).

In considering the resulting damage, there is as usual in environmental assessment a distinction to be made between localised events, which are shocking but produce no long-lasting effects, and the more insidious long-term consequences of regular operations. In both cases there can be:

●   decrease of aesthetic and economic value due to unsightly spills and oiled beaches (Plate 10);

●   damage to wildlife such as sea birds and marine animals;

●   decrease of fishing resource;

●   modification of habitats, delaying or preventing recolonisation by marine organisms;

●   contaminated sea-food entering the food web, perhaps reaching humans; and perhaps more permanently;

●   modification of the marine ecosystem by elimination of species, with decreasing diversity and productivity.

As with gas, the oil resource is under severe stress. As was noted in Chapter 1, the corresponding figures for the lifetime of proved reserves at 1989 production rates were a mere 5 years for the UK, and 44 years for the

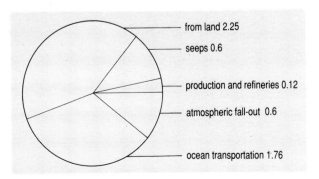

from land 2.25

seeps 0.6

production and refineries 0.12

atmospheric fall-out  0.6

ocean transportation 1.76

◄   *Figure 4.16 Sources of oil in the marine environment (in Mt).*

world, where the Middle East is even more dominant. Again, economic pressures will modify this picture, but continuing massive oil transportation and political instabilities seem inevitable. As the world transport system is so dependent on oil, it may gradually become more economic to expand synthetic oil production from coal by the various available methods (e.g. the synthesis method as in the South African SASOL process operating since 1955, or the potentially more efficient degradation process). There will be corresponding changes in the environmental effects of production, but not of use. However, the fundamental greenhouse problem will remain, perhaps forcing a more radical reconsideration of transport policy.

## 4.3   *Transport*

At this stage it may be helpful to change focus from the environmental effects of particular fuels to those of this particular end-use. At present in industrialised countries the transport and oil issues are almost synonymous. Another of the OECD Compass project books, *Environmental Effects of Automotive Transport* (OECD, 1986) notes that OECD member countries use some 70% of the world's energy and 20% of that is for transportation. Of this OECD transport energy over 99% is based on petroleum, of which 70% is on gasoline. About 75% of the transport petroleum is for road transport.

Q   What do these figures imply about OECD transport not based on petroleum?

A   It uses less than 1% of the energy, presumably as electricity, from coal or nuclear stations, for electric vehicles and trains.

Q   How much of the petroleum used for transport is not gasoline, and what is it?

A   29%, presumably kerosine, for jet aircraft, diesel for lorries and trains, heavy fuel oil for ships.

Q   What proportion of road transport energy is as diesel fuel?

A   We are told 70% of transport energy is gasoline (which is nearly all for non-diesel road transport), implying that the remaining 5% of road transport is diesel. Alternatively, 25% of transport energy is not for road transport, i.e. aircraft, trains, ships, so the remaining 4% of non-gasoline must be for road diesels. Either way, proportion of diesel in road transport energy seems to be 4–5 in 75, i.e. about 6%.

So it is our cars above all else that create the endless demands on (and power of) the oil industry, with all the environmental and political problems outlined above. In thinking of the future it is important to remember that a transport system doesn't have to be based on cars based on gasoline, but it will not be easy to change. We return to this in Chapter 5. Meanwhile we should consider more of the environmental effects of the system we already have.

The Compass study above suggests, as did the previous one (see Section 2.2), a comprehensive and somewhat laborious structure for considering environmental impact. In this case it takes the form of a $6 \times 4$ matrix, i.e. a diagram with 6 columns representing various aspects of the

| | Ecosystem | Resources | Physical environment | Health | Safety | Socio-economic |
|---|---|---|---|---|---|---|
| Vehicle and fuel production | | mineral shortages, capital for new developments | | | oil production accidents | |
| Infrastructure construction | habitat disturbance | | | | | |
| System operation | | | | vehicle exhausts, smog | | |
| Disposal | | | | | | who pays? |

▲   Figure 4.17   A transport–environment matrix.

environment and 4 rows for various parts of the transport system (Figure 4.17). In each of the 24 'cells', produced where rows and columns intersect, there is scope for considering impacts and damage – a daunting task.

The six environment areas chosen (with further subdivisions) are:

- ecosystems: terrestrial, aquatic and human/animal pathways;
- resources: mineral, natural (e.g. land and water), capital/labour;
- physical environment: air, water quality, waste disposal, noise, aesthetic;
- health: occupational, public;
- safety: occupational, public, social (this is to make a distinction between physical hazards and social or economic disruption);
- socio-economic: economic (e.g. employment, costs), institutional (e.g. firms, local authorities, government).

The four transport system areas (like the phases of Section 2.2) are:

- production of vehicles and fuel;
- construction of the infrastructure (i.e. the roads, bridges, railways, airports);
- operation of the components of the system;
- disposal.

Merely to list these topics is to recognise the endless ramifications of our transport system and its impact on (in some places domination of) our environment. This is not a unique scheme of classification, but it clearly brings out many more factors than the oil production, distribution and combustion effects we have already considered. It can be related to the 'system' ideas of Section 2 by regarding the rows as identifying innumerable primary energy-in-transport systems, which can each be analysed as interlinked components within a system boundary, and the columns as a range of options for extending the system boundary to examine various forms of environmental impact.

Some of the cells have already been filled in: the ones concerned with topics that we have already considered – oil production and distribution, and vehicle exhaust emissions.

*Activity 4*

Test your understanding of this matrix by filling in at least one topic
in each of the remaining cells if you can.

One recent change has been much hailed as an environmental advance:
the availability of lead-free petrol. It is only one small corner of the system,
but it removes an added hazard to the oil combustion pollutants that we
have already mentioned. Less obviously, the change is essential if catalytic
converters are to be used to control exhaust emissions, because they are
poisoned by lead. This has been as important a factor in the change as
direct concern about the health hazard of lead itself.

A different problem which stubbornly resists change is the appalling
level of casualties in the present system. (This might not be regarded as an
'environmental' problem in one sense, but when viewed as an influence of
one technical system on a larger human one it certainly is.)

In Britain, where figures are not unusual for an urban society, 57 700
people were killed on the roads in the ten years to 1987, and 3.1 million
injured; only 322 of the deaths were on buses or coaches; in the same
period there were 617 deaths and 23 780 injuries in railway accidents. In the
proper concern about tens of deaths and hundreds of injuries per year in
the energy industries, and about the major sea, rail and air accidents that
attract understandable attention, we must not lose sight of the daily human
cost of this major sector of energy use. There has been some modest
improvement in annual figures for motorists, but not for pedestrians and
cyclists, where the rates, suitably adjusted for numbers and distances, are
considerably higher than in some other European countries, particularly
Sweden and The Netherlands. The 10% reduction in total road casualties
achieved, from 344 000 in 1977 to 310 000 in 1987, sets the scale for the
target set in 1989 by Paul Channon, then Secretary of State for Transport,
for a one-third reduction by the year 2000 – requiring a threefold
improvement. Is this possible?

## 4.4   *Nuclear power*

The fossil fuel industries, and the transport sector in practice if not in
principle, are all contributors to greenhouse $CO_2$, and will have to change if
current projections continue to gain credence. Nuclear energy is a (non-
renewable) source that does not produce $CO_2$ directly, a fact to be put in its
favour alongside the smaller volumes of fuel that originally seemed to be
its advantage. It has its own environmental problems, of course, to which
we return below, but it cannot be entirely isolated from a discussion on
$CO_2$ production, for the following reason.

In the present system, any industrial process that uses electrical energy
depends on fossil-fuel power stations, which produce $CO_2$. In a study by
Mortimer presented by Friends of the Earth to two public inquiries in 1989,
figures were given for the $CO_2$ emissions associated with the production,
or saving, of 1000 MW of electricity by various methods, 'taking into
account related mining and fuel producing processes' (Table 4.4).

This study noted that efforts to increase nuclear power production
sharply 'would run into problems of declining uranium ore grade as world

Table 4.4 $CO_2$ emission associated with production/saving of 1000 MW of electricity

| Method | $CO_2$ (tonnes per year) |
|---|---|
| coal | 5 912 000 |
| nuclear | 230 000 |
| hydro | 78 000 |
| wind | 54 000 |
| tidal | 52 000 |
| loft insulation | 24 000 |
| low energy lighting | 12 000 |

Source: Mortimer (1989).

resources are depleted. The lower the grade, the more energy is required to extract and process it, and the more $CO_2$ released. At grades between 1 and 100 p.p.m. the amount released rises to levels equivalent to coal-fired power stations' (Mortimer, 1989).

Some aspects of nuclear policy will be discussed at more length in Chapter 8, but brief general comments are appropriate here, and we will then discuss the radioactive discharges from the Sellafield power station complex in Cumbria in order to illustrate the methods of environmental impact assessment described above.

## General environmental concerns

The fission process used in current reactor types – Magnox, advanced gas-cooled reactor (AGR) and pressurised water reactor (PWR) – produces large volumes of product isotopes, some highly radioactive. Most environmental criticisms of nuclear power arise from this, and fall into four groups:

1    Abnormal radiation levels from normal operations will cause cell damage, malignant cancers, genetic defects etc. – this possibility was recognised from the outset. It can be argued that the strict exposure levels and checks introduced have minimised this problem, at least in power stations.

2    Reactor operations and the transport of irradiated fuels cannot be guaranteed safe against catastrophic accidents such as those at Windscale in 1957, Three Mile Island in the USA in 1979, and Chernobyl in 1986. While stringent safety precautions may have been successful in nearly all cases (there were more than 400 operational reactors worldwide in 1990), the effects of these relatively few major failures have been so dramatic as to greatly weaken confidence in further expansion.

3    Radioactive waste has to be disposed of safely, which is difficult. An operational 1 GW burner reactor produces some 5 tonnes of radioactive waste a year (apart from uranium and plutonium, which it is present UK policy to recover by reprocessing); for fast breeders, which are nowhere operational, it would be less than 1 tonne per year. The activities and decay times mean that the more dangerous wastes must be isolated from the biosphere for at least 1000 years, an engineering challenge of exceptional stringency not yet satisfactorily resolved. Low-level wastes are vented to

the atmosphere, discharged into rivers and the sea or buried. The history of such sea disposal at Sellafield, summarised below, provides a vivid example of the environmental assessment method outlined in Section 2.

There is a further problem to be faced in decommissioning reactors at the end of their life, when much of the structure will have become radioactive. Recent reappraisals of the cost of this operation have cast further doubt on the commercial future of nuclear power. Indeed, after much technical and moral debate about the desirability of nuclear power, it seems that, in the UK at least, economic arguments are currently (1990) proving to be the most damaging. It will be interesting to see how these develop here and elsewhere over the next decade.

4    The large quantities of uranium enriched in its fissile isotope, and even more seriously, of plutonium, if separated by reprocessing, must somehow be kept secure from theft or other misappropriation for nuclear weapons (the threat of increased nuclear proliferation) by countries or groups that do not at present have them.

## Sellafield marine discharges

The history of radioactive discharges into the Irish Sea from the reprocessing plant at Sellafield provides a salutary insight into attitudes and environmental assessment methods in a particular case. While there would probably now be few defenders of the detailed policies adopted, particularly in the 1970s, it should be acknowledged that measurements of radioactivity can be carried out at very low levels, and that tracing the movement of particular isotopes has provided a clearer picture of ecosystem effects than used to be available. A great deal of environmental monitoring has been carried out and published, which was certainly not the case for chemical pollutants in the past. Attitudes to pollution standards and the ecological effects of pollutants in general have no doubt been significantly influenced by the monitoring of these radioactive effluents.

They are dwelt on here without any implication that they are *exceptionally* damaging but because the available data fit particularly well into the framework described above in Section 2: the *origin* of the effects is in the reprocessing operations at Windscale/Sellafield; the *residuals* considered are the authorised discharges of low-level radioactive wastes by pipeline into the sea; the *impact* is the resulting level of radioactivity in the marine environment and ecosystem; the *damage* in this case is judged by the dose of radioactivity received by human beings, in various critical groups, as a result. Let us look briefly at each of these in turn.

1    Windscale began as a plant for the production of plutonium for military use in 1950; uranium reactors create plutonium in their fuel rods, and this is extracted in the reprocessing operation. This practice has continued through the civil nuclear programme starting in the 1960s, the plutonium produced being stockpiled for future use, notionally in fast breeder reactors, though a considerable amount has been traded with the USA. The spent fuel also contains about 2% of other radioactive products which are 'waste'. During the initial plant design it was decided that low-level wastes could be disposed of in the sea, where they would be 'diluted and dispersed', like many other industrial effluents. It was argued that radioactivity is a natural property of the sea, so some added level could be negligible, but that discharges should be carefully controlled and monitored. This was at first done within the Atomic Energy Authority, but

since 1967 an annual report has been published on *Radioactivity in Surface and Coastal Waters* (from 1977 it has been called *Aquatic Environment Monitoring*) by the Lowestoft Radiobiological Laboratory of the Ministry of Agriculture, Fisheries and Food, who were charged with checking the safety of this operation (as well as the other nuclear installations, and other pollutants). Comparison of their reports over some 20 years provides an interesting reflection of changing perceptions, about nuclear power and the environment generally.

2    The nature and quantities of these particular residuals of the reprocessing operation, the low-level wastes discharged, were reported annually. They rose to a peak in the early 1970s. The Royal Commission on Environmental Protection reported unfavourably in its Sixth Report in 1976, and a general decline in discharge levels began about then. This discharge data gives a clear statement of the specified variation in time of a localised environmental disturbance – a giant 'blip' of radioactivity injected into the Irish Sea. However misguided the original decision may have been, it is vital to try to learn from it by mapping its consequences, both for public health and more general ecosystem effects.

3    A vast amount of tabulated data makes it possible, in principle, to construct something like the 'bubble of influence' postulated in Section 2 – that is, the impact, in space and time, of these residuals on chosen aspects of the physical environment and ecosystem, though there are so many variables that it is difficult to grasp the whole picture. Figures are given for the specific activity (the amount of radioactivity per unit mass) measured in the laboratory on samples of water, sand and silt, fish, crustaceans and molluscs of many species, taken from many locations. From these the environmental 'impact' has been mapped in some detail, showing how particular radioactive isotopes spread not only through the water and materials of the shore by physical processes, but are concentrated at higher levels in fish, in crustaceans like crabs and most of all in molluscs like winkles.

4    The resulting 'damage' from these complicated 'impacts', as far as the MAFF reports are concerned, is the possible effect on human health (more general ecosystem damage continues to be looked at elsewhere). The principal method used is to identify critical groups of the public whose movements and eating habits bring them into contact with the environmental radioactivity, and to ensure that in the worst case the received dose of radiation falls below some specified 'safe' level; then everyone else must be safer. Obviously there are lots of questions here: who are the critical groups, how do you assess the dose, what is safe? The answers given are complicated and varied over the period considered, and perhaps are still varying.

  The broad conclusion was that doses to critical groups never exceeded the prevailing 'safe' level, though they came close to it in the late 1970s. In 1985 the internationally recommended safe level was reduced – this new figure had been exceeded for about a decade, though current levels are well below it and continue to fall.

It is important to remember that the doses quoted in these reports are only estimates from a complicated procedure applied to selected environmental features believed to matter. As reports of leukaemia clusters etc. grow, more direct studies of the population itself are being made; for example, post-mortem measurements of radioactivity in human subjects (not necessarily showing apparent clinical effects) may indicate how good the estimates have been. No doubt there are already more data available than in these particular reports, and a clearer picture will gradually emerge. The recent (1990) conclusion of statistical studies (not new measurements) that childhood leukaemia can be linked, not to general environmental effects, but to occupational exposure of the father, was a disturbing surprise, and surely not the end of the story.

As a reminder of changed perceptions, a quotation from the first report in the MAFF series noted above (1967) is revealing:

'(This report) shows clearly that the discharge of radioactive wastes in this manner is *completely safe* . . . It is our policy to publish the results of our surveys, *so as to assist in creating an informed climate of public opinion in which the peaceful uses of nuclear energy may be fully exploited*' (emphasis added) – surely no part of the task of an independent assessment agency!

All the reports suggest a determination to show that the procedures *are* safe rather than to ask *whether* they are.

In fact, the effect of these studies, and others, has been to provide a map of the bubble of influence which has led to a change in practice (one of the general options considered in Section 2) – at least to a reduction in authorised discharges (which however increases the long-term waste disposal problem). Some would argue for a further change: the abandonment of the reprocessing of spent fuel, as has long been the case for civil nuclear power in the US. Others, taking in other environmental and economic concerns as well, would prefer the abandonment of nuclear power completely. Whatever the final conclusion, the studies do indicate the massive effort needed to assess environmental damage from pollutants, and also the need for this to be done as independently as possible from the polluting agency.

## 4.5   *Waste heat*

After the complexities of the previous sections, this can be dealt with fairly briefly. The first point is that all electric power stations (fossil fuel and nuclear) only convert about a third of the available energy into electricity, so the rest is lost as heat, removed into the environment as a residual. This can produce obvious local effects in the atmosphere or nearby waters used for cooling. Or the system can be changed so that the heat is used for district heating, so is no longer a residual – as has only rarely been done in the UK, but is common in other countries, particularly Denmark and Germany. This replaces further consumption of primary energy for heating, so is an evident improvement in energy efficiency.

The second point is that whatever use is made of primary energy, it all turns into heat in the end, more or less directly. So all the fossil fuel and nuclear energy, formerly locked up in the molecular and nuclear structure of materials, that is released for use adds to the heat input of the Earth, along with the absorbed solar radiation. The Earth is kept in balance by the re-radiation into space of whatever energy it receives from all sources; if this increases, the global temperature (as seen from outside) must increase too. This is a fundamental 'heat pollution' effect (not to be confused with the greenhouse effect caused by particular gases, which modifies the relationship between surface and upper atmosphere temperature, without changing the overall radiation to space). In fact heat pollution is not at present globally significant, with a total world fossil and nuclear power rating of some 10 TW to be compared with a solar input of some 100 PW, ten thousand times greater. There are 'heat islands' associated with big cities, due to higher energy use and changed surface conditions, but a negligible global effect. But it should be remembered that 'success' in meeting expanding energy demand from any non-solar source of supply (such as nuclear fusion) would be in danger of facing this fundamental heat pollution problem. There has been a tenfold increase in energy use this century; if there were a further tenfold increase in the next century, to 100 TW, this effect might begin to be of concern.

## 4.6   Solar energy sources

All the previous problems (chemical, nuclear, even heat pollution) are avoided if we make use of solar energy, either directly or indirectly via the climate and biomass systems, to meet our needs. Only two methods are at present in widespread use; others of future importance will be considered in Chapter 5.

### Hydroelectric power

A few per cent of world energy (some 0.35 TW) is provided by hydroelectric schemes, which depend on favourable topography for dam-building and storage of large volumes of water, which are raised to high level in the hydrological cycle (the solar-powered evaporation of water to form clouds, falling again as rain). It can also be raised by electric pumps, as at Dinorwic in North Wales, to provide effective storage of electricity produced in other ways. Turbines powered by the falling water can be brought in and out of use very quickly, providing flexibility in the electricity grid system. The total resource has been estimated at 2.2 TW worldwide. The large-scale engineering involved has seen its more complete exploitation in Europe and North America than elsewhere, though large schemes now often figure in development plans for the rest of the world. The local environmental effects are considerable, both during construction and in producing a permanent change to the local landscape.

These seem to have been accepted in general in developed countries, though new proposals are now subject to much more detailed planning scrutiny than formerly. The encouragement, or imposition, of large schemes in less developed countries has been much criticised by environmentalists, as often doing more damage to traditional ways of life and land use than is justified by the immediate needs of the local population – perhaps being more useful to an incoming mining company, for example. As always, the kind of scrutiny of environmental effects discussed in this chapter, and the even more difficult balancing of interests, is required in each individual case, implying a developed political framework and equitable planning procedures that are not always present (this general issue is taken up again by Smith in *Smith & Warr, 1991*, Chapters 5–6).

### Biomass

Wood as a fuel is no longer (at present) a significant part of the energy system in developed countries. But wood products like paper, and other vegetable and animal products, find many other uses, and form a large part of domestic and commercial wastes. In the UK, some 30 million tonnes a year of municipal solid waste is combustible, with over one-third of the energy content of coal. Most of it is buried (landfill), where the decay processes produce methane, hazardous both as an explosive and, as it leaks to the surface, a more potent greenhouse gas than $CO_2$. If incinerated, preferably in a combined heat and power (CHP) plant for electricity production and district heating, the $CO_2$ produced is returned as part of the normal carbon cycle (provided new biomass is being produced at the same rate as it is being destroyed), and coal or other fossil fuels with their various problems are replaced. Other European countries and Japan use the energy in wastes in this way – up to 75% in Luxembourg, but only 5% in the UK. There can be pollutant emissions from badly designed incinerators, but the same kind of controls as those for fossil fuel combustion can be imposed, and satisfied by good combustion engineering.

Alternatively, methane can be produced from biomass in a controlled way, collected and itself used as a clean fuel: this is particularly applicable to agricultural wastes and sewage.

In less developed parts of the world, fuelwood (and other biomass like animal dung) remains as a principal source of energy. It does not figure in commercial energy statistics, so its scale of use is difficult to estimate – a figure of 10–15% of total world energy use (i.e. over 1 TW) has been suggested. The collection of fuelwood can form a major part of the day's work. Under stressed conditions of population growth and land shortage it can contribute to deforestation. However, it is inappropriate to see this as a principal cause when set against large-scale forest clearances for commercial logging and ranching, and the general economic and political issue of land ownership. There is a growing interest in **agroforestry** (Plate 11). This practice allows the coproduction of woody and non-woody crops on the same area of land and has economic advantages over monoculture in some areas. Agroforestry also caters for multiple use of land for food, energy, amenity, etc. and has also been shown to be sustainable in some studies. Fundamentally, biomass use of all kinds is sustainable provided it takes place at the rate the biomass can be regrown – obvious, but often overlooked throughout history. At present, this is by no means the case, and progressive reduction in the forested area effectively adds to the greenhouse effect by increasing atmospheric $CO_2$, apart from its other environmental effects. Conversely, any increase in forested area would reduce atmospheric $CO_2$ of whatever origin (during the period of change). Strategies for reducing, and preferably reversing, deforestation must form part of the world response to the greenhouse effect.

## 4.7    *Summary*

Other aspects of energy policy and their environmental impact have been reviewed, with reference to their global and local effects. Petroleum use can be cleaner than coal, but still contributes to greenhouse $CO_2$ (and potentially methane); transport is a particularly significant user. Nuclear power does not produce $CO_2$ directly, though its introduction implies indirect $CO_2$ production; it presents other environmental problems. All non-renewable sources in principle contribute to heat pollution, though this is not significant at present. Solar energy sources (at present hydroelectric and biomass) are in principle sustainable, with only local environmental effects; changes in biomass production (deforestation or reafforestation) contribute to atmospheric $CO_2$ changes, in either direction.

# 5   Environmental economics and other values

If you look back at the 'origins' of environmental effects classified in Section 2, and the numerous details that have followed, it will be clear that there is immense diversity and human ingenuity in the present energy system, and that it is constantly changing. It is also clear that the primary reason for change is economic (new processes are adopted when they are cheaper) and that environmental effects have not usually been included in these considerations as we may now feel they should. How are environmental effects to be taken into account? I would like to suggest five approaches, which are not entirely distinguishable, but which provide a variety of perspectives as an introduction to the discussion in the next book in the series (*Smith & Warr, 1991*). They can be labelled technical, economic, legal, ethical and aesthetic.

## 5.1   Technical

Fortunately there are some changes where economic interest and environmental concerns coincide, so these should present least difficulty. All the measures broadly described as 'energy efficient' in Chapter 5 (insulation, CHP, efficient appliances) tend to be of this kind, in which case the only question is why they don't happen. A combination of inertia, lack of information and different perceptions of costs between initial outlay and running expenses, or between users and manufacturers, seems to be responsible; enthusiasts and educators can only be patient. Perhaps the most significant factor is that energy policy, at government level, say, has in the past been dominated by supply considerations. It is not in the economic interest of energy suppliers to see energy consumption reduced, and economic statistics can show increased energy consumption as desirable economic 'growth'. This perception has been changing in recent years, as reduction in demand has been seen to be more compatible with sustainable energy use; this will gradually be reflected in national policies.

## 5.2   Economic

This is sometimes crudely characterised as the 'polluter pays' principle, one that could hardly be disputed as desirable, but is not so easy to achieve. The difficulty is that in a free market a transaction between a buyer and seller takes place at one time, using the information then available; the environmental implications (for others as well as the buyer, of course) often only emerge at a later time, when the original transactors may not be recognisable, available or controllable. So the market has to be modified or regulated in some way by government and the law to prevent this, which implies planning, prediction, and policing – not entirely reliable processes, and of varying political acceptability.

However, planning is much used, particularly for large-scale investments, such as the building of power stations. An author who has tackled this particular issue is Hohmeyer (1988), in his *Social Costs of Energy Consumption*, a technical analysis (for West German conditions, but generally applicable to 'developed' economies) of the way 'external' effects (what we have called environmental impact and damage) can be included in the costing when comparing different systems. Cost comparisons of alternative methods (like wind) with existing methods (like nuclear) are then much more favourable. A related idea is the 'least-cost planning' required of US electricity supply utilities by some states, where approval to build a new power station is only given if it can be shown to be cheaper than investing in demand reduction by, for instance, efficiency measures.

A more general study of the way environmental issues can be incorporated in economic decision-making is the 'Pearce Report', by David Pearce and his colleagues for the UK Department of the Environment, and published in 1989 as a *Blueprint for a Green Economy*. This represents a positive move within orthodox 'neo-classical' economics to embrace the ideal of 'sustainable development' – another unarguable, but not so easily defined, doctrine associated with the 1987 World Commission on Environment and Development (WCED) report *Our Common Future* (the Brundtland Report), and discussed at length by Smith (in *Smith & Warr, 1991*, Chapters 5–6). Pearce recognises the idea of 'Environmental capital, goods and services', to be considered alongside the human-made varieties of normal economic theory. He specifically rejects the traditional idea that increases in gross national product can be used to measure the improved quality of life, since this can be achieved at the expense of environmental degradation, and proposes new measures which take better account of this.

In a society which is dominated by economics in decision-making, any way of including the environment is to be welcomed, but there are some difficulties, which the earlier examples in this chapter illustrate. They showed how difficult it is to trace the environmental effects of particular processes. Even when the broad links are clear it is not easy to prove who is responsible; often they are not clear, or unforeseen consequences emerge later. More difficult still is to move from environmental effects to environmental costs. It is central to Pearce's ideas that money values can be assigned to environmental factors, which raises difficulties, for instance, in comparing one person's treasured view with another's health or electricity costs, or any of these in different places and times. Finally, there is the mechanism for including these issues in market transactions. These will be much debated, but perhaps it is reasonable to consider charges, tax incentives or subsidies as 'economic' measures (which would have to be imposed on the market) while pure regulation would spill over into the next subsection.

## 5.3   *Legal*

National laws (like Clean Air Acts) and international 'regimes' of regulation (like the EC pollution directives) may be influenced by economic considerations, but they are surely not controlled by them. Longer term or wider ranging perceptions of human welfare are somehow distilled into these socially imposed constraints; their evolution is discussed by Greene (in *Smith & Warr, 1991*, Chapter 4). More controversial is the extent to which other parts of the ecosystem or the natural environment are also 'entitled' to protection, regardless of human welfare. Again attitudes are changing, and there is overlap with the next topic.

## 5.4   Ethical

Many of the world's religions include precepts on the way human beings should treat the natural world; these may as frequently cause conflict as agreement, particularly when different societies impinge on each other. In an increasingly interrelated world we are some way from shared ethical principles. The developed world, for all its residual religious conflicts, has in practice shared some beliefs over the last few centuries derived from a (Utilitarian?) enthusiasm for economic growth, driven by technical innovation and science. The growing environmental movement reveals dissatisfaction with this position, unhappily sometimes coinciding with a rejection of the strength of science – arguably as good an approach to 'truth' as we have, and at best, a creative recognition of the limits of knowledge. A better change of stance would be a greater wariness about innovation, separating it in our minds from improved scientific understanding. Returning to the earlier language of this chapter, we should assume that the residuals of energy, and other technical, processes are guilty until proved innocent, instead of regarding the technically possible as naturally desirable. We will need the best science for this assessment, but must apply it to asking *whether* practices will do more good than harm, not, as so often, demonstrating that they must: humility, not hubris (the Greeks always had a word for it). The implied objectivity of science can also be questioned: 'scientists' usually have employers; whoever sets the agenda of study may control the outcome. However, at best it does provide a systematic way of improving communicable models of the world, provided it is not arrogantly assumed that these instantly license change, which we should know by now often has unexpected consequences.

## 5.5   Aesthetic

We have an alternative method of judging the effects of our activities, our intuitive response: the joy and delight a child shows in a tree or a kitten, the outrage of Blake at a caged bird. It may not be objective, and may be culturally conditioned, but in some way it surely provides a link with our instinct for what is good for us, evolved over millions of years before we had speech, society, laws or economics. Dickens did not have to measure the damage produced by soot and smoke: he knew, a century before society was prepared to act. Such intuitive convictions may not always be right, but we do well to listen to them. Furthermore, aesthetic satisfactions are not only about intuition: there is also a highly complex intellectual process of pattern recognition and formation, in the matching of structure and imagery to underlying perceptions of connections, which artists like Dickens make with lightning concision.

So let us return to *Hard Times*, and its rogues' gallery of the architects of Coketown and its attitudes. It may provide a salutary counterbalance to the rest of the chapter.

Meet the politician and educator Thomas Gradgrind, with his celebrated 'In this life, we want nothing but Facts, Sir; nothing but Facts!':

> A man of realities. A man of facts and calculations . . . With a rule and a pair of scales, and the multiplication table always in his pocket, Sir, ready to weigh and measure any parcel of human nature, and tell you exactly what it comes to.

And his friend Mr Bounderby:

> He was a rich man: banker, merchant, manufacturer and what not. A big loud man, with a stare, and a metallic laugh . . . A man who could never sufficiently vaunt himself a self-made man . . . who was always proclaiming . . . his old ignorance and his old poverty . . . 'Josiah Bounderby of Coketown learnt his letters from the outsides of the shops . . . Tell Josiah Bounderby of Coketown, of your district schools and your model schools, and your training schools, and your whole kettle-of-fish of schools; and Josiah Bounderby of Coketown, tells you plainly, all right, all correct, – he hadn't such advantages – but let us have hard-headed, solid-fisted people – the education that made him won't do for everybody, he knows – such and such his education was, however . . .'

*Mr Harthouse dining at the Bounderbys'.*

And his schoolmaster M'Choakumchild:

> He and some one hundred and forty other schoomasters had been lately turned at the same time, in the same factory, on the same principles, like so many pianoforte legs. He had been put through an immense variety of paces, and had answered volumes of head-breaking questions. Orthography, etymology, syntax, and prosody, biography, astronomy, geography, and general cosmography, the sciences of compound proportion, algebra, land-surveying and levelling, vocal music, and drawing from models, were all at the ends of his ten chilled fingers.

And so on for another page (as it might be, environmental impact assessment, general systems theory, radioactivity and economics), culminating in the flamboyant rhetoric of this account of his teaching:

> He went to work in this preparatory lesson, not unlike Morgiana in the Forty Thieves: looking into all the vessels ranged before him, one after another, to see what they contained. Say, good M'Choakumchild. When from thy boiling store, thou shalt fill each jar brim full by-and-by, dost thou think that thou wilt always kill outright the robber Fancy lurking within – or sometimes only maim him and distort him!

# 6   *Conclusion*

Of course we can't quite leave the last word to Dickens' rhetoric, however heart-warming. His opposition of Fact and Fancy is a bit too neat for the complexities of the real world – surely we need reason *and* imagination, not one or the other – and we won't persuade our latter-day Gradgrinds to change by mocking them. We need passion and conviction to stir us into action, but we will also need patient analysis to make a case that will be listened to. The procedures of Section 2, either in the formal checklists of the OECD, or in the more open-ended form of systems theory, provide, it is suggested, a general way to assess environmental effects. Subsequent sections have shown that the Facts are by no means easy to find; there is plenty of scope for Fancy in deciding which larger systems are to be considered in determining impact and damage. There is then some evidence that such an analysis can gain general assent if carried out sufficiently thoroughly, in spite of kicking and screaming on the way (developing pollution control regimes, changes in radioactive waste policies, taxation). We still have some way to go, however, in arriving at value systems that will change the fundamental direction of globally damaging energy policies.

# Comments on Activities

## Activity 1

All the stages are involved, some more than once. There is no reason why you should know the details, but the following ideas are among those relevant:

- exploration. Someone had to establish, on general geological grounds, that Namibia contained uranium ores; they had to be found, and their grade established so that the economics of mining them could be assessed.
- harvesting. The mining operation itself. In fact, the ore is very low grade, and it only became economic to exploit, in a vast open-pit operation, in 1975, when uranium prices rose sharply. Of course this exploration and mining is conducted by companies in developed countries, with obvious political overtones.
- processing. The ore is processed at a mill using crushing and chemical operations to produce yellowcake, uranium oxide, which is the form in which it is shipped.
- transport. Yellowcake is shipped to UK.
- storage. It may be stockpiled in this form depending on strategic and market considerations.
- processing. It is converted into the forms used as nuclear fuels by British Nuclear Fuels Limited (BNFL): metallic uranium for the original Magnox reactors and 'enriched' uranium oxide with an increased proportion of the fissile isotope $^{235}U$ for the later AGRs and PWRs, which have differences in fuel element design.
- marketing. This is abnormal – there is a powerful world market for uranium in its various forms (even more for the plutonium derived from it after reprocessing), but it is tightly controlled for security reasons, so is very much in the hands of international bodies and government agencies, which make direct agreements with the multinational primary producers.
- transport. Fuel elements are transported (road and rail) to a nuclear power station.
- (1st) end use. The fuel is used in the nuclear power station to produce electricity.

● transport. The radioactive spent fuel is transported in specially robust flasks by rail to reprocessing plant – not part of the essential primary cycle, but seen as important, in particular for plutonium production.

● storage. Radioactive wastes, before and after reprocessing, are stored; this has to be secure for very long periods, e.g. hundreds of years.

● marketing. The electricity is marketed by the production company to the distribution companies. There are current (1990) uncertainties about the development of a partially privatised system with relatively uneconomic nuclear electricity retained under government control.

● storage. Apart from large-scale pumped storage of electricity as raised water, the transport application requires local electrochemical storage of electricity in batteries which can be carried on vehicles.

● marketing. This is now much more directly aimed at the consumer – marketing of electricity by area boards and of vehicles and batteries by their manufacturers.

● (2nd) end use. For final transport application.

You may know more of the details, though there is no reason to feel guilty if you don't know any of them: were you able to recognise that something like this process, with all its interlocking aspects, had to be involved?

*Activity 2*

There are no 'correct' answers, but possible suggestions are shown in Figure 4.18.

(a)

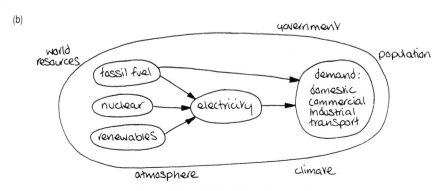

(b)

◀  *Figure 4.18*
*Answer to Activity 2:*
*(a) UK coal industry;*
*(b) UK energy system.*

## Activity 3

Detailed information will be found throughout Section 3. You may have noted

1   visible smoke, soot, etc., from domestic grates and poorly controlled industrial furnaces, now not allowed;

2   acid rain from invisible effluents ($SO_2$ and $NO_x$);

3   the enhanced greenhouse effect from $CO_2$ emission.

## Activity 4

Some suggestions are shown in Figure 4.19.

| | Ecosystem | Resources | Physical environment | Health | Safety | Socio-economic |
|---|---|---|---|---|---|---|
| Vehicle and fuel production | pollution from mines, oil, factories | mineral shortages, capital for new developments | air, water quality, wastes, aesthetic | occupational and public – toxic materials | oil platform, factory, distribution hazards | employment, geographical shifts |
| Infrastructure construction | habitat disturbance | materials and capital | dust, run-off noise | pollutants | construction accidents | costs, planning |
| System operation | toxic pollutants | fuel, maintenance skills | air and water quality, noise, aesthetic | exhausts, smog | accidents | costs to local government – politically sensitive |
| Disposal | some toxic materials | recycling | junk yards, tyres, batteries, ceramics disposal | toxic materials | accidents | responsibility for cost? |

▲   Figure 4.19   Answer to Activity 4.

## References

ELSWORTH, S. (1984) *Acid Rain*, Pluto Press, London.

HOHMEYER, O. (1988) *Social Costs of Energy Consumption*, Springer-Verlag, Berlin.

MORTIMER, N. (1989) Evidence to the House of Commons Select Committee on Energy bearing on the energy policy implications of the greenhouse effect *and* Proof of evidence, FOE 9, to the Hinkley Point C public enquiry, Friends of the Earth, London.

OECD (1983) *Environmental Effects of Energy Systems – the OECD Compass Project*, OECD, Paris.

OECD (1986) *Environmental Effects of Automotive Transport*, OECD, Paris.

PARK, C.C. (1987) *Acid Rain: rhetoric and reality*, Methuen, London.

PEARCE, D. *et al.* (1989) *Blueprint for a Green Economy*, Earthscan, London.

SMITH, P. M. & WARR, K. (eds) (1991) *Global Environmental Issues*, Hodder & Stoughton/The Open University, London (Book Four).

WORLD COMMISSION ON ENVIRONMENT AND DEVELOPMENT (1987) *Our Common Future* (The Brundtland Report), Oxford University Press, Oxford.

# 1 Introduction

The first chapter of this book outlined the use of natural energy resources to supply our needs. It placed particular emphasis on *numerical* matters: the existence of a common measure of energy of all kinds, the joule, in which all other energy units could be expressed, and the importance of one other unit, the watt, or joule per second, for the rate of conversion of energy from one form to another. We saw how the numbers of these units involved in energy storage and conversion processes vary over vast ranges as we move from the scale of individual human needs and particular appliances to the world scale of total energy demand and supply. As our future depends, among other things, on our ability to continue somehow providing for our energy needs, it will remain important to be clear about the general scale of these numbers.

However, we have also seen in Chapter 4 that present energy policies have many and complex environmental consequences, which cannot readily be assessed in numerical terms. The values (economic, ethical or aesthetic) to be used in judging between alternative options, and the ways these influence the political process, were introduced briefly there; they will continue to affect our discussion of the future, and are further considered by Smith (*Smith & Warr, 1991*, Chapters 5 and 6).

A major recent assessment of sustainable development worldwide, the 'Brundtland Report', *Our Common Future* (World Commission on the Environment and Development, 1987) concluded, as far as energy was concerned:

> Energy efficiency can only buy time for the world to develop 'low energy paths' based on renewable sources, which should form the foundation of the global energy structure during the 21st century.

These two topics, energy efficiency and renewables, form the two main strands of this chapter. The first is about ways of reducing energy *demand* while still satisfying human needs. Section 2 outlines the innumerable technical options available; Section 3 indicates some of the political factors involved in bringing them into use. The second is about forms of energy *supply* which are technically feasible and environmentally acceptable. Section 4 compares non-renewable and renewable energy contributions to future supply; Section 5 considers the potential environmental effects of renewables, including a more detailed case study of wind power. Although the discussion in this chapter is biased towards UK policy, this is representative of the issues in all industrialised countries. Furthermore, as these countries use most of the energy at present, creating most of the resulting environmental problems, any reductions in energy use and environmental damage that can be achieved without loss of amenity may help the rest of the world to avoid similar difficulties in their pursuit of an improved quality of life. Section 6 draws the threads of the previous sections together in some provisional conclusions about a sustainable energy future.

---

### Activity 1

Before reading on, reflect on the quantitative and environmental aspects of energy policy raised in Chapters 1 and 4. How has total world energy demand changed during the twentieth century? What does this imply for energy consumption per person in different regions? What is the likely effect on energy demand of a further doubling of world population in the next century, along with demand changes in the 'less developed' countries? What are the implications for the pressure on available fossil fuel, nuclear and solar resources? What are the environmental problems already recognised with fossil fuel and nuclear energy sources? Can these be included in economic considerations?

---

## 2   Energy efficiency

Any reduction in the amount of primary energy used to satisfy a particular human need represents an improvement in energy efficiency. It can occur anywhere in the long chain of conversion processes, from fuel extraction and refining, via combined heat and power plant, or improved manufacturing methods, to better insulation of buildings and more efficient domestic appliances. Some of these improvements have been referred to, particularly since the oil crises of the 1970s, as 'energy conservation'. Apart from the pedantic point that, scientifically, energy is *always* conserved, this may include proposals for reductions in the quality of service provided, which may well be resisted – such changes in behaviour should not be confused with reductions of energy use without loss of service. Otherwise the terms can be used interchangeably, but 'efficiency' has perhaps a more optimistic flavour than 'conservation', with its hint of puritanical cheese-paring.

The pursuit of energy efficiency is not new: it reappears with successive economic problems. In the 1920s, Norway and Sweden, with their cold climates and lack of indigenous fuel, had similar building insulation standards to those planned for the UK from 1990. Since the 1920s many communities in Denmark have used the 'waste' heat from diesel engine power plant in combined heat and power/district heating schemes. In 1934 the US government introduced mandatory thermal insulation requirements on all federally financed homes; they were progressively tightened in the 40s and 50s. When there were coal shortages in the UK in the 1940s it was widely agreed that a ton of coal saved was cheaper, safer and less polluting than a ton of coal mined. In the 1940s Swedish houses were developed with even more insulation and triple-glazing, producing further reductions in energy use.

However, the cheap oil and expectations from civil nuclear power of the 1950s distracted attention from energy efficiency, and it was largely forgotten until the oil crises of the 70s brought it back into consideration with renewed vigour. The vast worldwide reappraisal, often outside official government projects, particularly in countries with a history of such studies (Denmark, Sweden, Germany, Japan, USA) has shown much greater potential for energy efficiency than previously believed. In some applications, cost-effective reductions in energy use by as much as 90% were made. Representative studies in the USA, West Germany and the UK are listed at the end of this chapter. While energy supply experience is traditionally concentrated in large organisations, the best knowledge about energy efficiency is dispersed among many individuals in dozens of countries, with new ideas continuing to emerge.

The renewed emphasis has been on the demand, not for energy as such, but for *energy-related services*: comfortably warm homes, hot water on tap, cold food storage, machines to reduce domestic drudgery, modern telecommunications and health services, comfortable, well-ventilated and pleasantly lit offices, amenities relying on materials like steel, cement, paper and plastics. In 1990 energy demand in many countries is said to be unexpectedly buoyant. But if the required *services* can be provided using less energy, more cheaply and/or with less environmental impact, then rising energy use may well be seen, globally, as a failure. Unfortunately the separate energy supply organisations tend to regard increasing energy use as a success.

The way the present energy system of the UK is divided up, between different fuels, economic sectors and end uses, was summarised in Figure 1.14 of Chapter 1. It will be useful to remind yourself of the relative proportions of the various components before reading on. This breakdown is representative of that in industrialised countries, though obviously the availability of fuels, climatic and social factors produce many detailed variations.

*Q*  In the UK case, what fraction of the primary energy supplied is lost in conversion and delivery to the user?

*A*  About a third (particularly in electricity generation).

*Q*  What fraction of the delivered energy is used for heating?

*A*  About half.

*Q*  What fraction of delivered energy is used for transport?

*A*  About a third.

## 2.1   Space and water heating

In northern countries like Canada, Scandinavia, West Germany and the UK, 25–50% of all energy consumed is used to heat buildings. In the long term it should be possible to eliminate this drain on resources almost entirely.

Some heat input is of course essential to maintain an internal temperature above that outside. In any building, some of this heat is already provided by 'incidental gains' – solar (incoming sunlight), metabolic heat from the occupants, energy uses like cooking, lighting and electrical appliances. Only the balance has to be provided by the heating

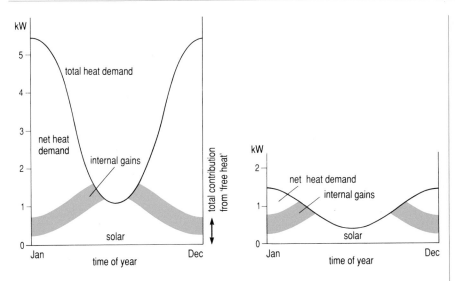

◀   Figure 5.1
Typical variation over the
year of the energy demand
for space heating in a UK
dwelling:

(left) conventional
UK dwelling
(90 m², semi-detached);

(right) superinsulated
dwelling.

system. If the heat losses from the building are greatly reduced and/or the use of solar energy is improved, this 'free heat' can account for most or all of the demand, and the residual requirement from the space heating system can be minimised. Figure 5.1 compares the best available with typical UK practice, showing that large reductions are possible in both the maximum heat required and in that part of the year for which it is needed: the annual heat demand is reduced by 90% or more. The heating system itself can be more efficient in its use of primary energy, as we shall see. The energy demand for water heating can likewise be reduced by more efficient use of hot water, and improved insulation of storage tanks and distribution pipes.

## Reduced heat loss

Techniques which have come to be called 'superinsulation' were developed in government research laboratories in Sweden, Canada, Denmark and the northern USA in the late 70s, though their origins are much older. The first such house was built with government support in Regina, Saskatchewan (Canada) in 1977, the second privately in Uppsala (Sweden) in 1978.

These houses have exceptional insulation, draughtproof construction, triple-glazing (or better) and a controlled ventilation system for winter use: usually arranged so that 70–80% of the heat in the outgoing stale air is recovered to preheat the fresh air intake. Constructional techniques have been developed in considerable detail in these countries; a representative design is shown in Figure 5.2. In severely cold climates 95% reductions in space heating costs have been documented; in more moderate climates, up to 100%. In a temperate climate such as the southern UK, a heat loss of less than 0.35 W per degree temperature difference (inside to outside) for each m³ of heated volume qualifies as 'superinsulated', to be compared with an average of about 1.6 W/m³ K for the current UK housing stock, and 1.1 W/m³ K for the 1990 UK building regulations. (K stands for kelvin, the unit of thermodynamic temperature.) With experience, such buildings cost little more to construct, the saving on the heating system largely offsetting

ROOF:

ROOFING SHEET
BATTENS
VENTILATION CAVITY
400mm MINERAL WOOL
LAMINATED RAFTERS
LATHS
VAPOUR BARRIER
GYPSUM BOARD

OUTER WALL:

RENDERING
LIGHTWEIGHT CONCRETE BLOCKS
200mm MINERAL WOOL
LIGHTWEIGHT CONCRETE BLOCKS
RENDERING

FLOOR:

PARQUET (FLOATING)
100mm RIGID MINERAL WOOL
VAPOUR BARRIER
LEVELLING
CONCRETE
LOOSE EXPANDED CLAY CLINKERS

BASE:

HARD BURNED BRICKS
CORRUGATED SHEET
BASE RENDERING
LIGHTWEIGHT CONCRETE BLOCKS
130mm POLYURETHANE FOAM
LIGHTWEIGHT CONCRETE BLOCKS

◀ *Figure 5.2*
*Construction of a Danish*
*superinsulated house.*

the costs of extra insulation and airtightness. Possible concerns about condensation and air quality seem to have been resolved with the careful detailing of these designs.

About half the new houses in Saskatchewan province were superinsulated by 1985. By 1989, Scandinavia and North America had hundreds of thousands, mainland Europe several thousand, and the UK about ten superinsulated buildings. The 1989 Swedish building regulations specified insulation that brings much new building into the superinsulated range.

It was also found in Canada and the USA that during major renovation of existing buildings, it was cheaper to superinsulate them than to provide the fuel to heat them. Suitable techniques were developed for different forms of construction such as timber-frame and masonry.

## Passive solar design

This refers to techniques developed since the 70s to make the best use of sunlight without summer overheating – an idea which is at least 50, if not 2000, years old, but has been refined with modern materials. Extra south-facing glazing, suitably heavy construction to store heat, orientation to favour heat capture in the winter and rejection in the summer is used in some 20% of new US housing. In less sunny regions like the UK more normal areas of glazing, but preferentially orientated to the winter sun, with rooms requiring heating concentrated on the sunny side, have proved successful when associated with high insulation and airtightness (Plate 13).

## Earth-sheltered design

Another development since 1973 has been towards partly underground, 'earth-sheltered' buildings, of which about 20 000 had been built in North America by 1989 (Plate 14). They exploit the fact that only 3 m into the earth, the temperature variation is just a few degrees, when outside it might be from +30 °C to −10 °C or below. Usually they have concrete walls and a concrete or timber roof, the insulation is less than that of above-ground superinsulated houses, and the floor-slab insulation and ventilation system are similar.

Earth-sheltered buildings have been found to reduce seasonal temperature variation, make efficient use of free heat, reduce the size of the space heating system and reduce or eliminate the need for summer cooling. In 1989 there were probably five earth-sheltered dwellings in the UK; one was superinsulated, and has negligible space heating requirements.

However, there is more to be learned about the manipulation of underground heat flow; a leading US energy efficiency centre, the Rocky Mountain Research Center, has been experimenting since 1981 on designs in which an insulation/waterproofing 'umbrella' around the house *encloses* a mass of earth large enough to provide inter-seasonal storage, so as to keep the interior warm in winter and cool in summer.

In the long term, a combination of such techniques could enable space heating energy use to be eliminated, even in cold climates.

## More efficient heating systems; combined heat and power

Conventional central heating systems, oil- and gas-fired alike, have been radically improved in efficiency during the 80s. In a typical UK domestic system, savings of 30–40% are not unrealistic through using a condensing boiler, thermostatic radiator valves and a room thermostat, pumped hot water and, in larger houses, separate zones with their own controls.

Worthwhile savings can be made by improving systems in this way. However, burning high-quality fuel to produce low-grade heat is thermodynamically wasteful. The savings from improved heating controls are dwarfed if a much more fundamental step is taken: namely, if the fuel which would normally be burnt to provide low-grade heat in the building is instead used for combined heat and power production.

Industrial nations like the USA, UK and France discard as much energy in the form of waste heat from power stations to rivers and up cooling towers as natural gas provides to their whole economies. With combined heat and power and district heating (CHP/DH), energy that would otherwise be thrown away is piped as hot water through insulated heat mains to individual buildings; their heating systems replace the cooling towers of the power station. Modern designs mean that losses are no more than about 10%, comparable to those in electricity distribution. (Note that district heating is sometimes provided by 'heat-only' boilers independent of electricity generation; waste heat from electricity generation can be used for other, say industrial, purposes, so the two ideas 'DH' and 'CHP' are in principle distinct, though often associated with each other.)

The temperature of the supply water of the DH system needs to be higher than the cold river or sea water used in conventional power station cooling, and this involves a small reduction in electrical efficiency. However, the extra fuel required to restore the amount of electricity produced provides low-grade heat to the DH system users at a lower *energy* cost than any other fossil fuel space and water heating system. There is an installation cost for the large insulated hot-water mains, which is larger than that of gas mains. Even so, the low cost of the heat available often makes this the cheapest way to heat towns and cities and provide their hot water.

About 50% of all buildings in Denmark and Finland are heated by DH, mainly from CHP plant. Denmark aims to increase this to 55% by the year 2000; it now only builds CHP stations. Cheaper plastic heat mains and connection systems have been developed to improve the economics, even for highly insulated or dispersed buildings which were previously thought unsuitable.

Recently, 'micro-CHP' plant has become available, based on internal combustion engines, usually burning natural gas or liquid petroleum gas (LPG), with outputs as low as 15 kW electricity and 25 kW heat. These make CHP feasible for small groups of 5–10 houses, individual office blocks, hospitals, etc. They also ease the development of extended DH schemes. Most countries with CHP/DH began with small schemes of 10–1000 dwellings, which slowly merged into town- and city-wide systems. At first, these embryonic schemes used fossil-fuelled heat-only boilers, which produced more expensive heat than CHP plant. Micro-CHP would improve the economics of this early stage.

However, except for Denmark, Finland, Sweden, Germany and Austria, other industrial countries, including the UK, have hardly begun to tap the potential for CHP/DH. The reasons for the UK situation are complex – perhaps the combination of a natural gas industry set up to compete with other energy industries, seeing DH as a rival; the lack of *local* government involvement in energy supply, unlike Germany or Scandinavia; and, until the 80s, low central heating ownership and thermal comfort standards.

Finally, the possibility should be mentioned of cheap and reliable CHP equipment being developed on a small enough scale for the individual house (perhaps based on a different type of heat engine called a Stirling engine). Such a system would take away the need for the heat mains of a DH system, and with suitable forms of grid connection to maintain continuity of electricity supply, begins to point to a more dispersed form of electricity generation. This is not yet available, but developments over the next decade should be watched.

## 2.2   *Space cooling*

In Japan, the southern USA and many developing countries, space cooling is more important for thermal comfort than space heating. Large amounts of electricity are used – thus, the USA uses 250 GW on hot summer afternoons (equal to the output from 250 large power stations) for this purpose alone, and demand is growing at 5 GW/year. Even in the UK, this is one of the fastest growing uses of electricity.

▲ Plate 1
Former china clay pit near
St Austell, Cornwall.

▲ Plate 2 Bom Futura in Rondônia, Brazil, is the world's largest tin-producing operation. In 1989 the 50 000 tonnes of tin concentrates it produced represented nearly 60% of Brazil's output.

◀ Plate 3
The aftermath of strip mining for coal near the city of Gillette, Wyoming. Much land dereliction of this kind remains unrehabilitated in the USA, especially in Appalachia.

▲ Plate 4   Open-cast coal excavation at Shipley Lake, Derbyshire. Bucket excavators dig out the coal, the overburden and soil having been separately tipped adjacent to the site for subsequent reinstatement.

▲ Plate 6   The same view of Shipley Lake as in Plate 4 after mineral extraction had ended. Open-cast working usually results in a high standard of rehabilitation achieved in a relatively short time.

▲　Plate 7　Acid drainage from a strip mine in New York state. Surface water drains into the local river system from workings which exploited an acidic material, garnet, used as an abrasive. This has produced an environment alien to aquatic life. Strip mining for coal which has been associated with sulphides and exposed to the weather is a more common cause of acid drainage problems in the USA.

▲　Plate 8　Baled-up drink containers awaiting recycling. Both aluminium and plastic can be reprocessed. In the USA, in states where there are mandatory deposit laws, 68 million kg of bottles made from polyethylene terephthalate were collected for this purpose in 1988.

◄ Plate 9
Damage to trees in the
Erzgebirge mountains of
central Europe.

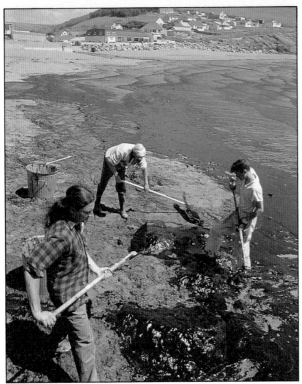

◄ Plate 10
Cleaning up after an oil
spill on the south Devon
coast.

▲　Plate 11　Agroforestry on farmland in China. Intercropping with Paulownia trees improves the yield of crop plants such as tea and wheat. The trees are fast growing and help to alleviate the shortage of timber, fuelwood and animal fodder.

▲ Plate 13
A passive solar house in the Milton Keynes Energy Park, Buckinghamshire. Large areas of glazing on the south side favour heat capture in winter.

▲ Plate 14 An earth-sheltered house in the United States. These houses are built partly underground with concrete walls to take advantage of the almost constant temperature 3 metres below ground, reducing the need for heating in winter and cooling in summer.

Countries where space cooling has always been essential for comfort have made major efficiency improvements. Electricity use for this purpose can be almost eliminated in cool and temperate climates, and greatly reduced even in subtropical regions. This depends on improved building construction and orientation to keep out summer heat, energy-efficient lighting and electronic equipment producing less waste heat to be removed, and improved efficiency in the refrigeration equipment itself.

These techniques enable new non-domestic buildings such as schools, shops, offices and hospitals to be kept cool with 90–95% less electricity than in 1980. In cooler climates like north-western Europe, refrigeration plant is not needed at all if natural or mechanical ventilation of suitably heavily constructed buildings is used at night to pre-cool the structure so that it can absorb the daytime gains from the sun, occupants and equipment. In the southern USA, similar techniques have been shown to reduce refrigeration requirements much more cheaply than the cost of the extra electricity. In the humid tropics, one carefully designed building, the headquarters of the Petroleum Corporation of Jamaica, uses less electricity for cooling than would be used for normal air-conditioning in the UK, at no extra cost.

## 2.3   Electrical appliances

Many industrialised countries use 30–40% of their electricity, 10–15% of total energy, to run electrical appliances: refrigerators and freezers, clothes and dish washing machines, television and other electronics, and so on. If everyone used the most efficient commercially available designs this consumption could be reduced by over 80% (some prototypes could achieve over 90%) without affecting the service provided.

Consider as one example the domestic refrigerator. A rough measure of energy performance is the annual energy consumption divided by storage volume: typical (1990) mass-produced designs sold in the UK achieve 2–3 kWh/litre. Developments in the US, Germany and Scandinavia show this can be reduced about 10-fold: the most efficient European mass-produced design in 1988, based on a 1984 prototype at the Technical University of Denmark, uses 0.4 kWh/l; later prototypes, and US pilot-scale production, use only 0.2 kWh/l, and their engineers estimate 0.1 kWh/l is achievable.

These radical improvements arise from attention to all stages of the use of electrical energy to transfer heat from the cold food storage space to the warmer surroundings. Poor insulation and loose door seals; an inefficient motor driving an inefficient compressor, with waste heat re-entering the cool space; an internal fan consuming energy and supplying heat; an undersized heat exchanger, reducing the thermodynamic performance – these have all been tackled to achieve the improvements described.

In climates like those of Canada, the northern USA and northern Europe where the external average temperature is only 8–10 °C, separating the condenser and mounting it outside, or using a 'through-the-wall heat pipe', can halve the electricity consumption again, or avoid the need to run the compressor in cold weather. In the USA, re-examination of the traditional inter-seasonal storage of ice made in the winter, but now using modern insulation materials, has shown that the electricity consumption of large refrigeration systems can be almost eliminated.

Decisions about appliance purchase are of course much influenced by costs, but it is not always easy to see their implications. Energy-efficient designs cost little more than standard models, and make major savings elsewhere in the energy system. Thus the most efficient European 200-litre mass-produced refrigerator mentioned above uses 80 kWh/yr and is estimated to cost only about £3 more to manufacture than a standard model using about 350 kWh/yr. To the user this implies a saving of 270 'units' of electricity a year, paying for itself in a year or so depending on the exact retail price charged for the refrigerator and the tariff charged by the electricity company. But it can also be viewed as 'generating' electricity at 270 kWh/yr – what has been termed the generation of 'negawatts', the power that is *not* required as a result of improved efficiency.

Q   What is this rate in W?

A   There are $24 \times 365 = 8760$ hours in a year, so
    annual saving, $270 \times 10^3$ Wh/yr, is at a rate of
    $270 \times 10^3 / 8.76 \times 10^3$ W = about 30 W.

Q   If a country has ten million such appliances, what is the power saved?

A   $10 \times 10^6 \times 30$ W $= 3 \times 10^8$ W $= 300$ MW
    which is equal to one moderate-sized power station.

How does the extra appliance cost compare with the costs of building power stations? These are usually expressed in pence per kilowatt-hour, p/kWh, over the life of the station, with much scope for ingenious 'discounted cash flow' accounting to include initial capital costs, continuous fuel costs and future decommissioning costs in a single figure. These are much debated by proponents of rival generation methods, as we shall see below, but competitive figures are always in the range of a few, say 2 to 5, pence per kilowatt-hour for the various options seriously considered. If our '30 negawatt' refrigerator is assumed to have a 12-year life, a similar calculation can be performed.

Q   If discounting is at first neglected, what is the apparent cost of the saved energy?

A   At an extra cost of £3 = 300p to save $12 \times 270 = 3240$ kWh,
    this represents 300/3240 = less than 0.1p/kWh saved.

Of course, this is overstating the case, as the discounting of future savings hasn't been done 'properly', whatever that is. With the kind of discount rate used in power station calculations, the figure is more like 0.2p/kWh, still considerably less than the cost of operating and fuelling existing stations, let alone building new ones. This is the basis of the 'least-cost accounting' required of some US utility companies. They are required to compare the cost of introducing efficiency measures with that of building new plant, and choose the cheaper option – often the former. This approach is not yet common elsewhere, however.

## 2.4   *Lighting*

In the UK some 17–18% of electricity is used for lighting; in developing countries the proportion is possibly higher, as this is often the first, and most valued, use of electricity. Methods available at present could reduce this by over 80%; many commercial buildings in the US, and a few in Europe, have achieved over 90% reductions from current standard levels.

During the 80s compact fluorescent lamps became available which can replace the small incandescent lamps still normally used in the home. There have been advances in the design of the 'ballast' used to control the current: the newer electronic types are smaller, lighter, more energy efficient and give a better performance – instant starting without hum or flicker – and the phosphors used now give a light quality resembling the 'warm' incandescent colouring. Replacing incandescent by compact fluorescent lamps reduces *total* domestic lighting costs because the higher initial cost is compensated by a much longer life and about 5 times lower electricity use.

Q    If a compact fluorescent lamp costing £12 has a rating of 11 W and a life of 8000 hours, and is equivalent to a 60 W incandescent lamp costing 50p with a life of 1000 hours, how do their total costs compare if electricity costs 6p per unit (kWh)?

A    Over its life, compact uses $11 \times 8000$ Wh $= 88$ kWh costing $88 \times 6 = 528$p.
Total cost (for 8000 h service) $= £12 + 5.28 = £17.28$.
Incandescent over its life uses $60 \times 1000$ Wh $= 60$ kWh costing $60 \times 6 = 360$p.
Total cost (for 1000 h service) $= £0.5 + 3.6 = £4.1$.
So for 8000 h (neglecting labour of replacement) total cost $= £32.8$, almost twice that of the compact.

This is again an over-simple calculation for accounting purposes, as it neglects the discounting of future costs. If these are included as in power station calculations, it can be shown that the effective cost saving offered by this appliance change is around 1p/kWh, again comparing favourably with the costs of building power stations. However, these benefits are not widely perceived because of the higher capital investment required. When seen as part of the least-cost planning of the total energy system, they have led some US utilities to give these efficient lamps away rather than build new plant. (The cost is of course absorbed in the price charged for electricity.)

Larger incandescent lamps, like the 500-W types mostly found in industry, can be replaced, usually by discharge lamps, with 75–90% energy reduction at low or negative cost.

Fluorescent tubes provide a little domestic, most public and commercial, and some industrial and agricultural lighting. They have been used since the 1930s, but surprising advances have been made since 1973, so that most systems installed even in the late 70s are technically obsolete. The best lamps in 1989, with good colour rendering and high-frequency electronic ballast, give about 2.5 times more light per watt of electricity than standard mid-70s types; US research suggests that 3.5 times by the mid-90s and 5 times by 2000 is achievable.

An integrated energy-efficient lighting system, as well as using the best lamps, makes greater use of daylight, improved 'luminaires' (fittings which waste less light and direct it where it is wanted), task lighting where appropriate, occupancy sensing or on-off schedules (which users can override), and, most simply, ceiling and wall finishes which absorb less light.

Some of these measures applied separately can save 50%; taken together they can save over 90% of the electricity used while maintaining the same lighting standard. Most energy-efficient lighting schemes have an extra capital cost of less than £4–5/GJ (1.5p/kW) of electricity saved; in some buildings designed for energy efficiency from the start, or in carefully planned renovations, they have cost *less* to install than conventional higher consumption schemes. In such cases the energy saving and environmental gain cost less than nothing. In general they cost much less than the operating cost of existing power stations.

## 2.5   Stationary motive power

Industrial motors consume 40% of the electricity generated in the USA, or 12–15% of its total primary energy. In western Europe the proportions are similar – in the UK about 30%, including the similar motor drives used in commercial buildings and agriculture.

It was shown in the late 70s by researchers at Imperial College in the UK that some 60% of this energy was lost in drives and controls. Electronic variable-speed drives and so on could eliminate most of the losses, reducing electricity consumption by up to 20%. The same principles can be applied to the smaller electric motors used in building ventilation systems and domestic electrical appliances.

## 2.6   Transport

This is in many ways the most problematic sector of energy use, as current (1990) trends are particularly unfavourable, in the UK at least, and significant changes over the next decade seem inevitable. The share of energy delivered that is used for transport is rising, in spite of the oil price rises – in the UK, from 17% in 1960 to 25% in 1980, 29% in 1987. Over 80% of this is used in road transport (passengers and freight) and 86% of all passenger transport is in private cars, with their current dependence on oil, the least available fossil fuel, and familiar problems of accidents, pollution, and congestion to weigh against their attractions for many of us.

Energy efficiency, to reduce demand, can be considered in the same general way as for the other sectors, first looking at technical improvements in existing methods, then considering less energy-intensive ways of providing the same service.

The conventional measure of energy efficiency for cars in the UK is miles per gallon (m.p.g.), typically between 30 and 45, with a current (1990) UK average of less than 35, considerably dependent on driving conditions. (For international comparisons we should really be using kilometres per litre, km/l; the above range corresponds to about 10–15 km/l.) German, Swedish and US manufacturers have demonstrated prototypes up to four times better than this over the last decade, but most of the lessons learned have been applied, in production cars, to higher performance. The number of new cars in the UK with top speeds over 120 m.p.h. trebled in the 80s. At the same time average fuel efficiency rose by only 5%; the best currently available is about 55 m.p.g. (nearly 20 km/l). It is clear that more efficient cars can be made: the world record achieved in the Shell Mileage Marathon in 1988 (admittedly for a very small low performance vehicle) is 6049 m.p.g.! This could surely be translated into a practical 200–300 m.p.g. if the manufacturers perceived a demand. A powerful tax incentive, such as an excise duty related to m.p.g., perhaps falling to zero at 100 m.p.g., would encourage changes in user outlook about environmental effects, and provide the best short-term improvement in transport energy efficiency. There would also be significant reductions in energy use if

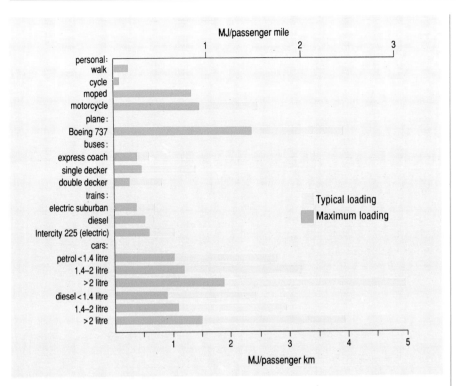

◀   Figure 5.3
Energy efficiency of
different transport modes.

speed limits were enforced, and tax advantages for company cars were removed – company cars are on average larger and less efficient than those bought privately.

A more general comparison of energy efficiency between different *modes* of transport is shown in Figure 5.3. In each case, the shorter bar represents fully loaded and the longer bar represents normal occupancy levels. Note that electric vehicles actually consume about three times as much primary energy if conventional power stations provide the electricity.

*Q*   What are the most and least efficient forms of car transport?

*A*   A fully loaded small diesel and a normally loaded >2 litre petrol car respectively.

*Q*   How do planes, buses and trains compare with cars?

*A*   Large jet aircraft are broadly comparable to large cars according to this measure of energy efficiency (when fully loaded, better than all normally loaded cars). Buses and trains are in general better than cars, much better than large cars, with a fully-loaded double-decker bus best of all. *Electric* trains of course have the *primary* energy disadvantage mentioned (though still better than large cars).

*Q*   What is the most energy-efficient form of transport of all?

*A*   Cycling.

It is clear, if unsurprising, that small cars are more efficient than large ones, diesel more efficient than petrol, and that perceptions of improved performance or prestige have so far outweighed the costs of vehicles, fuel and tax at present levels, although company car use and tax advantages confuse the picture. It is also evident that car sharing could have a large effect, but only if incentives were sufficient to encourage it, as in the Californian scheme of special lanes for full cars – this is not providing *exactly* the same service, but exchanging one amenity, independence, for another, shorter journey times.

This question of the *comparative* value of the service arises even more for the much more efficient public transport modes. (Air travel so clearly provides a different service that is hardly comparable, except to show that its fuel efficiency is no worse than a large car; the speed advantage over a fast train for internal trips has to be weighed against costs and accessibility.) The UK response to the perceived advantages of different modes over recent decades, whatever the reasons, is shown in Table 5.1.

Table 5.1    *Travel trends by mode (billion passenger km)*

| Mode | 1955 | 1960 | 1965 | 1970 | 1975 | 1980 | 1985 | 1989 |
|------|------|------|------|------|------|------|------|------|
| Bus, coach | 80 | 69 | 59 | 53 | 55 | 45 | 42 | 41 |
| Car, motorcycle, taxi | 77 | 127 | 231 | 293 | 328 | 403 | 448 | 563 |
| Cycle | 18 | 12 | 7 | 4 | 4 | 5 | 6 | 5 |
| Total road | 175 | 208 | 297 | 350 | 387 | 453 | 496 | 609 |
| Rail | 38 | 40 | 35 | 36 | 35 | 35 | 36 | 40 |
| Air | 0.3 | 0.8 | 1.7 | 2.0 | 2.2 | 3.0 | 3.6 | 4.9 |
| Total, all modes | 213 | 249 | 334 | 388 | 424 | 491 | 536 | 654 |

Source: compiled from Department of Transport, *Transport Statistics Great Britain*, HMSO, London.

Q  How has the total travel, in $10^9$ passenger-km/yr, changed from 1955 to 1989?

A  It has increased by 3 times, from 213 to 654.

Q  How have rail and air travel varied over this period?

A  Rail traffic has remained roughly constant, at 38 in 1955 and 40 in 1989 (varying from 40 to 35 in between) – so the percentage has fallen from 18% to 7%. Air travel has risen steadily from 0.3 to 4.9 (still <1%).

Q  How has the percentage of travel by road varied?

A  From 82% to 93%.

Q  How have the bus, cycle and car components of road travel varied?

A  Bus and cycle have both declined in real terms (80 to 41; 18 to 5) and even more in percentage terms (46% to 7%; 10% to 0.8% of total road travel). Car travel has increased by over 7 times (77 to 563), from 44% to 92% of total road travel, 36% to 86% of all travel, and is essentially responsible for the increased total travel, and the growing share of total energy use.

This shows such an overwhelming preference for car travel in the prevailing UK conditions that it will take very determined measures to reverse the trend for resource or environmental reasons. Fuel shortages will sooner or later be reflected in price rises, but this may cause severe economic disruption if the commitment to road transport continues. If greenhouse gas emissions, or other environmental problems, are to be controlled, taxation, subsidies or regulations will need to be modified before the perceived balance of amenity between private and public transport shifts.

There are some differences in car ownership and use in different developed countries which reflect their different traditions. Car ownership varies from 0.56 per capita in the US to 0.24 in Japan, with the UK, at 0.32, rather low among European countries. But 86% of travel in the UK is by car, almost the highest in Europe. Italy, for example, with ownership at 0.39 per capita, has only 71% car travel and Japan, with its lower ownership, only 47% (1986 figures). This no doubt reflects varying measures in different countries to promote public transport and/or restrict car use in cities; various forms of road pricing are now being explored. However, these differences are variants on a general problem that can only increase if the developing countries follow a similar path. At the very least, energy, transport and environmental policy have to be considered together.

Satisfying transport needs is not an end in itself, but is about providing *access* to people and services. Land use planning can seek to group homes, work, shops, schools, hospitals, entertainment in such a way that more journeys can be made by low energy means – on foot, by bicycle or public transport. It may be that modern telecommunications and information technology will significantly change work patterns so that less travel is necessary, though there is little sign of this yet – there is more communication, but just as much travel. Against these optimistic ideas is the reality of the individual response to the existing settlement and work pattern by ever increasing car use. It may be that this will be self-adjusting by cost or congestion, or that more controls will be needed to conserve resources or reduce pollution, or that more flexible systems can be developed, at least in cities, to combine the convenience of the car with the efficiency of public transport. There will always be different opinions about desirable life-styles, between the simple and the more technically based. A good transport system should provide the freedom to choose.

*Activity 2*

Consider your own use of transport. How far does it provide what you want, or is it constrained by work, housing patterns and availability of alternatives over which you have no control?

# 3  Energy efficient futures

## 3.1  Low energy strategies

After the oil crises of the 1970s, a number of workers in different countries made detailed studies of possible low energy strategies – not predictions or blueprints, but possible scenarios for energy demand reduction under sympathetic government policies.

To avoid confusion between energy policy and discussion of future lifestyles, official government projections for economic growth were used, and proposals for more efficient energy use and renewable supply were limited to the technology that was commercially available or at pilot/ prototype stage. (This leaves aside the growing conviction of recent years that the standard economic measure, gross domestic product (GDP) is not a good measure of national prosperity, since it takes no account of environmental degradation.)

Three of the most detailed studies, in the USA, West Germany and the UK, are listed at the end of this chapter. Similar analyses in Denmark, Sweden, Canada and other countries covered 95% of OECD energy use.

The US study assumed an increase in national wealth, as measured by GDP, of 1.5 times by 2000. It was shown that energy demand could fall to 50% by 2010, 80% of it coming from renewable sources (SERI, 1981).

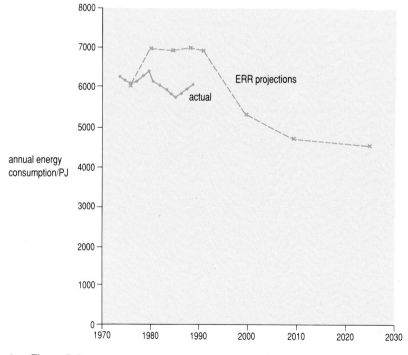

▲  Figure 5.4
UK total energy 1973–89 and projections of Earth Resources Research.

In West Germany, GDP was assumed to increase 2.3 times by 2025. Although it is already one of the world's more energy-efficient countries, its national consumption could fall by 45%, and renewable sources could supply 40% of the reduced demand (Krause *et al.*, 1980).

In the UK, a 2.9-fold increase in national wealth was assumed, and a 40% reduction in demand by 2025 was found, with 50% from renewable sources. A comparison of these projections with actual energy use in the 80s is shown in Figure 5.4. These show that the formerly rising energy use has indeed been checked, as was projected; *falling* energy use was projected only after 1990, so it will be interesting to watch over the next decade. It has to be said that this apparent agreement is almost entirely a coincidence, as the main cause has been reduced economic activity, not the widespread adoption of the efficiency measures proposed in the ERR report (Olivier *et al.*, 1983). There are now, however, environmental pressures for reduced energy use, in addition to the resource shortages driving the 70s studies, so perhaps the reductions will be achieved, if for different reasons.

To achieve efficient energy use, a mainly renewable energy system was projected for all these countries, even the least favoured like West Germany, the Netherlands, Denmark and the UK, which are cloudy, densely populated and highly industrialised. More recent studies, in the mid- to late-1980s, have been extended to the regional and global scale, and have included environmental aspects that were not considered in the earlier work. The Brundtland report of 1987, already mentioned, is an exhaustive account of the general possibility of 'sustainable development', with world energy policy based on a combination of demand reduction by efficiency measures, and supply essentially from renewable resources.

## 3.2   Making it happen

There can be no single worldwide prescription for the best way forward, but more efficient energy use seems an essential component of any strategy, as it automatically reduces environmental impact, whereas all supply options have some effect on the environment, considered below. The potential is unquestionably enormous for all countries. In effect, a vast 'source' of cheap energy is available, larger than the entire output of OPEC, and much more permanent. If energy use can indeed be halved or more in the developed countries, there could be a real objective of a more evenly balanced world energy use per head of 1–2 kW, which could accommodate a significant increase in the developing world. (Such a reduction in the US from 10 kW per head seems improbable, but in Europe a reduction from 4 kW is more conceivable, though massive attention to energy efficiency would be needed.)

Patterns of energy use, and energy waste, are deeply ingrained. Progress since 1973 has been patchy, and no country has tapped even a small fraction of the known potential. The most striking results have been confined to particular economic sectors in a restricted number of countries anxious to move away from dependence on oil. For example, in the Danish building stock, the primary energy used for space heating per unit floor area fell by 55% between 1973 and 1988, averaging 5% per year; in Sweden it fell by 50% between 1980 and 1988! Refrigerators sold in Denmark and the USA in 1988 consumed 50% less electricity per unit volume than those sold in 1973. The primary energy used to produce a ton of finished steel in Japan fell by 50% between 1973 and 1986.

The overall reduction in primary energy use per unit GDP was much less, however, as other sectors have had less vigorous or successful programmes. This is more true of other countries, like the UK, Norway and Italy, where there has been less, or less effective, government intervention.

The rate of progress also slackened after 1982, when energy prices fell. Energy use in Japan and the USA had been almost static since 1973, while economic activity rose by 40–50%, but in the mid-80s it began to rise significantly. In western Europe, primary energy consumption was well above its 1973 level by 1988 (though it wasn't in the UK, where GDP rise was low; see Figure 5.4).

Countries each have their own social and cultural traditions, which have to be taken into account in developing energy policy, but there are some common strands. Some governments in Europe and North America own the energy suppliers – the gas and electric utilities, oil and coal industries. Even those that don't own them recognise the need to regulate the natural monopolies, like gas and electricity supply, on behalf of the consumer. It is important to ensure that funds for users to introduce energy efficiency measures are available on the same terms as those for suppliers, and that utilities carry out 'least-cost planning', supporting demand reduction by improved efficiency when this is cheaper than increasing supply.

Three conditions seem to be required for a programme of efficiency improvement to succeed: users need (1) up-to-date technical information tailored to their personal circumstances, (2) equitable access to funds and (3) equitable access to the necessary skilled work. These have not usually all been met at once, with disappointing results. However, those countries that *have* set up a combined advice, financing and installation service have had notable success.

Sweden is a shining example. In the late 1970s, the government set a target of insulating and weatherstripping old buildings to reduce their space heating requirements by 30% by 1990. The state provided initial start-up funds, but local government administered the grants and loans, and provided inspection, technical advisers who could be phoned or visited, and builder training programmes. At first, 100% grants were available, and later, as familiarity with efficiency techniques grew, these were replaced by loans. The results, monitored by a parliamentary committee, exceeded the 30% target.

Mandatory efficiency standards can be set for new vehicles, electrical appliances, industrial boilers, etc. The United States has for some years required appliances such as refrigerators to be labelled with their energy consumption, so that buyers can make an informed choice; surely this should extend to other countries. Minimum standards eliminate the most inefficient items from the market, but incentives are needed to encourage the use of the best available designs.

There will always be arguments about the extent to which a 'free market' will provide these incentives – if it *were* free. On the one hand all users do not have access to the necessary information, often quite technical; on the other hand prices of different forms of energy are often manipulated so that they do not reflect the relative costs of providing them, and there are long time delays, so that a decision to invest in a particular method forces the choice of what is available later. More fundamentally, costs have not usually reflected environmental effects, either of using up a limited capital resource or of pollution and waste disposal. These underlying large-scale, often political, influences in the energy supply market imply a need for balancing intervention to influence demand.

## 3.3   Summary

An outline of the innumerable detailed possibilities for energy efficiency improvement was given in Section 2, showing vast potential for reduced energy use in most sectors without loss of amenity. The way these can be reflected in perceived economic advantage is a more open question, seeming to require much improved information and/or government intervention by regulation, taxation or subsidy. Transport looks to be an increasingly critical issue. General studies of total national energy strategies, initiated in the first instance by the oil crises of the 70s, but now supported by environmental concerns, were described in Section 3. Some local success has been achieved, though not very much in world terms; the possibilities are clear, but the politics of their realisation remain problematic. Energy policy is, however, now firmly on national and world agendas, and as environmental concern as well as likely fuel shortages are increasing, it will remain of vital importance.

# 4   Energy supply

In this section, the options for primary energy supply, and the 'vectors' used to transfer energy from one place to another are briefly reviewed. The problems with fossil and nuclear fuels are outlined, and then the possible renewable (or continuous) resources are discussed in more detail.

## 4.1   Non-renewable and continuous resources; energy vectors

The ancient Greeks introduced the myth of Prometheus, who stole fire from the gods for human use, and was punished for his presumption. What was then meant by 'fire' we might now call 'energy', with wood, fossil fuels, fission and fusion getting progressively nearer 'divine' origins, and correspondingly more serious punishments. (You can speculate for yourself about the symbolism of what happened to Prometheus – chained to a rock and having his liver eaten out by an eagle each day, to grow again each night, until he was rescued by Hercules.)

More practically, we now make a basic distinction between **'renewable'** and **'non-renewable' resources** – really a distinction about time and space scales. The renewables depend on the large-scale position of the Earth in the solar system, which is bathed in radiant energy from the sun and experiences gravitational effects from sun and moon that have some regular fluctuations but only change significantly over millions of years. The non-renewables are the Earth-bound treasure chests of stored solar energy in fossil fuels, and stored nuclear energy of earlier origin in radioactive, fission and fusion materials; these stocks are necessarily limited, though currently very large.

Humans are readily seduced by offers of unlimited wealth – with a modest inheritance it is usually considered prudent to live off the interest, but if it is large enough it doesn't seem to matter if the capital is spent as well. We have taken this attitude with non-renewables, spending the capital of fossil fuels and first generation fission, but after only a few hundred years the end is in sight. Fast reactor fission, and even more so, fusion, offer a renewed dream of vastly more capital to use up; if they offer thousands of years they tempt humans again not to worry about resource conservation. In the case of fusion the energy source is believed to be just that which powers the sun, so the choice is between using the fusion that is already happening there, and struggling to tame it on Earth (making the Prometheus image particularly apt, with who knows what punishment to look out for).

More like a source of income are the renewable resources, though the term 'renew*able*' is not entirely appropriate, as the primary resource is not under our control. No doubt the term has its origins in the particular case of wood, and other biomass, where we can make a choice to produce more if we wish from the effectively continuous supply of solar energy (**continuous resources** is perhaps a better description). The same applies to tidal (gravitational) and geothermal energy. The latter does have a finite terrestrial origin, the limited stock of internal radioactive minerals continuously heating the Earth, but we cannot change the rate at which they do it, so if we take heat away we are only modifying the rate at which it reaches the surface. All the energy supplied from these three continuous sources is steadily re-radiated to space, with the Earth adopting the mean temperature which keeps this balance. If we 'make use' of some of the energy we modify the route by which it degrades to low temperature, but we don't change this overall balance, so the temperature changes we make will be local, not global. The release of energy from *non*-renewable sources *does* change the overall balance, though so far apparently not significantly. The indirect effects of greenhouse gas emissions more immediately make a difference to the way surface temperatures relate to those higher in the atmosphere. This indicates the general importance of understanding the delicate feedback processes near the Earth's surface which maintain temperature and other conditions favourable for life, rather than perturbing them further. Another Greek myth, that of the Earth-goddess Gaia, has been invoked in recent years to stand for the hypothesis that life on Earth influences the environment so as to ensure its survival – in an extreme form, a view of the whole Earth as, in some sense, resembling a living organism. While the supernatural overtones of this idea seem to antagonise as many people as are attracted by them, there is much more recognition of the existence of stabilising feedback processes in the relationship between biosphere and geosphere than there used to be, and a growing interest in trying to understand them better.

Another energy supply distinction is between these *primary* energy sources and the energy **vectors** used to transfer energy from the point of origin to the point of use. The original examples are hot water, as in a district heating scheme, and fuels: wood, coal, oil and gas storing chemical energy, and transported in bulk from forest to mine to the consumer – or, in the case of vehicles, *by* the consumer. There may be considerable processing in between, e.g. at oil refineries, and the transport may be by pipeline as well as road, rail or water; and there will be losses on the way which make the *delivered* energy less than the primary. Conversions from coal or biomass to gas or liquid fuels may become convenient for heating and transport uses, and will have their own plant and energy costs and losses to influence the stage at which they become economic.

Alternatively, hydrogen, already used as a rocket fuel, has been strongly advocated as a future chemical energy vector for fuel in the 'hydrogen economy'. Various 'safe' handling methods have been developed, which would remain to be proved in large-scale use. Hydrogen would be produced by the electrolysis of water using whatever primary energy source was available to generate electricity.

Undoubtedly hazardous would be the plutonium 'nuclear energy vector' of a fast-reactor based nuclear economy. Plutonium is a commodity analogous to a fuel, but highly toxic, and much sought after for weapons use – strong arguments, it might be thought, against its widespread adoption, though they have not deterred governments from extensive study of this possibility.

The energy vector we now all take for granted is *electricity*, unique in its ease and speed of transport, along the wires of the grid system. This lies alongside the 'mass' handling of the conventional transport system and the 'information' handling of the telecommunications system to form the three crucial networks of industrialised society. The grid has been associated with the development of large-scale electrical power *generation*, but this is not an essential link. If there are fair tariffs for purchase as well as supply of electricity, it can be seen as a 'common carrier' for diverse suppliers and users of all sizes, balancing local and temporal fluctuations. Improved electronic communications about 'spot-prices' to reflect rapid supply and demand changes may bring about a more responsive 'market' system. This should have a bearing on the development of CHP generation, since the supplier who also has a market for otherwise wasted heat should be able to supply electricity more cheaply. (The difference between primary and delivered energy is particularly large for non-CHP power plant, as some two-thirds of the primary energy is wasted.) Renewable energy of all forms is often readily converted into electricity, so its development would also be encouraged by a grid with a fair tariff system.

Electricity can of course also be transported by conventional 'mass' methods when stored as chemical energy in batteries. While this is obviously convenient for small portable equipment (lamps, electronics) it is limited for supplying energy to vehicles by the energy/weight ratio of present batteries compared with chemical fuels. This may change with progress in electrochemistry, along with complementary improvements in fuel cells. In this case the energy vector would still be a suitable chemical 'fuel', but motive power would be obtained by the consumption of this fuel in a fuel cell to generate electricity to drive an electric motor. This would replace the present combustion of fuel to produce heat, which is converted into mechanical energy in a heat engine (with its thermodynamic efficiency constraints). The 'fuel' supplied to the fuel cell might not be immediately recognisable, as the electrochemical reaction used might not be the reaction with oxygen we call combustion. It would again have to be produced specially as an energy vector from some primary energy source.

Large vehicles like trains do better not to carry their energy with them but to pick it up from fixed wires or track – or more ingeniously from distributed electromagnets providing both levitation and propulsion. Still more fancifully, we can speculate about chemical energy vectors chosen to energise 'chemical motors' giving direct mechanical output as muscles do, not via heat or electricity. Maybe there will be analogous nuclear batteries, fuel cells or motors; or even some completely novel energy vector derived from improved understanding of nuclear processes. It should be recalled that chemical combustion and heat engines were known about long before nineteenth-century exploration of more subtle processes like electrolysis led to our present understanding of electricity, with all its subsequent applications. Perhaps there will be some equivalent advance in the application of nuclear processes to replace their present relatively crude use to produce heat.

> *Activity 3*
>
> Look back over Section 4.1 to make sure you can distinguish between the various forms of primary energy (non-renewable and continuous) and energy vector (existing and potential future types).

## 4.2   Fossil fuel limitations

The fossil fuel industries (coal, oil and gas) are deeply interwoven into the economic and employment structures of world trade and industry, so they will inevitably continue to contribute significantly to energy supply over the next century (with controls on their polluting effects), however much we theorise about it. We have already seen that resource limitation is bound to create shortages, which will be reflected in prices for oil and gas, less so for coal. One way or another the developed world will adapt, though conflict with developing countries will be hard to avoid as their internal demands increase and willingness to export their own resources reduces. A new factor in the manoeuvring will be the greenhouse effect. To the extent that current fears about the linkage between carbon dioxide emissions and climate change continue or grow, there may be strong institutional pressure (regulation, taxation, subsidy) within and between countries to control emissions. This may be a further source of international tension, as the developed countries are primarily responsible for present greenhouse gas levels, but the likely increase from developing countries (unless different energy policies are adopted) will dominate in future – wise counsels will be needed. A short-term effect of a carbon tax, say, to penalise carbon dioxide emission, will be to shift fossil fuel use, where possible, from coal to oil to gas, as that reduces emission per unit energy release, because of the different carbon–hydrogen ratios in the three types of fuel. Because this is just the direction in which available resources reduce, on present evidence, such a shift will make shortages worse.

A separate issue about fossil fuels is their value, not simply for their total energy content, but for their particular chemical structure, which makes them useful as chemical feedstocks. A large part of the chemical industry (dyestuffs, pharmaceuticals, and particularly plastics) is dependent on coal and oil for its raw materials.

The data on UK use of energy resources in Chapter 1 indicate that only some 1.6% of total delivered energy, 7.4% of that to 'other industry', is for chemical feedstocks. Thus this 'premium' use for these materials is only a small, but significant, proportion of industrial energy use. If there are to be shortages it would seem preferable to reserve them for this purpose, when they would last much longer. However, price will be the determining factor: if it rises it will of course be reflected in the resulting product prices.

## 4.3   Nuclear energy limitations

Three general possibilities were outlined in Chapter 1. Two are based on the **fission**, or splitting, of the nuclei of heavy elements. In burner reactors, the only type in commercial use, the essential fuel is a particular isotope of uranium, only present as 0.7% of natural uranium. In breeder reactors, demonstrated in principle but nowhere commercial, the uranium is better used by converting its main isotope into plutonium, which then becomes the essential fuel. The third possibility is **fusion**, the combining of the nuclei of light elements, such as the deuterium and tritium isotopes of hydrogen. This has not yet been demonstrated in a controlled form.

### Fission

In spite of vast research and development spending by developed countries worldwide, and the euphoria of the 1950s about 'electricity too cheap to meter', the 1980s have seen a general disenchantment with nuclear power as a solution to energy supply. This in spite of the established position of the nuclear power industry, with strong links to government decision-making (not least because of the overwhelming political significance of nuclear weapons). If nuclear power is losing favour it will not be for lack of encouragement and funds. Doubts about economics had already led US utilities to stop ordering reactors before the Three Mile Island accident (1979). The Chernobyl accident (1986) strengthened opposition in Europe. The UK, still committed to a limited programme, had to withdraw its existing stations from the 1989 electricity privatisation proposals when an independent cost analysis showed that at 6.3p/kWh the comparison with coal at 3.5p/kWh was unfavourable. Only France among European countries, with some 75% of its electricity produced by 55 nuclear reactors (in 1990), has a continuing strong commitment (Figure 5.5) – it will be interesting to see how views of reliability and the finances (the state-owned utility EDF is said to have vast debts) develop over the next decade.

◀   Figure 5.5
French and European
nuclear power.

More generally, as already noted, the uranium resource for this 'burner' use is less than that of oil – Sir Alan Cottrell in 1988 put it at 'about half that of the world's oil'. Assuming continuing growth, 'it is quite possible by 2030 and virtually certain by 2050 that any remaining PWR stations [the currently favoured Pressurised Water Reactors] will then have to stand idle because of prohibitively expensive fuel costs.' At the other end of the process, the safe disposal of radioactive wastes continues to be a problem everywhere, as Chapter 8 will consider in more detail.

The limited uranium resource was long ago the reason for proposing the 'fast breeder', which certainly stretches the resource to be as good or better than coal, but introduces a further set of cost and environmental hazards. The UK research and development (R&D) spending on its fast reactor programme since 1955 is shown in Figure 5.6, where it is compared with total renewables R&D over the same period. In spite of this massive effort, funding was cut in 1988 and there are no plans for a practical reactor, though collaborative studies in Europe continue. Quite apart from these evident technical difficulties in producing a safe and economic design, there are the major implications already mentioned of reliance on a system involving the production and trading of large quantities of the highly dangerous plutonium.

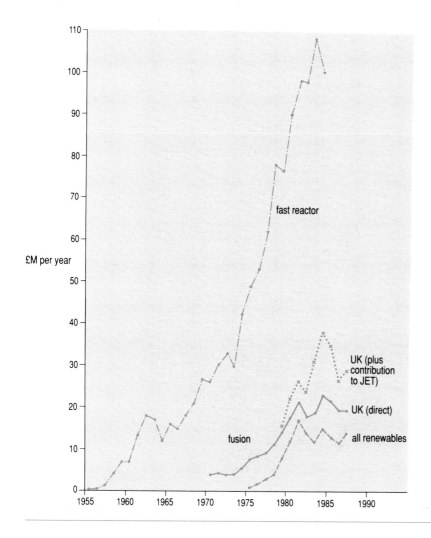

◀ *Figure 5.6
Some UK Department of Energy research and development budgets.*

## Fusion

This is in a different category from all the other options, as there is as yet no evidence that a practical reactor can be made at all, let alone any details of its economics and unforeseen difficulties. The attraction is a theoretical one, which has again provided massive research funding worldwide. The UK figures are also shown in Figure 5.6. The appeal is so powerful to a society dependent on large-scale electricity generation from concentrated energy sources that it is unlikely that work on the problems will, or should, cease, but policy priorities should surely regard it as a long-term possibility meriting basic physics research rather than engineering commitment. The assumption that its application would inevitably be in thermal power stations has focused emphasis on large expensive installations as well as exploratory studies. A typical large research machine, the Joint European Torus, JET, is shown in Figure 5.7. (The surge of interest in 'cold fusion' in 1989 should perhaps also be mentioned. Although this particular idea seems to be a dead end, it emphasises that all is not understood, and that some completely novel application of nuclear energy may yet emerge – also that hope springs eternal for some magically simple energy source.) In contrast, renewables, requiring inventive engineering using *established* physics principles, have found the funding to move from exploratory studies to larger scale prototypes hard to obtain.

▲   Figure 5.7   The Joint European Torus.

## 4.4   *Continuous (renewable) energy resources*

We now come to a more detailed review of the continuous resources. They have always been available and used in traditional ways; they were displaced by the exploitation of fossil fuels in the industrial revolution and of nuclear energy in the twentieth century for what seemed like good reasons of cost and convenience. Can they be reintroduced in a twenty-first century industrial, or post-industrial, society?

### *Solar energy*

#### *Direct*

Radiation from the sun (infra-red, visible light, ultra-violet) can be used directly to produce heat, as has always happened, or less obviously to produce electricity. The most basic form of heat production is achieved by re-examining traditional practices of building design with more scientific analysis and modern materials – the **passive solar** design, already mentioned above under efficiency. Orientation to the sun, window design and heat flow through the structure are arranged to make the best use of the winter sun without summer overheating. It is closely linked to insulation and ventilation control in an integrated low-energy design, the importance of the 'solar gain' part obviously varying with climate.

When solar heating systems also include moving parts such as pumps, they are called **active solar**, the simplest example being the 'flat plate' collectors for water heating often seen on roofs in sunny countries (Figure 5.8). More advanced (and expensive) versions have focusing mirrors or lenses and computer controlled tracking to make better use of the sun. They are proving economic for heat production even in relatively cloudy parts of north-western USA, and in the sunnier conditions of south-western USA they can raise steam for electricity generation (Figure 5.9) competitively with fossil fuels.

A much simpler idea, with its own design subtleties, is a **solar pond**: essentially a pit with a dark coloured base filled with brine of carefully controlled concentration. Because the density of brine increases with its

▲   *Figure 5.8   A flat plate solar collector.*

◄   *Figure 5.9*
*A solar power plant*
*in California.*

concentration, it is possible to maintain a variation in concentration, from very high at the bottom to pure water at the top. Incoming solar radiation is absorbed at the dark bottom surface, heating the lower brine layers to 100 °C or more. In a suitable design this heated brine remains at the bottom, without convection; the only heat loss is by conduction through the purer water above. This is low enough for the whole structure to act as an integrated heat collection and storage system from which heat may be extracted as required. In sunny regions such as Israel and southern USA, well-designed solar ponds appear to be competitive heat sources, and it is claimed that electricity generation from them will also be competitive if fossil fuel prices rise again to the levels of the early 1980s.

A more distinctively high-technology development is the direct generation of electricity from sunlight using **photovoltaic devices**. These use semiconductor materials resembling those of electronics, and are used extensively for small-scale applications like exposure meters and pocket calculators, and in space, where cost is not a limitation. A great deal of development, particularly in Japan and the USA, has been directed to reducing the cost of manufacturing large-area panels of high enough efficiency to meet more general energy needs – it is now (1990) claimed that about 200 W average demand can be supplied competitively in the US to any house more than 400 m from the grid. Further cost reductions seem likely. Hybrid devices in which *both* heat and electricity are produced in a domestic scale 'solar CHP' system are also possible; again costs will determine whether, or when, these become available.

*Indirect*

The longest tradition in the indirect use of solar energy is in the burning of fuelwood, still believed to account for some 15% of world energy use. More generally, photosynthesis produces plant material, and hence animal material, of all kinds, collectively known as **biomass**.

Q   How much of the incoming solar energy is converted into biomass?

A   Solar radiation = $5.4 \times 10^{24}$ J/yr = $1.7 \times 10^{17}$ W (from Chapter 1).
Photosynthetic energy stored in biomass = $1 \times 10^{22}$ J/yr
= $3 \times 10^{14}$ W = about 0.2% of solar energy.

Q   How does this compare with total world energy demand?

A   About 30 times greater – present demand is about 10 TW = $10^{13}$ W.

So this is a large resource, though, like the primary solar energy, it is dispersed over the Earth's surface, and requires concentration to meet our needs – at its least satisfactory, by individuals collecting wood over a large area. More systematically, 'energy crops' (fast-growing trees or other plants) can be grown in forests or plantations, harvested mechanically, and marketed directly, compressed or converted into gaseous, liquid or solid fuels of higher energy density by controlled heating, anaerobic digestion by bacteria, etc. A wide range of possibilities is being explored in different countries, the growth of sugarcane in Brazil to produce alcohol as a vehicle fuel being a well-publicised example. As always, economic factors will determine their success, in ways dependent on the system chosen, alternative fuel prices and competing land uses. Energy crops are usually seen as competing with food crops, and may also be visually unattractive, as with timber forestry and intensive agriculture. Agroforestry systems seek to integrate timber, food and energy production in ways that take advantage of complementary species as in natural ecosystems, and aim to be at once economic and attractive – an appealing objective that may have increasing impact.

A large amount of biomass suitable for conversion into heat and fuels is already available as wastes from agriculture, industry and the home: 'dry biomass' as straw, wood and refuse, 'wet' as animal slurries, sewage, and food industry residues. For the UK this is estimated as 10% of fossil fuel demand. Some countries already make substantial use of this resource: Denmark, for example, uses about 75% of available wastes. The UK, which uses only about 6% of this resource, has a large unrealised potential for avoiding waste and environmental damage. The burning of straw or the dumping of sewage are direct nuisances. Burying refuse leads to the hazards of producing methane, which is potentially explosive and is a 'greenhouse gas'. Refuse incinerators can also be polluting, but well-designed plant can produce heat, methane and/or refuse-derived-fuel (RDF) without adverse effects (Figure 5.10).

The second group of indirect solar methods derive from the hydrological and weather systems: the evaporation and precipitation of water, the vertical and horizontal movements of air masses, driven by solar heating and modified by the Earth's gravity and rotation, i.e. water and wind power. The first of these has a long history, as the water power that preceded fossil fuels in the industrial revolution, and more recently as the **hydroelectricity** that currently supplies some 4% of world energy needs. These depend on the kinetic energy of falling water, in turn derived from its potential energy in a mountain lake or reservoir. The power available depends on the 'head', the height through which the water can fall, as well as the volume of water available, so mountainous countries like Norway and Switzerland make more use of hydroelectricity. The high costs and engineering skills involved in large schemes have concentrated them in Europe and North America, which have already exploited most of the available sites. Many more remain elsewhere: a world resource of some

◀   Figure 5.10
A modern refuse plant
in Edmonton, London.

2 TW, 20% of energy demand, has been estimated. Large dams have figured significantly in aid schemes to the developing world, though they have been much criticised for their environmental effects and inappropriateness to local needs. In developed and developing world alike there is also considerable scope for the use of smaller turbines in fast flowing rivers, which may satisfy local needs better.

The second weather-derived energy source again has a long tradition, as windpumps for water and windmills for corn, though the use of modern forms of **wind turbine** for electricity generation is comparatively recent. The total energy involved in the world wind pattern is about $3 \times 10^{23}$ J/yr $= 10^{16}$ W, but of course much is higher in the atmosphere than can be tapped by Earth-bound turbines: a maximum UK resource of $2 \times 10^{18}$ J/yr $= 60$ GW has been estimated, for example. Most current machines are

◀ Figure 5.11
A wind farm in California.

'horizontal axis', with blades influenced by aircraft propeller design; they drive electric generators, for local use or to feed into the grid, with ratings varying from a few kW to a few MW, the most cost-effective currently being 200–1000 kW. Some large machines have been developed for use in shallow water offshore, where the greater wind speeds and lack of visual intrusion can compensate for the cost of transferring power back to land. There are also more novel 'vertical axis' machines with certain advantages (they don't need to be turned into the wind, generators can be at ground level, some types eliminate towers), but there is little operating experience as yet (Plate 12).

Like solar and biomass energy, wind is a distributed resource, so while all three can supply the local needs of small communities without difficulty, their use to replace the concentrated energy supplies provided by fossil and nuclear power stations involves collection over large areas. We take it for granted that food supply for urban communities requires large farms; by analogy large arrays of wind turbines are called **wind farms**. A modern power station may have a rating of 1.3 GW, which can only be replaced by hundreds of large, or thousands of medium-sized wind turbines. Several large arrays of medium-sized turbines have been built, particularly in the Altamont Pass region of California, where tax concessions encouraged such renewable developments (Figure 5.11); by 1988 a total of 1.5 GW had been installed in the USA. It was the operating experience with these schemes that led to the confidence now placed in medium power designs. Denmark and Holland plan to have about 1 GW installed by the end of the century. The UK had 8 MW in 1990, with a total renewables objective of 0.6 GW by the year 2000.

The final indirect solar resource is *wave* power, produced by wind blowing over the sea, with a world resource of $3 \times 10^{22}$ J/yr = $10^{15}$ W, of which about 5 GW might be available around British coasts. Average power levels of 15 to 70 kW per metre of wave front are estimated for favourable regions around the UK, so tens of kilometres of wave energy conversion machines are needed to match the output of large power stations. The machines must be able to withstand adverse and very variable conditions (peak power levels hundreds of times higher than average). A number of promising designs have been explored ('nodding duck', hinged raft, oscillating water column), generating electricity which can be transmitted to shore by cable (Figure 5.12). Various prototypes on scales up to a megawatt or so have been tested in the UK, Norway, Japan and the USA on or near the shore, but the feasibility of a full-scale deep-water system remains to be proved. Models of deep sea systems on a 1/10 scale were tested in the UK in the early 80s, but work stopped in 1982; it is currently (1990) being reappraised by the Department of Energy.

## Tidal (gravitational) energy

The exploitation of tidal energy resembles that of hydropower – a high tide is trapped behind a dam-like structure or 'barrage' across a suitable estuary, the water then being passed through turbines to generate electricity. The effective 'head' of water is much smaller than in hydroelectric schemes, but the volume of water is much greater. The water flow can be arranged to generate on the ebb (falling) tide only, or on the flood (rising) as well. Successful pilot schemes have been demonstrated in the USSR and France, where a 240 MW plant has operated for over 20 years on the Rance estuary in Brittany. Major new projects are under way in

Figure 5.12
Wave machines:
(a) raft,
(b) duck.

Canada and the USSR. A number of possibilities have been investigated in the UK, of which the largest would be the Severn Barrage. This would be able to produce 8.64 GW when operating, with 1.3 GW average output (about 7% of the total UK electricity demand), at apparently competitive costs over its 120-year life, estimated at 3.79p/kWh (Figure 5.13). However the capital cost for this large undertaking (say £8500 million at 1989 prices) would be large and the environmental effects considerable, so no decision to build it had been reached at the time of writing.

A general impression of possible sites around the UK for offshore wind, wave and tidal power generation is given in Figure 5.14.

*Tidal scheme performance (estimates, 1986)*

|  | Mean tidal range/m | Barrage length/m | Installed capacity/MW | Annual energy output/GWh | Cost of energy/(p/kWh) |
|---|---|---|---|---|---|
| Severn – Inner line | 7.0 | 17 000 | 7 200 | 12 900 | 3.7 |
| Severn – Outer line | 6.0 | 20 000 | 12 000 | 19 700 | 4.3 |
| Morecambe Bay | 6.3 | 16 600 | 3 040 | 5 400 | 4.6 |
| Solway Firth | 5.5 | 30 000 | 5 580 | 10 050 | 4.9 |
| Dee | 5.95 | 9 500 | 800 | 1 250 | 6.4 |
| Humber | 4.1 | 8 300 | 1 200 | 2 010 | 7.0 |
| Wash | 4.45 | 19 600 | 2 760 | 4 690 | 7.2 |
| Thames | 4.2 | 9 000 | 1 120 | 1 370 | 8.3 |
| Langstone Harbour | 3.13 | 550 | 24 | 53 | 5.3 |
| Padstow | 4.75 | 550 | 28 | 55 | 4.2 |
| Hamford Water | 3.0 | 3 200 | 20 | 38 | 8.5 |
| Loch Etive | 1.95 | 350 | 28 | 55 | 11.7 |
| Cromarty Firth | 2.75 | 1 350 | 47 | 100 | 11.8 |
| Dovey | 2.90 | 1 300 | 20 | 45 | 7.2 |
| Loch Broom | 3.15 | 500 | 29 | 42 | 13.9 |
| Milford Haven | 4.5 | 1 150 | 96 | 180 | 10.0 |
| Mersey | 6.45 | 1 750 | 620 | 1 320 | 3.6 |

Source: A. C. Baker, ICE Symposium Paper, Oct. 86.

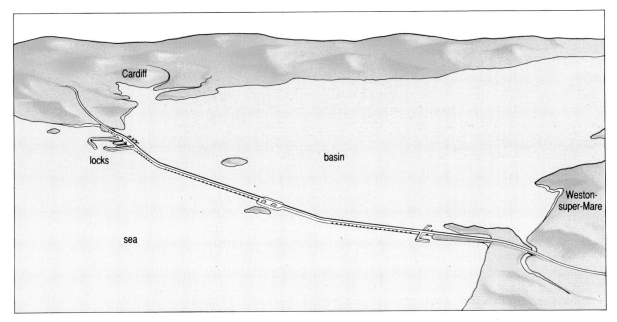

▲   *Figure 5.13   The Severn Barrage.*

Wave power areas

Offshore wind power areas

    possible

    probable

▶ Tidal power sites

Strangford Lough

Solway Firth

Morecambe Bay

Dee & Mersey

River Humber

Menai Strait

The Wash

Carmarthen Bay

Thames Estuary

Severn Estuary

◀ Figure 5.14
*Possible sites for offshore wind, wave and tidal sites in the UK.*

## Geothermal energy

The total heat escaping from the Earth is about $10^{21}$ J/yr = 30 TW, fairly evenly distributed at about 60 MW/m$^2$. In some volcanic 'hyperthermal' areas, however, this rate can be much greater, so much so that steam can be tapped from boreholes and used for space heating, industrial processes and in power stations. The total world electrical capacity from such systems in 1982 was over 3 GW, and non-electrical over 7 GW; the ultimate potential is perhaps 360 GW. In other 'non-thermal' regions favourable geological conditions can provide useful heat from below the surface. If the surface rocks have better than average thermal insulation, underlying porous rock may contain hot water – such aquifers 1–2 km below the surface have been exploited for district heating in Paris. Alternatively, underlying rocks may have a higher than average amount of radioactivity and therefore an enhanced temperature; these 'hot dry rocks' lie at about 5 km depth below the surface in south-west England, for example. Techniques have been developed for fracturing such rocks at depth and pumping water through them to make this a usable resource (Figure 5.15). The total energy available in the UK from this source is said to be comparable to the coal reserves.

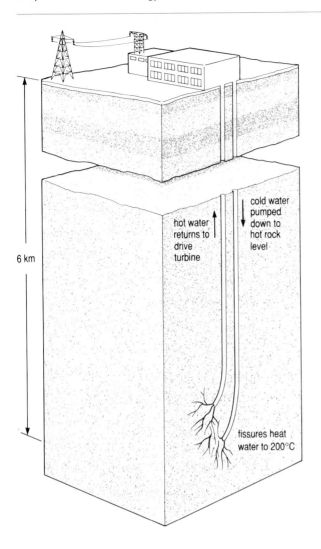

◀   *Figure 5.15*
*A hot dry rock*
*geothermal station.*

## Potential and costs

The relative merits of these various renewable techniques are hotly argued
by their protagonists. The economics vary in different countries and with
time, depending on the scale of R&D funding. The comparative UK
spending on fast reactors, fusion and renewables, for example, has already
been noted (Figure 5.6); a comparison between 1986 government R&D
spending in various developed countries on renewables and other forms of
energy is given in Table 5.2, showing the UK level to be exceptionally low.
So it is unlikely that there will be any final merit order; it can change with
new developments worldwide. The *total* resource is in many cases a
significant proportion of total demand; where opinions and estimates
differ is in the rate at which renewables can be introduced in competition
with existing methods, and the reduction of demand that might be
achieved by better efficiency, so that the renewables proportion increases.

If we limit ourselves for the moment to UK policy, we will get a more
detailed impression of the kind of arguments involved. Thus, for example
the UK Department of Energy in 1988 gave estimates for the 'technical
potential' of various favoured methods (some, like active solar and

*Table 5.2   Government R&D spending on renewables in selected countries, 1986*

| Country | Renewables R&D spending/$10^6$ | Share of energy R&D budget/% | Spending per capita/$ |
|---|---|---|---|
| Sweden | 17.3 | 21.8 | 2.06 |
| Switzerland | 10.2 | 14.7 | 1.57 |
| Netherlands | 17.0 | 10.6 | 1.17 |
| West Germany | 65.9 | 11.6 | 1.09 |
| Greece | 9.7 | 63.2 | 0.97 |
| Japan | 99.2 | 4.3 | 0.82 |
| United States | 177.2 | 7.8 | 0.73 |
| Italy | 29.5 | 3.9 | 0.52 |
| Denmark | 2.6 | 17.8 | 0.51 |
| Spain | 19.4 | 27.6 | 0.50 |
| United Kingdom | 16.6 | 4.4 | 0.29 |

Sources: International Energy Agency (1987) *Energy Policies and Programmes of IEA Countries: 1986 Review*, Organisation for Economic Co-operation and Development, Paris; Population Reference Bureau (1986) *1986 World Population Data Sheet*, Washington, D.C.

photovoltaic were excluded, rightly or wrongly), and an estimate of the contribution they might make competitively by 2025 (Table 5.3).

Table 5.3 implies a total potential of about 100 GW, with a contribution by 2025 of up to about 20 GW, on these estimates, to be compared with a 1988 total UK primary energy demand of about 285 GW, of which about 28 GW was supplied as electricity.

Similarly, the Central Electricity Generating Board (CEGB) in 1988 presented an estimate of an 'upper limit of renewable energy contributions as a percentage of likely UK electricity demand' (Figure 5.16), showing a proportion rising to about 18% by 2030. Similar figures were used in their 1989 estimates of the reduction in carbon dioxide emissions that could be achieved by 2005.

Obviously there can be detailed argument about all of these figures, particularly the percentage of the total represented by renewables if that total were significantly reduced by energy-efficiency measures. Both institutions (Department of Energy and CEGB) have a history of extravagant projections of total demand, and of the necessary nuclear component of it, which little resemble the actual history of the past two decades. Nevertheless, these figures do indicate that renewables are now 'on the official agenda', and that matching the intermittent nature of the sources to the complex demand fluctuations is not seen as a problem, at least up to about 20% renewables. As wind and wave power are greatest in the winter when demand is highest, and regional differences in both, and in tides, can be averaged out by the grid, it can be argued that a higher proportion could be accommodated. This will remain to be seen after the establishment of a privatised electricity industry and possibly more open access to a grid 'market'.

What *will* determine the development of all the techniques will be costs, or perhaps better, perceptions of costs, since these are so dependent on how they are calculated. A comparative set of figures from the

Table 5.3   Technical potential of renewable resources

| | Technical potential (translated here into GW average power) | Estimated contribution by 2025 |
|---|---|---|
| *Electricity producers* (quoted in TWh/hr) | | |
| Wind power | | |
|    Onshore | 5.1 | 0–3.4 |
|    Offshore | 16.0 | ? |
| Tidal | 6.2 | 0–3.2 |
| Geothermal (hot dry rocks) | 24.0 | 0–1 |
| Wave | 5.7 | 0–0.02 |
| Small-scale hydro | 0.2 | 0.03–0.08 |
| | | |
| *Heat producers* (quoted in mtce/yr) | | |
| Passive solar | 7–12 | 0.8–1.7 |
| Biofuels | | |
|    Wet and dry wastes (includes landfill gas) | 18.0 | 2.5–8 |
| Forestry | at least 17 | 1–4 |

Note a possible confusion about units. It was explained in Chapter 1 that whenever energy is converted from one form to another, the *rate* of conversion can be expressed as an average power in joules per second, or watts. The average over a short period, like an hour in the winter, can be very much higher than over the whole year. So some authorities only express the *maximum* power that can be obtained in watts. Thus the 'installed capacity' of UK power stations, if they were all working at once, is about 60 GW. The total energy requirement in a year is often expressed in 'energy units per year': for electricity this is kWh/yr, for heat it is mtce/yr. However, these can equally well be expressed as *average* ratings in watts, as has been done here, as long as it is understood that these will be much less than the maximum ratings. UK power stations actually deliver about 250 TWh/yr, an average rating of about 28 GW.

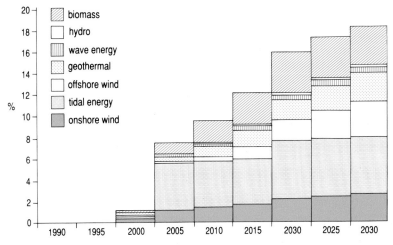

▲   Figure 5.16   *Upper limit of renewable energy contributions (CEGB estimate).*

Table 5.4    *Comparative cost of renewables (in p/kWh)*

|  | Watt Committee | Department of Energy |
|---|---|---|
| Mini hydroelectric | 1.35 | – |
| Wind | 2.26 | 2.5–3.2 |
| Geothermal (hot rocks) | 3.01 | 3–6 |
| Onshore wave | 3.17 | – |
| Tidal | 3.23 | 3–7 |
| Deep-sea wave | 5 | 9–4 |

These figures are based on conditions before privatisation.

independent Watt Committee on Energy and the Department of Energy from 1987 gives their views of costs in p/kWh, the usual basis of comparison (Table 5.4).

Again there is clearly a difference of opinion, the Department being more cautious. New techniques should have falling costs with experience; existing techniques may become more expensive with higher environmental protection and/or fuel costs. However, on any basis, some renewables are seen as competitive with the Watt Committee's figure of 'break-even' for private generation, 2.49p/kWh and the CEGB's electricity costs of 3.5–6.3p/kWh – all of which are very dependent on the assumed discount rate (commercial 10% or more, public sector 5%, say). This is one reason that wind power schemes, however tentatively, are beginning to go ahead.

This basic cost comparison is to ignore the environmental problems of fossil fuels and nuclear power. These impose separate reasons for encouraging alternatives, even while the initial cost advantages are not clear, a view certainly taken by some governments, like Denmark and, at times, the USA. The disparity in UK government support for nuclear and renewable energy has already been pointed out. Nevertheless, the responsible Minister, Michael Spicer, in 1988 said: 'The renewable technologies would not be best served in the long term by distorting the market by grant aid or other subsidies for their use' – an argument which has clearly not been applied to nuclear power, or indeed to coal.

On the other side, the British Renewable Energy Forum had already argued in a 1986 report that 'Market forces alone will be insufficient in an environment where such forces are already heavily distorted by selective taxation and multiple support of existing sources.'

This debate will surely continue to rage in the new framework of privatised UK electricity, the European market and world environmental concerns.

# 5    *Environmental impact of renewables*

It is a little ironic that environmental groups here and abroad are the most vociferous in questioning these (renewable) technologies. The Severn and Mersey barrage proposals are said to have potentially serious impacts on bird and marine life, and some people are suddenly seeing windmills as being noisy and obtrusive, at least on the scale that would be required to provide significant amounts of electricity.

On a recent visit to Denmark, which has a large number of windmills producing electricity, I found tremendous controversy among environmental groups, some of which were vociferously for and some of which were equally vociferously against wind power as an energy source. That environmental uncertainty is one of the strongest reasons for the Government's continued involvement in research into this area.

(Michael Spicer, UK Parliamentary Under-Secretary of State for Energy, 30 October 1987)

*Activity 4*

Consider the environmental effects that have been identified for traditional fossil fuel and nuclear power generation, and compare the effects that can be foreseen for the renewable methods described in Section 4.

## 5.1    *A general comparison*

The massive environmental effects on all scales of existing power sources, from the local visual effects of open-cast coal mining to the regional scale of pollution and the world scale of possible climate change are obviously not shared by the renewables. But in tackling one set of problems we introduce new ones, mostly local in scale. They must be considered sympathetically, weighing the environmental disturbance against the social value and cost of the energy produced, and the interests of local communities against more remote beneficiaries. Most of the solar sources (whether direct, biomass, wind or wave) are essentially diffuse, of low energy density, so any attempt to use them to produce the large concentrations of power associated with existing plant involves collection over large areas. Thus, a 2-MW wind turbine has *larger* blades than those of the steam turbine shown in Figure 5.17, but the vastly greater power of the jets of steam striking these blades than that of the wind gives a steam turbine a rating of some 500 MW, emphasising the concentration achieved with fossil or nuclear fuels. (This disparity is less pronounced for hydro, tidal or geothermal schemes, which take advantage of geographical factors to give energy concentration, and correspondingly greater power production.) All of the diffuse sources can more readily meet distributed local needs than those of large urban populations. In the long run this might influence

settlement patterns, but at present we will have to accept, along with large
farms for food production, similar large land areas for energy production
by these means – though the uses are not incompatible: energy and food
crops can be mixed, and farming can continue between wind turbines. An
advantage of such distributed schemes is that they can be expanded or
contracted without massive investment or decommissioning costs.

As the renewables involve the 'harvesting' of energy from natural
flows, rather than the exploitation of concentrated energy stores, a possible
primary measure of their environmental effect is the extent of disturbance
of these flows; different methods also have individual 'secondary' effects
of various kinds. (This approach is adopted in a study by Alexi Clarke listed
under 'Further reading'.) Thus

- *solar energy* is normally absorbed and re-radiated at lower temperature;
collection only modifies this process to redistribute the heat produced, so
the primary effects are small; secondary effects might be visual intrusion or
reflected glare;

- *biomass production* is the normal response of the ecosystem to solar
input, though the natural system shows much species diversity; any
agricultural system (for food, timber or energy) disturbs this process, with
perhaps more risk to its sustainability the nearer it is to a monoculture, and
the more agrochemicals are used; secondary effects might be visual,
conflicts over land use and amenity, and the noise and pollution from
mechanical harvesting and processing;

- the use of biomass *wastes* is in a sense a complementary process, as
they only exist as a result of our earlier disturbance of the natural flow, and
we *reduce* the environmental effects of burning or burying them by
controlled energy production; secondary effects might be visual and other
pollution from collection and processing;

- *wind energy* is extracted by wind turbines, so the natural air flow is reduced downstream, but only to a very small extent as so little of the total energy is accessible; secondary effects are visual, noise, etc., considered in more detail below;

- *wave energy* is likewise extracted by conversion machines, though soon replaced by the wind; coastal erosion might be *reduced*; the movements of shipping and marine organisms would be affected;

- *tidal energy* is extracted by significantly modifying natural water flows so the local effect is considerable, as it is with large *hydropower* schemes; secondary ecosystem and visual effects, and disturbance during construction, may be large, and are site dependent;

- *geothermal energy* is extracted from the natural flow of heat within the Earth's crust, originating from the fluid interior, or more local radioactivity; the relation between the rate of extraction and the rate of replenishment determines the temperature reduction, and hence the continuing use of the site, or conceivably, larger geological changes, as with other mining operations; secondary effects are like those of mines, but with no spoil.

The worst case for its immediate environmental effects is evidently tidal, with specific dependence on the particular site. Thus, the Severn Barrage scheme has raised concern about the effects of the modified water flow on mud flats which are feeding areas for birds, on the deposition of silt and on effluents which will no longer be swept out to sea (but should be cleaned up anyway?) – to be measured against 120 years of pollution-free electricity generation on a very large scale. The balance of local opinion seems to be in favour, but a decision to proceed depends on issues of private and public financing which have not yet been resolved. Similar debates will take place over each other new scheme (Mersey and Humber, for example) as it arises.

Less severe, but more general, questions are now being asked about wind power. This is currently a sufficiently financially attractive option for a serious deployment programme. The environmental concerns now being expressed, as the introduction of wind farms is starting in the UK, make this appropriate for a more detailed case study, which forms the rest of this chapter.

## 5.2   The wind resource

We have already seen that the USA has installed over 1.5 GW of wind power, and that Denmark and Holland are committed to reaching 1 GW each by 2000; the UK has begun to embark upon the commercial exploitation of the resource. What conditions are required for wind power to be useful, and what difficulties are foreseen?

The fact that wind is intermittent means that operation can only be expected for 30–40% of the time whereas conventional power stations operate for 55–70% of the time, allowing for maintenance, mechanical problems and fluctuating demand. So up to twice the installed capacity would be required from wind to replace more conventional sources. But unless the proportion of wind energy were to exceed about 20%, the use of the grid to smooth out contributions from different parts of the country, and from existing plant, seems able to cater for local fluctuations. The total number of turbines of existing designs (around 1 MW) needed to replace a large (e.g. 1.3 GW) power station is very large. Where will these thousands

1  Didcot cooling tower          5  Nelson's Column
2  St Paul's Cathedral           6  400 kV pylon
3  3 MW turbine, Orkney          7  Carmarthen Bay 300 kW (CEGB)
4  Richborough 1 MW turbine      8  Carmarthen Bay 200 kW turbine

▲    *Figure 5.18    Figures in a landscape – sizes of wind turbines.*

of machines be sited, and how will they be regarded – as ugly intrusions, or as environmentally appropriate, since they use a continuous resource, and are non-polluting?

Without going far into the complexities of technical wind turbine design, it is worth trying to grasp two basic principles which influence their size and location. The first is that the power depends on the 'swept area' covered by the blades. You may remember that the area of a circle is $\pi r^2$, that is, a number, 'pi', times the radius 'squared' (i.e. multiplied by itself). What this means is that doubling the blade length multiplies the power by four, so there is a considerable advantage in increasing their size, with a corresponding increase in the height of the tower – which also enables them to reach levels of higher wind speeds. There are then increasing structural difficulties, which at present limit designs to a few MW, with debate about the most reliable and cost-effective size, perhaps 'medium-power' of about 300 kW. What this means in terms of relative size is shown in Figure 5.18, with heights of 40–70 m, spanning the height of grid pylons or Nelson's Column in Trafalgar Square.

The second point is that power is even more dependent on wind speed – in fact on speed 'cubed', $v^3$, that is, speed multiplied by itself twice over so that doubling the speed increases the power by eight times. So it is highly rewarding to seek out areas of high wind speed. High, exposed areas may readily have average wind speeds 1.6 times higher than surrounding lowlands (higher peak speeds and also fewer calm periods) so the power available is about four times greater.

The basic pattern of lowland wind speed over Britain is shown in maps like Figure 5.19, where 'isovent' lines join places where the annual average speed 10 m above the ground, for altitudes 0–70 m above sea-level, has a particular value, ranging from less than 4 to more than 8 m/s.

Q    Where are the highest lowland wind speeds?

A    The Orkneys and extreme north-west of Scotland.

Q    Where are the lowest?

A    Inland regions of eastern Scotland; the Pennines, West Midlands and London regions of England.

The legend reads:

Isovent showing wind speed in mean annual metres per second at 10 metres above ground

General areas of above 5.5 m/s mean wind speeds

General upland areas where hill sites with suitable wind speeds can be found

● Proposed wind park

Labels on map: Langdon Common, Capel Cynon, Cold Northcott

▲   *Figure 5.19   Wind resources and CEGB wind park sites in Britain.*

A wind speed of 5.5 m/s is usually taken as a guideline for wind energy conversion to be practicable. Coastal and lowland regions where this is exceeded are also shown in Figure 5.19. These include the western peninsulas of England and Wales, i.e. Cornwall/Devon, Pembrokeshire, Lleyn; Anglesey, the Lancashire and Cumbrian coasts, western Scottish coasts, much of Sutherland and Caithness; Mull, Skye and other Western Isles; Orkney, Shetland and the Outer Hebrides. This value is also reached along a narrow strip of the east coast of Scotland and much of England, a few promontories and exposed parts of the south coast, and virtually all offshore regions.

However, this is only the lowland resource. Inland regions *within* the 5.5-m isovent can still have suitable winds on sufficiently high ground. Candidate areas (see Figure 5.19) are largely in Scotland, central northern England, central Wales and the Pennines. The 'speed-cubed' rule makes it well worth while to seek out suitable sites, but this is not straightforward. Wind speeds generally increase as air masses rise over hills, ridges and plateaux, but the details depend on the particular lie of the land.

Complete surveys are not yet available. As long ago as the 1950s the Electrical Research Association found over 1500 sites, mainly between the west coast of Scotland and the 4.5 m/s isovent, where, it was estimated, over 2000 wind turbines producing over 5.6 GW could be accommodated; no environmental constraints were considered. The government's Energy Technology Support Unit has studied a $100 \times 100$ km square area of south-west Scotland in which 'first-order' siting constraints were considered. Sites were excluded if they were already used for buildings and works, military zones and radio masts, airports, road and rail junctions, forestry, golf and race courses, parks and the National Trust.

Such studies imply that 10–20%, maybe even 100%, of UK electricity demand could be met by wind power, particularly if the huge offshore potential is included. More detailed 'second-order' environmental impacts, however, remain to be considered.

## 5.3   *Environmental constraints*

As usual with discussions of changes which impinge on the environment, the factors involved are many and interrelated. Consider first some technical matters which set the scale of the problem, before going on to more subjective questions about how we perceive their effects.

First, how big are the new turbines going to be? Setting aside 'small' machines of less than 100 kW power, which will no doubt be scattered about without too much impact, the choice for substantial generation is between 'medium' (100 kW to 1 MW) with blade diameters below about 50 m, like pylons or Nelson's Column, and 'large' ($>1$ MW), maybe up to 100 m, like large cooling towers or St Paul's Cathedral. The emphasis in the practical wind farm schemes in the USA, Denmark and Holland has been on medium size. Research in the USA, and by the CEGB in the UK, has looked at large machines – obviously fewer will be needed, but there is less operating experience, and the relative impact remains uncertain, depending on siting. At present the economics seem to favour medium size, and they have been adopted in the CEGB wind park proposals.

Second, how much *land* will they occupy? With one more bit of technical information you can estimate this for yourself: adjacent wind turbines do not interfere with each other if they are separated by from 5 to 15 times the blade diameter – say 10 times as a standard figure.

To get a general idea, let us keep to simple numbers – 1 MW turbines of 50 m diameter replacing a power station of 1 GW output.

Q   How many turbines are needed to provide the same power (when operating) as the power station?

A   1 GW/1 MW $= 10^9/10^6 = 10^3 = 1000$.

Q   If the wind turbines only operate for 35% of the time, while the power station operates for 70% ('load factor'), how many turbines are needed?

A   Twice as many, 2000.

Q   If these were divided into 20 'farms' of 100 turbines each, arranged in a $10 \times 10$ square array, what would be the area of each farm, and the total area?

A   Turbine spacing $= 10 \times$ blade diameter $= 10 \times 50$ m $= 500$ m;
    array length $= 10 \times 500$ m $= 5$ km
    (strictly, $9 \times 500$ m $= 4.5$ km between end turbines, but this allows an
    extra 250 m at each end as a 'buffer zone' discussed below).
    Farm area $= 5 \times 5 = 25$ km$^2$.
    Total area $= 20 \times 25 = 500$ km$^2$.

Obviously the exact figure depends on the assumptions about power/size relationships, load factors, array shapes and spacings, and can be a source of contention – the CEGB said that a wind replacement for Sizewell would occupy $27 \times 27 = 729$ km$^2$ whereas a wind enthusiast can get it down to $17 \times 17 = 289$ km$^2$ by making different assumptions. The *general* idea of the area involved is not in doubt, but a factor of two or more in detailed planning is quite important!

The two basic design points made above in Section 5.2 are relevant. What is the effect of blade length and wind speed on these estimates?

Doubling the blade length increases the power by four, but also doubles the required spacing, so increases the area by four, leaving the power per unit area about the same. So the choice between medium and large turbines doesn't have much effect on this question if the spacing *pattern* is kept the same; it might be possible to find a better detailed arrangement for fewer large machines.

On the other hand, the 'wind-speed cubed' rule means that using the same size of turbine at different sites can make a big difference to its power: an increase in wind speed from 5.5 m/s to 7 m/s more than doubles the power ($7/5.5 = 1.27$; $1.27^3 = 2.06$), turning our 1 MW model into a 2 MW, and halving the number of turbines and area of land required. This emphasises the importance of seeking out the windy sites, and the sensitivity of the calculations to site data which are not always available.

Even more important is the fact that these comparatively large land areas are not in fact used up by building wind farms on them. The proportion of the area occupied by the towers and necessary services has been variously estimated at from 3% to 5%, the rest being still available for agriculture. The land actually occupied is reduced to a few tens of square kilometres, not much more than a large power station site. It would not be expected to be all in one place, but distributed over several farms. This permits a site-dependent compromise about land use – lower wind speed areas where more turbines are needed may share use with arable farming; windy hill-tops with fewer, well-spaced large machines may be used for livestock, or not farmed at all, with amenity and visual impact becoming more important.

The next consideration is that of 'buffer zones' between wind farms and the public, both for general access and habitation. Two issues, noise and safety, fortunately point to similar requirements, and also help with the most controversial, visual impact, which can be assessed against the whole of this more technical background.

1   *Noise* from wind turbines comes from three sources: the regular rhythmic swish of the rotating blades, mechanical noise from the gearbox and an electrical hum from the generator. The latter two are internal, and in good designs are reduced by conventional sound-proofing. The blade noise is more fundamental, and improved aerodynamic design to reduce it is being eagerly sought. It is most noticeable in light winds; as the wind gets stronger its own noise in trees, buildings, etc. dominates. Turbine noise carries downwind, but reduces with distance. How much reduction

is required depends on the background noise level, and the activities, around the particular site. Urban background levels are higher than rural; permanent homes obviously require quieter conditions than working areas, industrial or agricultural, or chance passers-by. The requirements for remote 'wilderness' sites with very low background levels may be particularly exacting. While a buffer zone of 1 km or so is usually completely satisfactory, this may drastically reduce the wind capacity available in some areas, so careful assessment is needed. Concern to avoid noise disturbance is essential, but it would be a pity to limit the use of wind power by restrictions which are unnecessarily stringent.

2    A similar buffer zone is also needed for *safety* reasons. Like all large engineering structures, wind turbines can fail if the design, construction, inspection or maintenance are faulty. The development period of modern machines, from the 1940s to the 1980s, did see some spectacular tower collapses and runaway in high winds causing blade break-up in the USA, Denmark, Holland and France, though without casualties or adjacent property damage. These have led to improvements in design and quality control, better understanding of blade fatigue, better control and braking mechanisms in high winds and tighter regulation. The risk from current established designs is considered to be negligible – very much lower than from road transport, for example.

Denmark, with much experience, has a proposed buffer zone 'formula' of >90 m + 2.7 × blade diameter from open public areas, roads and buildings.

Q    What does this imply for 50-m and 100-m diameter blades?

A    50 m: $90 + 2.7 \times 50 = 90 + 135 = 225$ m
     $100$ m $= 90 + 2.7 \times 100 = 90 + 270 = 360$ m

There is thus little difficulty in providing adequate noise and safety buffer zones in remote locations, but in areas of scattered settlement they can restrict the available wind resource considerably. In a Cornwall study using 70-m diameter 2-MW turbines for reference, 350-m (5 diameters) spacings and buffer zones enabled sites of 1.4 GW capacity to be identified, whereas 700-m (10 diameters) zones reduced this to 0.132 GW. A Danish study of the national resource used 7 diameters, giving 200–300 m distances for different sizes of turbine, and based on *experience* of 100, 200 and 500 m distances rather than calculation or regulation. Distances greater than 300 m from buildings were considered to make siting in general impossible in the normal Danish landscape of scattered agricultural buildings.

Evidently, whatever formula is chosen for the size of buffer zones constrains the size of turbine that can be used on each site and the total resource available.

Further technical factors in choosing sites are ease of *access* to the electricity grid and the road system, and *electromagnetic interference* disturbing radio and television reception, microwave communication links and radar – this may require the introduction of additional 'booster' transmitters, which are, however, comparatively cheap in relation to turbine costs.

With all these practical matters dealt with, we are led to the most controversial and subjective question, of the *visual impact* of wind turbines. They are large structures on unobstructed hill and coastal sites, moving so that they attract attention, and possibly spread out in large numbers as wind farms. Many of the most suitable sites are in the highlands of the north and west of the UK, much valued as National Parks and unspoilt landscape. Individual reactions can obviously vary from outrage at ugly intrusions to enthusiastic support for glorious symbols of environmentally appropriate engineering; which reactions dominate will be dependent on the site and the imagination and sensitivity shown in its detailed use.

It seems to be accepted that we have an exaggerated perception of vertical objects compared with horizontal, regarding anything more than 50 m high as 'large', which is consistent with the distinction between medium and large turbines. 'Extreme dominance' is said to be felt within distances of three times the height, dominance within ten times. (So the buffer zones already required go most of the way to removing 'dominance'). Features are dissociated if separated by more than three times their height, which again will occur with the spacings required to avoid interference, though not if you can see through several staggered rows, with their blades forming a 'thicket'. Most experience is with medium size turbines. The comparative effect of fewer, more widely spaced large machines with fewer access roads may be less; at sufficiently large distance they will be less likely to coalesce. Conditions in the UK rarely permit visibility of slender structures beyond 5–8 miles. Rotation speeds of less than 45 r.p.m. are thought to be restful. Solid towers are preferred to open gridwork. (Why are traditional windmills picturesque? Are slender modern aerodynamic designs equally attractive?) There are 22 000 pylons and many aerial masts that are already tolerated up to a point, though whether similar structures should be added will again depend on the site. Substations and access roads have to be included in the landscaping.

This all adds up to a complicated set of judgements to be made about each site in turn; most important is that the visual effects of proposed schemes should be clearly presented in local consultation.

A separate concern that has been expressed about wind turbines and the environment is their effect on wildlife – specifically, *birds*, the only form that seems to be involved. Turbines are large moving structures with high blade tip speeds, so are potential obstacles and hazards. It must be said immediately that this has not deterred us from putting up power cables, pylons, masts and lighthouses, which are similar stationary objects with which birds frequently collide in bad weather, or from building motorways and aircraft, which kill large numbers of mammals and birds. Bird strikes by aircraft seem to be treated more as hazards to the machines than to the birds. Nevertheless, it is appropriate and natural that a development proposed as environmentally benign should be scrutinised carefully for adverse effects.

A number of detailed studies have been done on turbine sites in Holland, Denmark and the USA; the research turbines in the Orkneys are near bird sanctuaries, and a joint study is being done with the Royal Society for the Protection of Birds (RSPB). The dependence of bird behaviour on species, site, number of turbines and weather conditions continue to be examined, but the major concern that has emerged so far is about the disturbance caused by increased human activity around wind farms, not the machines. While any doubts remain it may be better to avoid known breeding grounds and migration routes for wind farms, and use underground cables for grid connection where there is much birdlife. At coastal sites a recommendation has been made to site turbines as far inland as possible.

The exploitation of the substantial resource still available after all these factors have been considered, together with the even greater offshore possibilities, can meet perhaps 20% of our electricity needs. Conflict will however only be avoided with sensitive consideration of each site, and full consultation with the people who will be affected. Apart from the areas specifically designated as National Parks or Areas of Outstanding Natural Beauty (AONB) all areas will raise some questions of visual intrusion. The reactions to the CEGB wind park proposals will now be considered.

## 5.4   The 1988 CEGB wind park programme

In April 1988 the CEGB announced a £28 million programme to develop three 8-MW wind 'parks' of 25 medium-power turbines at selected sites in the Northern Pennines, Wales and Cornwall (see Figure 5.19). Construction would begin, after local consultation, in 1990 and be completed in 1993. This was against the background already described of developments elsewhere, of research studies by the CEGB and others, and of growing pressure from wind and renewables proponents. There was also a background of resistance, some from environmental worries in the USA and Denmark, some from prevailing convictions in UK government. In a 1986 debate, Peter Walker, then Secretary of State for Energy, defending UK nuclear policy after the Chernobyl disaster, had described wind turbines 'having a noise equivalent to a helicopter', an image echoed in a 1987 debate on renewable energy by MPs asking 'whether we want every beauty spot turned into an electricity generating site with 100-m blades making a noise like that of a landing helicopter every minute of the day' and expressing 'reservations about peppering our countryside with 75 ft high monster windmills'.

In January 1988 Michael Spicer, the Minister then responsible, said, more reasonably, 'Popular enthusiasm for renewable energy needs to be accompanied by realism. Benign as they may appear, their exploitation, like that of any other resource, will extract some environmental price . . . (which) must be evaluated before exploitation is embarked upon on any substantial scale.' Lord Marshall's announcement of the CEGB project emphasised 'the reaction of the British public to these new wind parks. We shall be carefully monitoring the visual and other amenity aspects of them – noise output, interference with communications and their compatibility with the simultaneous use of land for other purposes.'

In this controversial atmosphere, with realism urged on enthusiasts, while fixed opinions were often repeated, the choice of sites for the CEGB scheme, and the manner of consultation, were obviously critical. Before choosing them, the CEGB sent a shortlist of seven sites for comment to the Countryside Commission. Their response was to rank them for environmental sensitivity, placing the Langdon Common site in the Northern Pennines, about to be designated as part of an AONB, at the top of the list as the most sensitive; the Cornwall and Wales sites came last. It is a matter of opinion whether the CEGB's choice of these three sites should be seen as provocative (even conspiratorial) or as a shrewd test of a range of options from worst to best – both views have been expressed. Certainly the initial enthusiasm of environmental groups for the project was tempered by the details. The declared aim of the government, 'to examine environmental impact and public acceptability' (Michael Spicer, February 1989), is being carried out, though now in the new climate of privatised electricity supply.

## 5.5   National and local reactions

The first reactions were from national environmental bodies and the windpower community. Understandably, after the advice it had given, the Countryside Commission opposed the Langdon Common proposal. *Windpower Monthly* in October 1988 collected a range of opinions broadly supportive of renewable energy, but variously critical of the detailed CEGB approach, from environmental bodies like the Council for the Preservation of Rural England, the Ramblers' Association and the RSPB. The Green Party, uniquely, considered that there was no need for government funded demonstrations at all, but that diverse *private* generation schemes, including wind, should be allowed to flourish, encouraged by changes in rating and terms for electricity sale – a view particularly appropriate to the new privatised supply industry – while national funding should continue to concentrate on research.

Friends of the Earth recognised the inevitable environmental effects of *all* energy supply, but emphasised that it is also necessary to consider worst possible accidents, reversibility and the scope for individual or community control, where wind comes out well. The importance of local consultation had been stressed for the Severn Barrage scheme and applies similarly to these wind proposals. Finding a middle way between a Luddite objection to all new schemes and a failure to protect the countryside and wildlife requires sensitive assessment of losses and gains by the local community, not a distant authority.

These national reactions were indeed followed by evidence of local concern. The county council response to the Langdon Common scheme was to propose nearby sites that would be less sensitive; in September 1990 plans for this site were in fact abandoned. A different kind of problem arose in Cornwall. Many farmers only became aware that the CEGB was proposing to 'take over' their land for wind farms within a day or two of the national announcement, and there was predictable resistance to allowing access for further studies – it was too late for the CEGB to insist that local consultation was only beginning. It was perceived as 'riding roughshod' over local opinion, and there was talk of compulsory purchase orders. These preliminary skirmishes died down as questions of compensation for loss of land, organised visits to experimental wind installations, and indeed the possibility of farmers making their own use of their land for private wind generators, took over – but not without bad feeling about the manner in which the CEGB had handled things. Other local interests (tourism, employment and so on) are also involved, and public responses will become clearer as wind farms become established. Since privatisation and the reorganisation of the CEGB, the future of the two remaining wind parks hangs in the balance. Meanwhile, the new framework has created a specific market for private wind energy developers. How will sensitive planning and local consultation fare? See Rand (1990) and Rand & Harper (1991) for further discussion.

This reflects a more general question about the use of a distributed resource like the wind, which has arisen in the USA and Denmark too. A resource clearly seen to be used for local needs is much more acceptable than an intrusive scheme imposed by a powerful 'outside' body that does not seem to produce a local benefit. In Denmark, environmental objections have mostly been concerned with wind farms proposed by public utilities. Locally based community schemes, admittedly smaller, developed either privately or by wind co-operatives, have seemed to provide a better perception of local benefit without unacceptable environmental loss.

However, given the nature of our present society, we are likely to continue having large institutions, providing for large urban populations, proposing large schemes that may impinge uncomfortably on local and rural concerns. When the CEGB *did* embark on its modest scheme, as we have seen, its way of proceeding managed to arouse antagonism. How can we arrange that local and national interests, energy needs and environmental protection are better judged? If renewable energy is seen as generally less environmentally damaging, it will be a pity if it has to be pushed through by the confrontational methods associated with previous energy policies. Our landscape once comfortably embraced 10 000 windmills. Should it do so again?

## 5.6   *Conclusion – renewable energy futures*

The many renewable forms of energy described in Section 4 are together able to provide a supply system that can gradually replace existing methods. Whether and how quickly it will do so will (apparently) depend on costs, but these will in turn depend on underlying factors of availability, technical ingenuity, political intervention and environmental effects – expressed both by better accounting for existing methods and careful scrutiny of alternatives. We have already seen that all energy supply involves *some* environmental effect; how this should be assessed raises difficult questions of values. Current ideas of 'environmental accounting' propose that money values should be attached to the environmental costs of policies, including energy policies. Certainly this seems better than neglecting them, but you will have your own view of whether money is the right measure in every case. How do you weigh a view of Great Gable in the Lake District against more convenient commuting to work – or Third World starvation?

It is important that *some* judgement be made about new policies, and we have seen the need for careful consideration of their effects, and consultation of local opinion, before introducing them. In the case of renewable energy, sensitive use of natural energy flows may even be seen as *enhancing* the environment, unlike the affronts produced by thoughtless exploitation of natural energy stores.

# 6   *Sustainable energy futures*

The methods of energy demand reduction described in Sections 2 and 3, and of alternative supply described in Sections 4 and 5, offer a general way forward to developing sustainable energy policies. The balance between them will vary country by country, and in response to changing perceptions of environmental issues and political responses to them.

We have emphasised immediate UK policy, but in the longer term and world wide the same issues arise, with the additional pressing inequity of large differences in energy use between different countries, more urgently calling for sustainable policies. A general point about industrial society is that it places in individual hands a large number (millions) of technically complex energy *consuming* devices (motor cars, refrigerators, television sets) and these are no doubt sought everywhere. Although some of the large energy demand comes from the industrial and service infrastructure that provides these goods, as much of it comes from their widespread use, and is sensitive to efficiency improvements, as we have seen.

Energy *production* on the other hand is traditionally concentrated in large units (mines, oil refineries, power stations) and the centralised financial and governmental institutions which control them. A shift of emphasis to renewable energy production, particularly that based on the distributed solar energy resource, lends itself to the distribution of many small units, down to the local or even domestic scale (small hybrid solar, or biomass fuelled, CHP; small wind, wave and hydro machines). The experience with energy-consuming devices suggests that there is no reason why these should not be technically complex if they are well designed for ease of use. As well as meeting local needs, they could all be coupled to the grid to provide an energy trading and support system. This would limit the required centralised institutions to control of the transport, grid and communications networks, and of specialised manufacture, distribution and maintenance, rather than the present monolithic energy suppliers. Along with an increasing use of information (rather than goods and energy) transfer, this raises implications for social and political organisation in all parts of the world which may be very different from those of existing industrial societies.

## *References and further reading*

SOLAR ENERGY RESEARCH INSTITUTE FOR US DEPT OF ENERGY (1981) *A New Prosperity: building a sustainable energy future*, Brick House Publishing, Andover, Massachusetts.

KRAUSE, F. *et al.* (1980) *Energie Wende: Wachstum und Wohlst ohne Erdol und Uran*, S. Fischer Verlag, Frankfurt (M).

OLIVIER, D. *et al.* (1983) *Energy-efficient Futures: opening the solar option*, Earth Resources Research, 258 Pentonville Rd, London N1 9JY.


CLARKE, A. (1989) *Comparative Environmental Impact of Renewables*. Open University Technology Policy Group, Milton Keynes.

LOVINS, A. B. (1988) *The State-of-the-art: Lighting*, Rocky Mountain Institute, Colorado.

RAND, M. (1990) *Developing Wind Energy for the UK*, Friends of the Earth, London.

RAND, M. & HARPER, M. (1991) *Removing the Windbrakes*, Friends of the Earth, London.

SMITH, P. & WARR, K. (eds) (1991) *Global Environmental Issues*, Hodder & Stoughton/The Open University, London (Book Four).

UK ISIS (1987) *Proceedings of the 1st UK ISIS Conference on Superinsulation*, UK ISIS, London.

WORLD COMMISSION ON THE ENVIRONMENT AND DEVELOPMENT (1987) *Our Common Future*, The Brundtland Report, Oxford University Press, Oxford.

## *Notes on Activities*

### *Activity 1*

World energy consumption has increased from a rate of about 1 to about 10 TW (i.e. from $10^{12}$ to $10^{13}$ W) during the twentieth century. With a current world population of about $5 \times 10^9$ this makes the *average* rate of consumption now about 2 kW per person, but this ranges from <1 kW in less developed countries through about 4 kW in Europe to over 10 kW in the USA. With a doubled population in the next century, and some increase of average consumption, say to 3 kW each, the total would be 30 TW, with extreme possibilities such as: worldwide attention to energy efficiency bringing the average *down* to 1 kW each, so a total of 10 TW, as now, or world profligacy matching the US at 10 kW each, so a total of 100 TW. These *rates* of energy consumption imply an *annual* consumption of around $10^{21}$ J (there are $3.1 \times 10^7$ seconds in a year, so 30 TW = $3 \times 10^{13}$ J/ s = $3 \times 10^{13} \times 3.1 \times 10^7$ J/year = $9.3 \times 10^{20}$ J/year). A resource of $10^{22}$ J would last about 10 years, $10^{23}$ J about 100 years, at this rate. Some impression of the pressure on the various fuels is gained by comparing their 'reserves' and 'resources' with these figures; exceeding 'proved reserves' produces price increases as less accessible resources are brought into use. Of course this is a *total* consumption estimate, so shouldn't strictly be compared with resources of any one fuel, as they are to some extent interchangeable, though conversions to less favourable fuels again lead to increased costs. However, a comparison with each fuel in turn gives a broad picture of availability. In these terms, it is clear that the oil and gas reserves, of 5 and $4 \times 10^{21}$ J, are under severe stress, and their total resources, of a few times $10^{22}$ J, are not much better. Uranium, with reserves of about $10^{21}$ J for use in burner reactors, will be even less readily available. Coal, with quoted reserves of $2.6 \times 10^{22}$ J and resources more than 10 times higher, might be available for a century or so; uranium used in breeder reactors (providing some $10^{23}$ J) is rather better – but in both cases the environmental price is high. The only terrestrial resource apparently almost unlimited is the deuterium in sea water, estimated to provide over $10^{30}$ J if it could be successfully used in a fusion reactor – this is yet to be proved possible. Solar energy on the other hand arrives continuously at the Earth's surface at a rate of some $2.4 \times 10^{24}$ J/year, some 2000 times larger than this projected demand – though much of it arrives where it is not wanted, making its systematic use depend on changed priorities. Even the small percentage of solar energy converted into biomass energy, some $10^{22}$ J/year, is well above the total demand, though the same problem of its wide dispersal arises.

The environmental problems identified for fossil fuels include the gross local pollution of uncontrolled coal burning; the $SO_2$, $NO_x$, CO and hydrocarbon emissions, leading to acid rain and photochemical smog, from coal and oil combustion, now under increasingly tight control; and the inevitable $CO_2$ production from all fossil fuels, with its projected effects on the climate from the enhanced greenhouse effect (gas is somewhat preferable to oil, in turn preferable to coal).

Nuclear power does not produce $CO_2$ directly, though it has been argued that increased nuclear generation would imply increased energy use, in fuel production and construction, that would at present be derived from fossil fuels, with their direct $CO_2$ output. Nuclear has its own environmental problems – radioactive hazards, of catastrophic accidents and routine waste disposal; 'proliferation' of nuclear weapons from stolen materials, particularly plutonium in a breeder-based system.

The economic effects of direct supply and demand fluctuations for fossil and nuclear fuels are already considerable, but environmental effects are not included. GDP is often used as a measure of economic prosperity, and energy intensity (energy use per unit GDP) as a measure of energy efficiency, but it is increasingly recognised that high GDP can be achieved by destruction of environmental 'capital'. New 'environmental economics' measures are under discussion, but are not yet in general use.

*Activity 2*

There can be no general answer, as it will depend on your personal circumstances. No doubt you will have noted something about the relative locations of your home and work, and perhaps domestic, financial or amenity difficulties in bringing them closer together. You very likely find a car convenient for you and your family because of the ease of door-to-door transport and carrying shopping it provides; perhaps public transport is inadequate in accessibility, availability or cost. Maybe you are a model user of cycle or moped – or perhaps you would be if you didn't feel so vulnerable, to other vehicles or the weather. What changes would you like to be made?

*Activity 3*

The primary energy sources are the non-renewable fossil fuels (coal, oil and gas) and nuclear fuels (uranium and potentially deuterium), and the continuous (or renewable) solar, gravitational or geothermal energy. Energy vectors are traditionally hot water, refined fuels, wood and electricity. A potential chemical energy vector is hydrogen, and a nuclear one plutonium. More speculative chemical fuels might be transported for use in fuel cells, or more hypothetically in chemical motors; there might be nuclear equivalents.

*Activity 4*

The environmental effects of fossil fuels and nuclear power, on all scales from the local to the global, have already been discussed under Activity 1. Renewables do have environmental effects, discussed at more length in what follows. They are essentially *local*, the visual effects of machinery in the landscape or changed land use. The most severe are those from large tidal and hydroelectric schemes, which might influence not only the local landscape and ecosystem but also water flows at greater distances.

# 1   Introduction

Look back at Figure 2.11 in Chapter 2 which offers a diagrammatic résumé of many of the ideas under discussion in this book. In Chapters 2 and 3 attention is given to the circumstances under which the extraction and processing of minerals impact on the environment. Also considered are the constraints on such processes; for example, whether they are imposed to ameliorate environmental damage, or are of a political/economic kind and result in extractive and processing activities at one location rather than another.

This chapter develops this theme by considering the use of such materials in industrial and manufacturing processes and the problems which may arise. The emphasis here is much more on the means by which policies of environmental control have been initiated and developed by government.

From your studies so far in this book, it should already be apparent that there are essential differences between air and water pollution. Since such differences provide a rationale for the way in which the material contained in this chapter is dealt with, it is as well to be reminded of what they are.

### Activity 1

Briefly outline what you think are the essential differences between air and water pollution, commenting especially on their impact on people and how they affect people's lives.

It is unlikely that your response will have contained the detail provided in the answer to this Activity. The important point is that the problem of polluted water is usually relatively restricted in its impact and often may be largely regarded as one of amenity, a matter remarked upon in Section 4 of Chapter 3. Air pollution, by contrast, may well be of much wider significance, especially in terms of human well-being.

It is for these reasons that this chapter now concentrates on air pollution, although not to the total exclusion of water pollution considerations. Even here the sheer variety of industrial and manufacturing processes poses a problem for what must be a relatively short account, so it is necessary to be further selective. The obvious focus then becomes that of air pollution from the chemical industry, not only because of its wide range of potential pollutants, but also because it was the stimulus to the first government pollution regulation in Britain.

The argument of the chapter falls into three stages. Section 2 traces the early development of industrialisation, the production processes which gave rise to the most serious forms of air pollution and the origins of an approach to regulation which lasted until the 1970s. Special attention is paid to the location and concentration of industry and to the need to distinguish between particulate and gaseous emissions for which separate control systems have emerged.

Section 3 considers a case study of a fertiliser works near Stanlow in Cheshire, using it to identify some of the problems of that regulatory approach, notably failures of local and central government to act in concert.

Section 4 identifies some approaches to regulation which have been proposed in the European Community and shows how they have been selectively incorporated into the Environmental Protection Bill currently passing through the Houses of Parliament (July 1990). The key issue is how far legislators are prepared to press environmental controls when these have the effect of increasing costs.

The conclusion assesses progress to date and refers to some approaches to pollution reduction which have not yet been incorporated into legislation.

# 2    Industrialisation in the nineteenth century

## 2.1    Introduction

In the nineteenth century, the twin forces of industrialisation and mass urbanisation transformed Britain's landscape as the entrepreneurs and inventors of the new economic order sought ways to supply power, labour and raw materials rapidly and reliably to the expanding production centres. The two engravings of Figures 6.1 and 6.2 illustrate the striking contrast between the old and the new. Figure 6.1 shows a water-driven grinding wheel in Endcliffe Wood near Sheffield and Figure 6.2 shows a steam-powered cutlery works in the same city. They illustrate the decline of small scattered rural workshops on the hill streams typical of the eighteenth century and the subsequent concentration of industries in cities, in a mass of furnaces, chimneys and congested workers' dwellings. The steam engine was the driving force of this industrial and urban expansion. Exploiting technological advances begun in the previous century, steam power both drove and demanded advances in the iron and engineering industries, in mechanisation, and in the exploitation of coal which provided the fuel for furnaces and engines. James Watt's improved 'fire engines' were already at work in textile factories, ironworks, coalmines, breweries, flour mills, potteries, waterworks and other industries at the end of the eighteenth century. Increasing reliance on this form of power through the nineteenth century produced urban concentrations on Britain's coalfields, including factories emitting smoke, dust and various gases which stimulated the beginnings of concern about industrial pollution.

◀   Figure 6.1
A water-driven grinding
wheel near Sheffield in the
nineteenth century.

◀   Figure 6.2
Steam-powered cutlery
works in Sheffield in the
nineteenth century.

As important sectors of British industry came to be typified by large-scale organisation, so there was a tendency for location to become more specialised: particular areas developed their own industrial character and this was to have important consequences for many aspects of their social circumstances, not least those associated with their environment. Cotton spinning mills and weaving sheds concentrated in the towns of Lancashire, combining with associated engineering works and finishing factories to form vast industrial complexes in cities like Manchester (Figure 6.3). So monstrous were the clouds of smoke 'vomited forth from the numberless chimneys' that in the 1840s the French traveller Leon Faucher compared Manchester to an active volcano (Faucher, 1844). The application of steam power to the chemistry and art of pottery manufacture made the concentration of the industry in North Staffordshire more pronounced. Inside the factories workers inhaled dust from ball and china clays, flint nodules found in deposits of chalk, plaster of Paris (gypsum), calcinated bones, and feldspar derived from igneous rocks. Outside, according to Arlidge (1892), they were exposed to 'an abundant share of coal dust and coal smoke' which was disgorged from the ovens 'in the shape of dense black smoke, intermingled with gases of combustion' (Figure 6.4). The glass industry was akin to pottery manufacture in its reliance on minerals as raw minerals including sand, lime and sodium carbonate (soda ash), and on coal for firing its furnaces. Here, too, the industry became increasingly mechanised and concentrated in the factories of a few large firms. One of these, Pilkingtons, employed about 3000 workers at St Helens in Lancashire around 1900 and was one of the largest glass-manufacturing works in the world. Its complex of sheet and rolled plate glassworks, collieries and brickworks are illustrated in a panorama of 1879 (Figure 6.5).

▲  *Figure 6.3   Steam-powered cotton spinning mills in Manchester, with engineering works alongside on the left and galleried tenements for workers on the right (engraving by Thomas Slack c. 1815).*

▲    Figure 6.4    Josiah Wedgwood's Etruria factory in the North Staffordshire Potteries.

▲    Figure 6.5    Pilkington's glassworks in St Helens.

While primary attention must be concentrated upon industrial sources of air pollution, it should not be forgotten that until relatively recently the domestic hearth was a major contributor to urban air pollution. A city like Glasgow could burn up to 1 million tons of coal a year, most of it on domestic fires though some was used in the production of gas. It was estimated that 95% of London's 'black canopy of smoke' was produced by open fires which discharged 200 tons of soot every day. Small wonder that to Charles Dickens fog had become the 'London particular' producing 'night in the daytime' and blotting out every familiar landmark (Figures 6.6 and 6.7). It is of interest to note that the Hon. F. A. R. Russell, who in 1880 identified a relationship between high smoke concentration and excess

▲  *Figure 6.6*
*A clear view of London and Westminster from Islington about 1820.*

◀  *Figure 6.7*
*A scene near Temple Bar during the fog in 1844.*

mortality in London, later advocated the imposition of a tax on bituminous coal (a fuel which produces a good deal of smoke when burnt) in order to finance a subsidy on anthracite, a solid fuel which generates relatively little smoke.

## 2.2   The synthetic alkali industry in Britain

Somewhat different in its impact both on the environment and on environmental regulation in Britain was the heavy chemicals industry. Originally the chemicals required by the textile and other industries such as glass and soap making (the detergents, bleaches and alkalis) were supplied from natural products using very slow processes. Many of these products were difficult to obtain and in limited supply. Sustained industrial growth would have been impossible without the development of synthetic substitutes at the end of the eighteenth century. There was not enough cheap meadowland or sour milk in all Britain to whiten the cloth of the mechanised Lancashire industry and it would have taken unattainable quantities of human urine to dissolve the grease adhering to the raw wool used in the steam-powered mills of west Yorkshire.

The heavy chemicals industry developed to provide the necessary acids and alkalis. Its significance to the national economy may be judged from the fact that by 1862 the alkali industry was employing 1900 workers and producing finished goods worth £2.5 million.

The production of soda, sulphuric acid and bleaching powder necessitated locations close to large supplies of the two basic inputs of salt and coal. Thus these works became concentrated on Tyneside, Clydeside and Merseyside, locations which in turn were in close association with the industrial consumers of their output, the chemicals industry. Indeed, in 1864, of the 84 soda makers, 38 were in south Lancashire and north Cheshire and 19 on Tyneside.

The mass production of these chemicals also produced damaging waste gases and the industrial complexes producing them were soon dominated by chimneys of great height as part of an effort to disperse the gases (Figure 6.8). In the production of soda, for example, three major pollutants were involved: the hydrochloric acid gas emitted in the initial reaction of salt and sulphuric acid, the hydrogen sulphide from the sulphide waste heaps and the smoke from the large quantities of coal burned.

◄   *Figure 6.8*
*The St Rollox Works in Glasgow manufacturing chlorine bleaching powder (chloride of lime).*

Their combined environmental impact was noxious and destructive but the mix of pollutants and their wide dispersion made it difficult to attribute blame to any particular works. Owners of land damaged by these emissions had little success in seeking redress through actions in nuisance in the civil courts. The first attempt to apply controls by statute, the Alkali Act of 1863, only related to emissions of hydrogen chloride gas from soda and potash works (95% of which had to be condensed). The technology to achieve that reduction in gaseous emissions, essentially a tower in which the hydrogen chloride came in contact with water, had been available for more than 30 years.

## 2.3   Pollution control

### Issues and interests

The transformation of some parts of Britain's countryside into what one historian has called 'the drab lifeless grey of industrial wasteland' (McLeod, 1965) brought unprecedented economic progress to Britain as well as attendant social and environmental ills. Regulation to mitigate these negative features inevitably raised fundamental issues about the nature and purpose of intervention and about its impact on the interests concerned. In very few cases were either the issues or the interests clear cut, and it is for this reason that control over pollution was so controversial and difficult to achieve. This was particularly the case in relation to pollution of the atmosphere – a part of the environment which everyone needed but no-one could own, not even the State. In this section the interests involved and their attitudes to pollution will be discussed before going on to discuss the outcome in two specific cases – the control of smoke and the control of emissions from the alkali industry.

Landowners who made up the agricultural interest, which was still a dominant force in Parliament throughout most of the nineteenth century, were particularly affected by air pollution. In the fields around places like Widnes and St Helens it was said 'the spring never comes hither . . . the foul gases . . . have killed every tree and blade of grass for miles around' (RCNV, 1878). Even in light winds the gases from alkali works could carry for distances of up to nine miles damaging farms 'just as if a fire had gone over them' killing trees and hedges, stunting wheat and putting cattle off their feed. Agricultural rents declined disastrously, and landowners complained that old ancestral seats were being destroyed by pollution from the air. Not surprisingly, agricultural estate owners were active in seeking measures to protect their property and the House of Lords Select Committee on Injury from Noxious Vapours (1862) had among its members five great landlords and was chaired by Lord Derby, the 'king' of Lancashire. Indeed, the 1863 Alkali Act was for many years known as Lord Derby's Act, reflecting the safeguards it achieved for the land-owning class. Even here, however, the issue was scarcely clear cut since the majority of landowners also had extensive interests in the new industrial order, either directly as in Lord Derby's case through the exploitation of coal and other mineral resources from their estates, or indirectly through rising rents from building land in the expanding towns.

The industrialists themselves organised powerful opposition to even the mildest measures to control smoke and other emissions, arguing that the expense and disruption that would be caused would lead to economic stagnation. The Royal Commission on Noxious Vapours (1878) was told

that these vapours were the inevitable and largely unalterable price of
prosperity, since 'half or two-thirds of your income is derived directly or
indirectly from manufacturing industry, and you must take the rough with
the smooth.' Faced with the prospect of shutting up trade and the dire
warnings of the manufacturers, legislators were cautious and even the
great Public Health Act of 1875 required the abatement of smoke from
furnaces only 'as far as practicable, having regard to the nature of the
manufacture or trade . . .' Several industries which had the worst pollution
were exempted, notably the manufacture of coke from coal, brickmaking
and iron-ore smelting, on the grounds that a proven control technology
had yet to be devised.

Where improvements were secured, these proceeded chiefly on the
grounds of more efficient operating of plant. This device protected the
position of manufacturers because it was predicated on the view that it was
not industry itself but rather plant operating below maximum efficiency
and profitability that was the source of pollution problems. Controlling
smoke emissions by more complete combustion could be shown to reduce
consumption of coal. Recovering hydrochloric acid as a marketable
product when it had previously escaped from the chimneys of alkali works
is a striking example of the way in which pollution control measures could
succeed when they were allied to the interests of industry. To use the
currently popular phrase, 'preventing pollution pays'.

Local newspapers and essayists who purported to reflect public
opinion often echoed this enthusiasm for expanding industrial activity
even if it meant valleys studded with factories and chimneys discharging
volumes of gas and smoke close to houses. Their presence was welcomed
by those living nearby, it was said, because 'It is all good for trade, we want
more of it, we find no fault with smoke' (Smith, 1850). Absence of smoke,
by contrast, might well mean 'the quenching of the fire on many a
domestic hearth, want of employment to many a willing labourer, and
want of bread to many an honest family' (Cooke Taylor, 1842). Reliance on
the 'general nose of the public' as the primary line of attack against air
pollution therefore carried little weight and neither individual common law
prosecutions for nuisance nor police powers to report individual offenders
to local magistrates were greatly used.

Although there were a number of vociferous local pressure groups
such as the Manchester Association for the Prevention of Smoke and the
Lancashire and Cheshire Association for Controlling the Escape of Noxious
Vapours, public opinion whether organised or not could not make much
impact on the situation. Unlike other areas of public health reform,
progress on air pollution did not rely on popular passion. This
characteristic may be related to the fact that throughout the nineteenth
century there was little hard evidence that airborne pollutants actually
caused ill health. Even reformers like Sir John Simon (Chief Medical Officer
of the City of London) and the Rev. John Molesworth, vicar of Rochdale
and Chairman of the Manchester Association for the Prevention of Smoke,
could only argue that the effect was indirect. Simon spoke of air pollution
causing not specific illnesses but 'states of unhealth where a man was
constantly below par' (RCNV, 1878), and Molesworth argued that airborne
dirt made people poorer because of the cost of keeping clean so that by this
and other means their tendency to disease was increased.

Given the ambivalence of the growing urban electorate to the presence
of industry and its pollutants, it is not surprising that the local authorities
of the time felt able to take only limited action against it. Indeed, as MPs
pointed out, in the manufacturing districts the manufacturers themselves

not infrequently constituted a large proportion of the sanitary authorities. Many councillors simply appealed to the law of averages, arguing that if their town was no worse than others why should it try to be better? Any action might simply mean industry removing to a more tolerant area causing unemployment, a weakened local tax base and increased demands for poor relief. Though many local authorities included air pollution clauses in local by-laws, nuisance acts and improvement acts, progress was minor and slow. Provisions were weak, fines were low and convictions minimal. Many local acts relied on the principle of practicability and the goodwill of manufacturers. Many excluded the very industries most detrimental to air quality – Leeds, for example, excluded dyeworks, ironworks and brickworks and Liverpool excluded all manufacturers who had merely 'done their best' to prevent the escape of smoke. Despite some claims to have rendered the atmosphere in towns purer, many councils admitted that their record was unimpressive. They could claim neither great rigour nor expertise in dealing with the sources of air pollution, and confidence in them was consequently undermined.

Significant improvements, it seemed, required action by the national government to introduce comprehensive, compulsory legislation backed up by a system of rigorous inspection. Action by Parliament, however, had not only to overcome the opposition of MPs representing manufacturing constituencies, but also had to satisfy the need for legislation that met the criteria of uniformity, legitimacy and practicability while preserving the liberty of the individual.

It is now time to turn to the case of smoke prevention and control of other emissions to see how these requirements were met and the various interests were settled. The regulation of the two had separate and contrasting histories until the mid-twentieth century, after which they began to coalesce. They thus provide interesting examples of alternative methods of air pollution control.

## Smoke control

Until the nineteenth century, individuals suffering specific nuisances from individual works could seek redress only through prosecutions of the perpetrators under common law. With the expansion of industry powered by furnaces generating steam, the problem became one for towns as a whole and the issue was redefined as one of public rather than private nuisance. The emphasis shifted from prosecution to prevention and the police were given powers to compel owners of steam engines to use appliances that had been invented to enable smoke to be consumed more efficiently within furnaces and not discharged to the atmosphere. Pressure for Parliament to become involved in framing statutes to deal with the problem recurred throughout the nineteenth century, but the decades are strewn with unsuccessful attempts to enact the necessary legislation. When legislation did emerge, the interests of manufacturers were largely protected and the initiative was left to local authorities acting within guidelines set by Parliament and anxious not to disrupt economic activity.

In its regular attempts to frame legislation for the abatement of smoke from industrial premises, Parliament looked for specific criteria. MPs continually stressed the need for technically effective means of consuming smoke, for acceptable means of doing so given the nature of particular industrial processes and especially those where furnaces were frequently quenched and restarted, for a workable definition of 'smoke' itself, and for the determination of whether smoke constituted a health hazard or simply a nuisance. Only the first of these conditions proved easy to achieve and in 1843 the Select Committee on Smoke Prevention accepted that suitable techniques were available that were both easy and cheap to install. Acceptability was only achieved, however, by confining mandatory powers to new furnaces, and by exempting altogether those processes where furnaces were used intermittently, such as iron foundries and pottery kilns. The absence of any definition of smoke ensured that several bills were rejected on this ground alone, and successful prosecutions were rare even in cases where statutes allowed actions to be brought. It is no wonder that local authorities who were responsible for bringing polluters to court relied on the deterrent value of their powers while rarely actually invoking them.

From 1853, smoke control acts contained clauses exempting polluters from prosecution if they could demonstrate that they had used the **'best practicable means'** (BPM) to abate smoke. This fundamental principle was to play a vital part in the story of pollution control as will be seen in the discussion of the alkali industry. In the case of smoke control, judgement on this issue lay with local authorities who brought prosecutions and also with local magistrates before whom cases were heard. In these circumstances the inclination was to give defendants the benefit of the doubt, but the system did give individual citizens a direct route for complaints through their local councillors. This local accountability for smoke control persisted through the present century, and was extended in the 1956 Clean Air Act to enable local councils to declare smoke-control areas where only smokeless fuels could be used. The same Act, however, took control away from councils in those industrial premises where there were technical difficulties in achieving smoke abatement. Here control passed to the central inspectorate – the Alkali Inspectorate. This step saw the beginnings of the coalescence of the two systems which has continued to the present day. But it is to an assessment of the legislation relating to the heavy chemicals industry that this chapter now turns.

## Control of emissions from alkali and other scheduled works

From the beginning, powers to control emissions from the heavy chemicals industries took a different route from that pertaining to smoke control. From the outset in 1863, control was placed not in the hands of elected local authorities but in the hands of the **Alkali Inspectorate** – a central body of professional scientific inspectors (chemists or chemical engineers) answerable to Parliament through a Minister of the Crown. Unlike smoke, accurate chemical measurement of hydrogen chloride gas was possible and such data could, if necessary, be cited as evidence in any prosecution of a polluter. Although initially viewed with suspicion by both industry and Parliament, the Inspectorate gradually established itself and pressed for more effective controls over a wider range of polluting industry. In 1874 the Alkali Act was amended to include a statutory emission limit on hydrogen chloride emission (in addition to the 95% condensation requirement) and to require the use of BPM to minimise the discharge of other noxious gases (e.g. smoke and sulphur dioxide) from alkali works.

In 1881 the jurisdiction of the Alkali Inspectorate was extended to include a further 12 types of chemical works listed in a schedule of the amending statute – hence the term 'scheduled works'. Sulphuric acid works were included and these were also subject to fixed limits on acid emission. The use of statutory limits in the early Alkali Acts is interesting for it is often stated that these devices are foreign to the British approach:

this is not strictly true. The type of plant to which the fixed limits applied gradually become obsolete and control was exercised entirely through BPM. It is also necessary to note that the Inspectorate has adopted a practice in which each scheduled process is assigned a 'presumptive limit' for its particular noxious gas; if emissions do not exceed that limit, then adherence to BPM can be presumed. But it must be emphasised that these presumptive limits are non-statutory and are intended to serve as general guidelines, each works being subject to control as the Inspector sees fit.

All works operating scheduled processes had to obtain a certificate of registration to be renewed annually. In the case of new works certification was only granted where the works met the requirements of the Act, but existing works were allowed to continue. In operation, the Alkali Acts relied heavily on the decisions of the Chief Alkali Inspector and his team of local inspectors. Their *modus operandi* is the key to understanding the significance and impact of the legislation.

Various piecemeal amendments were consolidated by the 1906 Alkali etc. Works Regulation Act which remained substantially in force until 1983. It set out specific cases where statutory standards were to be applied to emissions, namely alkali works, hydrochloric acid plant and some sulphuric acid works. It also listed other classes of works which were required to prevent the emissions of 'noxious or offensive gases' and to render those gases that were discharged 'harmless and inoffensive'. In these cases, the measure to be applied in judging the action taken was that it should represent 'the best practicable means'. There is no statutory definition of this phrase nor any explicit formulation attempted by any Chief Inspector. In practice it is settled by local inspectors in collaboration with those who operate plants. Its weakness as a tool for controlling emissions has also been its strength – it has provided an elastic means for reconciling the conflicting interests of the public who suffer the effects of pollution, of manufacturers concerned to operate efficiently and profitably, and of the nation as a whole in its demands for economic growth and full employment.

In determining whether BPM has been used, local inspectors consider not only the current state of technical knowledge but also local conditions and circumstances as well as the financial implications. The methods adopted by the Inspectorate have been those of gradual gentle persuasion, using the intellect and not the 'cane' and rejecting any action that might smack of militancy or 'policemanlike' behaviour. Indeed, so close have relationships between local inspectors and manufacturers been that accusations have been levied that this is a case of poachers turned gamekeepers (Frankel, 1974, p. 15).

In comparison with their influence over sources of smoke, local authorities and their electors have little influence over scheduled works within their area. Local authorities in general have not been able to match the scientific expertise of the Inspectorate and have been forced in practice to leave discretion to them alone, even though the judgements inspectors make are at least as much economic and political as they are technical. However, because the decisions made are *represented* as resting on technical expertise they are difficult to challenge. Little information about decisions or even about the rare cases of prosecution are released to local authorities and still less to the public. Inspectors generally maintain that they have sufficient flexibility to consider local circumstances. The input of local authorities is limited to representation on local liaison committees where these have been established and to the use of planning controls, although these are tightly restricted in the case of works falling under the

Alkali Acts. No local authority may bring a prosecution for nuisance against scheduled works without the express permission of the responsible Minister. These features of the pollution control system established under the Alkali Acts are particularly apparent in areas where there is a concentration of industry and it is to one such example that consideration is given next.

*Activity 2*

Write brief notes comparing and contrasting smoke and gaseous pollution (a) in terms of the hazards posed and (b) in terms of form of regulation. What problems might result from a proposal to construct a new factory producing both smoke and gas pollution in an area near other factories and houses?

# 3    Air pollution in North Cheshire: a case study

## 3.1    Introduction

This case study is based upon an in-depth examination (Miller & Wood, 1983, pp. 35–61) of a highly industrialised area of North Cheshire in which, over the last quarter of a century, a variety of agencies have been involved in mediating between the conflicting interests of industry and environment. Among these are residents' groups, industrial organisations, both tiers of local government, different departments of the central executive and, ultimately, the European Commission. While none of the controversies discussed below attracted the level of national attention which now inevitably attaches to major projects, such as the siting of a nuclear power station, local disputes can prove no less fruitful sources of insight into the way in which competing claims on the environment are resolved within an advanced democracy.

The area of interest (Figure 6.9) lies on the south bank of the Mersey Estuary extending from the mouth of the River Weaver to the east as far as the industrial area of Ellesmere Port to the north-west; the M56 and M53 motorways form the southern and western boundaries. The Stanlow petrochemical complex, covering some 800 hectares, dominates the area, but it is the chemical fertiliser plant to the west at Ince on which attention needs to be focused. Two oil-fired power stations, Ince A and B, complete the industrial land uses in the area of interest, although Ince A was subsequently decommissioned. The villages of Elton and Ince (combined population of about 3000) lie at the centre of the case study area. Just to the east are the larger towns of Helsby (pop. 5000) and Frodsham (11 000) lying beneath Helsby Hill (141 m) and Overton Hill (146 m), two escarpments which form the northern edge of the Mid-Cheshire Ridge and are the most striking natural features in otherwise flat and unimpressive landscape. Originally the area was marshland; Helsby and Frodsham Marshes were

1  Elton village expansion     2  UKF fertiliser plant

▲  *Figure 6.9   The case study area of North Cheshire.*

drained during the second world war and given over to agricultural (dairy) use. Colonies of a number of rare plant species thrive on the peat subsoil of the marshes; these and its importance in terms of migratory wildfowl, especially teal and pintail, led to this part of the estuary being designated a 'site of special scientific interest' by the Nature Conservancy Council.

Thus the area possesses all the necessary ingredients (industry, housing, agriculture, wildlife) for an archetypal conflict over land use, and one made even more acute by the fact the industries present are all sources of atmospheric pollution.

## 3.2   *The fertiliser plant*

The Shell Oil Company's refinery at Stanlow dates from 1923; 40 years later, its subsidiary, Shell Chemicals, entered into a partnership with an American chemical concern with the aim of building a plant capable of producing ammonia using naphtha, a derivative of petroleum. The ammonia was to be used to manufacture more than half a million tonnes of fertiliser (ammonium nitrate) per annum.

The chosen site was some 70 hectares of land owned by Shell Chemicals on Ince Marshes. The planning application, required to develop the land under the 1947 Town and Country Planning Act, was made to Ellesmere Port Borough Council, but was subsequently 'called in' for determination by central government. This was because such a sizeable industrial development represented a departure from the 1958 County Development Plan, which had designated the area as 'white land', i.e.

indicating a presumption that the existing land use (in this case, agriculture) should be retained.

After an uneventful public inquiry in which none of the local authorities involved raised objections to the proposals, the planning inspector's recommendation to grant planning consent was accepted. In addition, the Minister of Housing and Local Government observed in his decision letter of June 1966 that 'it is reasonable on the information available to plan on the assumption that this area [Ince Marshes], with its particular locational advantages for petrochemical industries may all be required eventually for industrial expansion'.

Thus a strong presumption in favour of the industrial development of Ince Marshes was established. At the same time, a property development company was acquiring land in and around the nearby village of Elton with the aim of expanding its population from 300 to 6000. Although the local planning authority was not opposed to the scheme in principle (the expansion of this village had been anticipated in 1961 when the West Cheshire green belt had been drawn up), they thought this figure seemed unacceptably high since it would overload the sewage disposal works which Chester Rural District Council were about to build. To the west, the development reached to within 400 m of the boundary of the Stanlow complex; Ince A power station lay a similar distance to the north, but would partially obscure the fertiliser plant to be constructed about a mile to the north-east.

Since part of the development encroached upon approved 'green belt' and was therefore a departure from the County Development Plan, this proposal was referred, like the fertiliser plant, to central government. However, the Minister chose not to intervene and left the county authorities to decide the matter as they saw fit. Despite certain misgivings of some county planners on the wisdom of residential expansion in an area surrounded by industry, outline planning permission was granted in July 1967. After protracted discussion over the capacity of the sewage disposal works and housing density, agreement was reached between the developers and the rural district council (to whom the determination of detailed planning consent had been devolved) on a development in six phases leading to a target population of 4500 by 1977. The first phase, nearest the refinery, was occupied in 1969 and immediately the new inhabitants began to make complaints about pollution, especially odour.

At the same time, residents of Helsby began to lodge their complaints about the newly commissioned fertiliser plant (Figure 6.10). The works had been beset with problems from the outset. Two attempts to 'start up' the ammonia plant were unsuccessful. Major changes to the plant were necessary following the decision to use natural gas from the North Sea as the basic feedstock, rather than naphtha from Stanlow as originally intended. A serious fire in 1971 further delayed production. In 1973 Shell sold the plant to UKF (Unie van Kunstmestfabrieken), a Dutch company reputed to have far more experience in the operation of this type of chemical plant. The new owners immediately embarked upon a programme of work to improve the plant performance; but by 1975 the annual output of 430 000 tonnes was still only 77% of the target envisaged in 1966.

Despite UKF's best efforts, the plant had acquired a very poor reputation in the locality on account of noise, odour and gaseous emissions. So much so that when planning permission was sought in 1974 to expand the plant, the company was to face far more opposition than its predecessor experienced in 1966, and anodyne statements such as

Figure 6.10
The UKF Fertiliser Plant
viewed from Helsby in 1990.

'ammonia would be completely contained and leaks could not be tolerated for safety reasons' would not again go unchallenged.

The expansion of the fertiliser plant involved development of a further 10 hectares of Ince Marshes which, with its 'white land' designation, meant that the decision on the planning application would be made by the county rather than the district (Ellesmere Port and Neston Borough) council. As part of its structure plan preparation, the county planning department had earlier commissioned Cremer and Warner, leading chemical engineering consultants, to carry out a county-wide survey of the environmental threats posed by the chemical industry. This company was also asked to examine the hazard and pollution potential of the fertiliser plant extension. After a thorough investigation of the proposals, with the full co-operation of UKF management, Cremer and Warner concluded that they could cite no technical grounds for opposing the development, although they did list a series of measures for minimising noise, hazard and air pollution.

While considering their consultants' report, the county planners learned, to their surprise, that the Secretary of State for the Environment had decided to determine this application himself 'in view of the need to consider the environmental implications of further petrochemical plants in this area, and the questions which the application raised about safety and the risks of pollution and noise disturbance.'

This unexpected intervention by the central executive served only to strengthen the resolve of the local authorities to secure what they held to be adequate safeguards should the project be permitted. The planning officers of both Cheshire County and Ellesmere Port Borough Councils were satisfied that the Cremer and Warner report had identified no compelling reason to depart from the long acknowledged planning aim of supporting expansion of the petrochemical industry in this part of the county. But the elected members of both councils rejected their officers' advice. They were opposed to the development and, if the Secretary of State were eventually to grant consent, that consent should carry conditions giving the local planning authorities stringent controls over noise and air pollution.

The particular condition which became a formidable bone of contention required the plant operators to undertake a scheme by which atmospheric emissions of ammonia and particulate matter could be monitored and the data collected made available to the local planning authority. The level of local hostility to the UKF expansion was such that the elected members of the local authorities involved were determined to be able to claim to have an enforceable means of informing themselves of the performance of the plant's pollution control system. However, the management could not accept this demand: the plant involved a 'scheduled process' and the enforcement of 'best practicable means' to minimise atmospheric emissions was the responsibility of HM Alkali and Clean Air Inspectorate. If they were to accede to the planners' requirement on monitoring, they would effectively be serving two masters.

This dispute was to be publicly aired in January 1976 at the public inquiry into the planning application. UKF began by stating the economic *raison d'être* of their proposal: there was a need for Britain to become self-sufficient in ammonia because, although only 15% of demand was met by imports, these came from sources which could no longer be considered reliable following the oil crisis of 1974. Given the projected increase in demand for ammonia and ammonia-based fertiliser, a 350 000 tonne shortfall by 1980 was anticipated. By expanding at Ince, it was possible to exploit the existing rail and road network, as well as the technical expertise which had been acquired by the staff of the works.

On the question of environmental effects, three eminent chemical engineers gave evidence in support of UKF's contention that the design and operating procedures of the proposed plant were such that, even in the event of a major breakdown occurring during the least favourable meteorological conditions, emissions would still pose no conceivable risk to the health of the nearest residents. In his evidence, the District Alkali Inspector was able to concur with this view and held that the design of the proposed plant appeared to be consistent with the 'best practicable means' requirement for this class of scheduled process.

Cheshire's chief environmental health officer was similarly prepared to accept that the proposed plant incorporated state-of-the-art technology to minimise emissions. The insistence upon a monitoring scheme was essentially a political response and one motivated by a desire to reconcile the need for industrial expansion in this part of the county with the hostility of residents who had suffered from the effects of the existing plant's initial problems. In addition, the officers of the local authorities were conscious of their failure at the 1966 inquiry to subject Shell's proposals to a depth of scrutiny appropriate to a development of that scale and pollution potential.

The most determined opposition to the development came from representatives of residents of Helsby and Frodsham. They questioned the company's figures on the projected shortfall of ammonia supply over demand. They also questioned the long-term wisdom of using natural gas as a feedstock, but if there were a need for increased capacity it would be better sited on the east coast close to the gas terminals. Finally, the inquiry was given a brief résumé of the evidence in the scientific literature of the association between cancer and the ingestion of nitrate (ammonium nitrate in the form of a powder or 'prill' was the product of the fertiliser plant and was the particulate pollutant of most concern to the authorities).

The planning inspector recommended that the development be approved. His report reveals his doubts on the legal validity of planning conditions which encroach upon the jurisdiction of the Alkali Inspectorate but, nevertheless, he did suggest that a condition 'requiring the monitoring of chemical emissions from the proposed ammonia plant in a manner to be agreed by the local planning authority' should be appended to any planning consent granted by the Secretary of State. When justifying his conclusion on this vexed question, he commented 'that the powers of the Alkali Inspectorate relate to individual works; in my opinion only planning authorities can control the cumulative build-up of atmospheric pollution in industrial areas.'

Although the Secretary of State accepted his inspector's recommendation that outline planning consent be granted, he was categorically opposed to the imposition of a planning condition requiring the developer to monitor atmospheric emissions. While he was aware of the need for and value in monitoring, he considered it wrong to give planning authorities powers which duplicated those vested in any statutory pollution control agency (in this case, HM Alkali and Clean Air Inspectorate).

Many of the issues raised by the UKF decision were to be debated again some six months later at the 'Examination in Public' of Cheshire's revised structure plan.

## 3.3   *Cheshire county structure plan*

Within the county-wide survey which preceded the written statement of land-use policies, considerable attention was paid to pollution of the atmosphere, water and land. During this period both officers and elected members became conscious of the level of local concern over environmental quality, especially in the north of the county around the concentration of chemical industries on the banks of the Mersey estuary.

There was a clear political need to reconcile this public concern with Cheshire's longstanding policy of assisting the industry, which formed the basis of the local economy and on which a large proportion of the population depended for employment. How could further expansion of the petrochemical industry be achieved without the increased pollution burden posing a threat to public health? The solution proposed by the county planners was, at the time, innovatory and was to be the source of controversy.

In essence, planning consent for any future development would take account of any resulting addition to existing concentrations of air pollution. The pollutants of immediate concern were sulphur dioxide and smoke. If any development was estimated to cause the concentration of either pollutant, in any particular locality, to exceed the target level suggested by the World Health Organisation, then there should be a presumption against granting planning approval for that development. This policy, Cheshire argued, was necessary because although the Alkali Inspectorate was able to exercise control over emissions from the major polluters, their limited statutory powers, namely the enforcement of best practicable means, did not address the problem of the gradual deterioration of atmospheric quality as a result of multiple sources; these might include scheduled processes which individually satisfied the BPM criterion as well as sources (e.g. transport and domestic) which lay outside the Inspectorate's remit.

Among the opponents of the county's proposals were representatives of the Departments of Industry and of the Environment, the Alkali Inspectorate, the Confederation of British Industry as well as a consortium of oil and petrochemical companies with interests in the area. The county's supporters consisted predominantly of amenity groups and residents' associations, some of whom wished to see the proposals extended to include pollutants other than smoke and sulphur dioxide.

The principal objection, expressed most emphatically by the District Alkali Inspector, was that tying industrial development to quantitative air quality standards left no room for discretion and flexibility. In other words, it was incompatible with the pragmatism enshrined in the 'best practicable means' approach. In addition, the proposal would be difficult to enforce because assessing the effect of the emission of an individual source upon the average concentration of that pollutant in the adjacent area would depend upon a mathematical model of atmospheric dispersion. This, in addition to information on the amount and form of the pollutant to be discharged, would also require data on local meteorology and topography, all of which, like the choice of model, could be the subject of lengthy technical debate if challenged during an appeal or any enforcement proceedings.

The policy on air pollution which proved to be uncontentious was that which stated a presumption against sensitive development (housing, in particular) being allowed in areas already subject to nuisance from existing sources of air pollution. The discussion of this policy at the examination in public gave the industrialists an opportunity to express their regret that it had not been observed earlier and more rigorously by those local authorities (especially Ellesmere Port and Cheshire City Councils) which could and should have established 'buffer zones' around the petrochemical complex. In this connection, the chairman of the inquiry considered the decision to allow the expansion of Elton Village to be 'the height of folly' (Figure 6.11).

While the inquiry panel was conscious of the problem faced by Cheshire in attempting to reconcile the needs of its principal industrial base with popular demands for improved environmental quality, it was not

▲   Figure 6.11   The UKF Fertiliser Plant viewed from Elton in 1990.

prepared to endorse its methods. Its recommended policy on air pollution sources contained no reference to quantitative atmospheric quality standards; the 'acceptability of a given level of pollution' was to be gauged by reference to 'available scientific evidence' and 'the advice of the authorities responsible for controlling air pollution'. This recommendation was subsequently accepted by the Department of the Environment and was incorporated in the final version of the structure plan. In defending the rejection of reference to WHO standards, the Secretary of State argued that 'it would be inappropriate for him to approve policies based on standards which have not been accepted nationally and which are likely to give rise to difficulties in implementation'.

This comment, it should be noted, was made in 1979; since 1976 the UK government had been aware of an EEC directive (then in draft) which would make mandatory the attainment throughout the Community of air quality limit values, for sulphur dioxide and suspended particulates, based upon World Health Organisation Report 506 (WHO, 1972). An explanation of this apparent contradiction can no longer be found within a single local case study but requires a far wider discussion of the influence of the European Economic Community on UK environmental legislation.

### Activity 3

Re-read Section 3 and use the particular events described to construct a summary of the powers and procedures involved in the British system of town and country planning.

## 4    Recent approaches to pollution control

### 4.1    The European Community

The various forms of air pollution control discussed hitherto have had, as their primary objective, the safeguarding of public health, with the prevention of nuisance being a subordinate aim. In the 1906 Alkali Act for example, 'best practicable means' was to be used primarily to prevent the emission of noxious or offensive gases and secondly to render 'harmless and inoffensive' any such gases which were nevertheless discharged. The 1956 Clean Air Act, which finally conferred upon local authorities effective powers to limit the discharge of smoke from domestic hearths, was similarly aimed at reducing morbidity from those forms of respiratory disease which were exacerbated by long-term exposure to high concentrations of air pollutants. In the notorious London smog of December 1952, low temperature combined with atmospheric conditions of a persistent low-level inversion layer led to unusually high concentrations of smoke and sulphur dioxide (recorded maxima were 1600 and 3800 $\mu g/m^3$ respectively) for more than four days with an estimated 4000 excess deaths in London, mostly among the elderly and chronically ill, and a further 2000 in the neighbouring counties. Chronic bronchitis was long known as the 'English disease' and descriptions of the 'pea-soup' fogs of the metropolis are commonplace in Victorian novels. But similar pollution episodes were not unknown in continental Europe. In Seraing, situated in a deep gorge in the valley of the River Meuse in Belgium, concentrations of sulphur dioxide in December 1930 are believed to have been even higher than those of London in 1952; but the lower population density meant that the death toll (60) was far lower.

The 1980 directive on air quality can therefore be seen as the result of a common desire among the member states of the European Community to reduce the risk to public health posed by the principal pollutants (smoke and sulphur dioxide) resulting from fossil fuel combustion. But this directive and later analogues concerned with nitrogen dioxide and lead were aimed at ensuring that *concentrations* remained below the levels at which impairment of health was believed to arise. Within western Europe, there remain only isolated pockets where such conditions prevail but to the east, in Poland especially, the absence of controls over emissions has meant that environmental conditions in the industrial areas are comparable to those of mid-Victorian Britain (see Chapter 3, Box 3.1).

The directive (EEC, 1980) on air quality was not the first piece of European legislation to have an influence on the UK pollution control system: earlier controls (which were essentially 'product standards') over the sulphur content of gas oil (a term which includes diesel fuel as well as the oil used in domestic central heating boilers) and the lead content of petrol had been introduced as regulations under the Control of Pollution Act 1974 and following directives in 1975 and 1978. Nor did it raise any novel issues of principle. Differences between the British and European approaches to pollution control had already been well exposed in connection with various directives concerned with water pollution.

At the risk of grossly over-simplifying matters in which national self-interest and administrative convenience were no less influential than scientific or technical considerations, the difference may be summarised thus: the UK government favoured the approach of an **environmental quality objective** (EQO) in which a standard or objective was set for the quality of the pollution-receiving medium and maximum permitted emissions from individual sources were then determined accordingly; the majority of member states advocated a regulatory regime based upon uniform **emission limits** (EL) over individual emissions of a given pollutant to a given medium (i.e. surface water, underground water or the sea). Clearly the two approaches are not entirely unrelated and represent two means to the same end: that is, ensuring that the concentration of any pollutant does not exceed the level at which damage to human health arises. Why then did they become the subject of such contentious debate?

Britain is an island with short fast-flowing rivers. Given its ample rainfall and its numerous upland catchment areas, it is not particularly dependent, especially in the important industrial areas in the north, on riverine or underground sources for drinking water. These natural geographical advantages and the absorptive capacities of tidal estuaries and coastal waters have fostered an adherence to the EQO approach. Here a limit must still be set on any source of discharge such that the particular EQO is not breached, but that limit can take account of the existing quality and the dilutant effect of the receiving waters.

This notion of variation in permitted discharges among equivalent industrial sources was viewed with suspicion in continental Europe. Uniform emission limits are much simpler to administer; they are not

dependent upon assumptions and complex mathematical models of
pollution dispersion, and they are easier to enforce since measurement of
amounts of pollutant at the point of discharge (i.e. the end of a pipe) is far
easier than measurement of very low (parts per billion or less)
concentration after dilution in the receiving medium. When that medium is
a river (the Rhine being the example most commonly cited) which crosses
national boundaries, the inherent merits of a system based on ELs become
more apparent: if an EQO is applied throughout the river, a downstream
state is clearly disadvantaged because its own discharges have to be
reduced to take account of those of its upstream neighbour. If an overall
reduction in total load is necessary (e.g. to save the North Sea fisheries
from extinction) then this is most equitably achieved by imposing a
Community-wide tightening of uniform emission limits on all sources of
the pollutant in question (whether located on the Humber, the Rhine, the
Seine or, for that matter, the Ebro).

It must also be recognised that *uniformity* of control over pollution
sources is the approach most consistent with the original aim of the
European Economic Community to create a 'common market' by the
abolition of barriers to trade: a state whose indifference to pollution
safeguards resulted in lower costs of manufactured goods than those of its
more environmentally concerned competitors could be said to have an
unfair trading advantage.

## 4.2   *Air quality standards*

Having argued the case for environmental quality objectives in regard to
water, the British government's rather unenthusiastic acceptance of the
first attempt to apply the idea to atmospheric pollution is at first sight
rather surprising. In fact the drafts of Directive 80/779 provoked very little
comment in Parliament. The major role in scrutinising the domestic
implication of draft European legislation had been given to a Select
Committee of the House of Lords. It recommended only minor
amendments and made no explicit comments either for or against the
proposal. In 1976 the Royal Commission on Environmental Pollution, some
of whose members also sat on the Lords Committee, had earlier expressed
their opposition to the idea of binding air quality standards (RCEP, 1976).
They were, however, prepared to endorse the concept of non-mandatory
air quality 'objectives', against which the progress of pollution control
policies might be gauged. These objectives should be expressed in terms of
target bands rather than a single figure and with different bands applicable
to urban and rural areas.

The final version of the directive contains both 'guide' values, which
set long-term objectives for concentrations of smoke and sulphur dioxide,
and 'limit' values to be attained throughout the Community by April 1983 if
possible, but by 1993 at the latest. If there then remains any area where the
smoke or sulphur dioxide concentration exceeds the appropriate limit
value then that member state must answer to the European Commission
and possibly the Court of Justice. There is no provision for legal action
against individual sources even though it might be theoretically possible to
attribute a localised violation of a limit value to a particular works, e.g.
power station or steel works. The directive places a binding obligation on
each member state to maintain and improve the quality of its atmosphere;
this requirement represented a major shift in the UK approach which had
hitherto been primarily concerned (as Cheshire's planners had argued)

with the technology of controls at source. Before pursuing this changed approach, it is necessary to make some remarks on the nature of the limit values and the way in which the concentrations are monitored.

The limit values adopted by the European Commission were based upon those suggested earlier by the World Health Organisation. The principal author of these latter standards was Professor Patrick Lawther, an eminent epidemiologist and an internationally acknowledged authority on the effects of air pollution on human health. That the EC values were based largely upon research originating in Britain partly accounts for the relative lack of detailed scrutiny given to them by Parliament. The coupling of the limits for sulphur dioxide and smoke stems from the mistaken but widely held belief in a synergistic effect between these two pollutants. As Professor Lawther explained to the House of Lords Committee: wherever coal or oil is burnt in large quantities, smoke and sulphur dioxide are inevitably emitted simultaneously and thus epidemiological studies of the incidence of respiratory diseases (e.g. chronic bronchitis) cannot distinguish between their separate effects. To claim therefore that their combined effect is worse than the sum of their individual effects (i.e. synergistic) is scientifically meaningless.

One consequence of this fallacy is apparent in Figure 6.12: the two axes represent the mean values of the concentration of smoke and sulphur dioxide in winter; the shaded area indicates compliance with the directive; its shape derives from the fact that, in any location where the smoke level is relatively low (less than 60 $\mu g/m^3$), a less stringent limit value for sulphur dioxide applies. A similar concession applies in the limit values for the annual means.

At any monitoring station it is necessary to install and service apparatus capable of measuring the average value of the smoke and sulphur dioxide concentrations over successive periods of 24 hours. Having collected these daily mean values over one year it is possible to calculate the annual mean (of the 365 daily averages), the mean for the winter months (1 October to 31 March) as well as the 98th percentile; and hence compliance with the various limit values can be judged. The apparatus required is not particularly expensive or sophisticated (Figure 6.13) but a network of such monitoring sites, concentrated upon

▲    Figure 6.12
Graphical representation of smoke and
sulphur dioxide limit values in
EEC Directive 80/779.

▲    Figure 6.13    The apparatus used in the National Survey of Smoke
and Sulphur Dioxide (the pump, gas meter and seven pairs of smoke filter
papers and sulphur dioxide absorption bottles are visible).

urban and industrial centres, is necessary to ensure that localised violations do not arise.

Such an extensive network already existed in the UK well before the air quality directive. Co-ordinated by the Warren Spring Laboratory of the Department of Industry, it had been set up to monitor the implementation of the Clean Air Acts of 1956 and 1968, especially the domestic smoke control programme. At its height the network consisted of more than a thousand sites, most of which were serviced by the technical staff of local authority environmental health departments. As the domestic smoke control programmes began to take effect, and as supplies of (very low sulphur) gas from the North Sea came on stream, so the data revealed a steady decline in average concentrations of sulphur dioxide and an even greater fall in smoke. So much so that by the late 1970s a far smaller network was being contemplated. The advent of the air quality directive has necessitated the retention of some 400 stations.

What the data continue to reveal is that there are residual pockets where ambient concentrations breach, or threaten to breach, the limit values and that these tend to arise in coal mining areas. Since miners receive free allowances of coal, they have a clear reason to resist pressure to convert to smokeless fuel or other less polluting forms of space heating. Their local councillors, who might well be miners themselves, might therefore be disinclined to establish smoke control areas under the Clean Air Act 1956. The Secretary of State is empowered to order a local authority to embark upon smoke control, but this power has never been used and is unlikely to be while it remains central government policy to limit public sector expenditure.

Nevertheless a Department of the Environment Circular (DOE, 1981) refers to the key role of local authority initiatives in the control of domestic sources of smoke 'within a framework based on the concept of an air quality standard'. Without referring directly to Cheshire County Council's initiative, the circular goes on to make clear that the directive does not prohibit the siting, in areas below the limit values, of new plant which might be sources of sulphur dioxide or smoke. It continues: 'Local authorities with areas exceeding the limit values should take into account the need to attain the limit values within a reasonable time when preparing or reviewing structure plans or local plans.' Whether this statement can be seen as a belated vindication of Cheshire's earlier activities is debatable. But with regard to the use of planning conditions (like those which Cheshire sought to have applied to the UKF consent) which refer to scheduled works, the view of the central executive remained unequivocal: 'conditions should not be used to regulate pollution where appropriate specific powers can be used, and in particular planning permission should be refused only where the authority is satisfied that the development in question would result in a significant deterioration of local air quality even after the use of specific powers to control pollution.'

The substance of this Circular should not be seen simply as a riposte to local authorities like Cheshire County Council, which had arguably exceeded its powers in its determination to secure environmental safeguards. It must also be viewed in the context of the commitment of the Conservative administration, which had taken office in 1979, to remove unnecessary bureaucratic restrictions to wealth-creating industrial and commercial activities. But in retrospect, the eighties was a decade in which an increased recognition of the scale of 'environmental problems' and of the urgency of the need to combat them gradually overcame ideological antipathy to state intervention.

## 4.3    Transboundary pollution

During the 1980s, the rationale of Community legislation became focused upon other and ultimately graver threats: acid rain, for example. Acidification of lakes in Scandinavia is not a particularly novel phenomenon nor, for that matter, is the occurrence of localised damage (traditionally attributed to disease or adverse meteorological conditions) to forests. But during the late 1970s the scale of the harm being suffered by the forests of northern and central Europe became apparent, as did the urgent need for action to avert ecological catastrophe.

Since air pollution is no respecter of state frontiers, intervention would have to be internationally co-ordinated with the industrial economies of the European Community leading by example. The 1980s have witnessed a shift in the underlying motivation of the Community's air pollution policies away from a desire to safeguard human health towards a concern for the wider effects on the environment. For example, even though, save for a few isolated pockets, the Community generally conformed to its health-directed air quality limit value for concentrations of sulphur dioxide, total emissions of this pollutant could, perhaps in combination with other chemical species, nevertheless pose a threat to forests, lakes and other parts of the ecosystem of such gravity that substantial cuts in that total become necessary irrespective of any immediately apparent reduction in mortality or morbidity from respiratory illness.

As the decade progressed, acid deposition was joined by other global pollution problems, most notably 'greenhouse' warming and depletion of the ozone layer, as regular items on the agenda of the meetings of environment ministers. Consensus was not to be a common characteristic of these meetings. There were many occasions in which the UK representative was to be found in the minority; the refusal to join the '30% Club' is perhaps the best known. Until very recently the UK had refused to join those nations committed to reducing their sulphur dioxide emissions by 30% between 1980 and 1993. The UK case was that adopting 1980 as the benchmark penalised them unduly since UK emissions had been falling steadily since 1970, and the overall reduction would be more equitably achieved if this were to be taken as the base year. Less well publicised is the UK insistence that action to curb acid deposition should not be concentrated on sulphur dioxide, but should give equal weight to reducing the discharge of oxides of nitrogen (produced when nitrogen reacts with oxygen at the high temperatures which arise in power plants and in vehicle engines). This stance stemmed in part from the belief, advocated by the Central Electricity Generating Board, that the dieback of the German forests could not be attributed to acid deposition alone and was better explained by damage from ozone. On continental Europe, an alternative explanation tended to be preferred. Named the 'Ulrich hypothesis' after its originator, it held that tree damage was attributable to the effect on the roots of toxic aluminium ions made more mobile by increased acidity in the soil.

It should not be assumed that this scientific debate has been resolved or that the differences between the politicians derived solely from conflicting advice from their respective scientific advisers; national self-interest was only thinly disguised. But this should be seen as yet another occasion when political action, this time at the supra-national level, cannot await unanimity among scientists.

An awareness of the vast areas of uncertainty in scientific understanding of the complexities of the long-term effects of anthropogenic pollution on the ecosystem prompted the development in West Germany of the **Vorsorgeprinzip**. The usual translation (prevention principle) does scant justice to a sophisticated concept which seeks to set pollution control within the wider context of environmental management. Discharges should be reduced as far as technology permits for, even if such control represents an economically inefficient distribution of resources and cannot be justified in terms of immediate health benefits, the prospect of their causing as yet unsuspected and irreversible detriment to the ecosystem demands that it is better to err on the side of caution. *Vorsorge* goes beyond the presumption enunciated in the Community's Second Action Programme on the Environment of 1977 in favour of regulating pollution at source rather than remedial measures applied in the environment. The level of regulation is usually linked to some notion of economic feasibility but, in theory at least, *Vorsorge* takes precedence over this constraint.

To what extent the *Vorsorgeprinzip* will underpin the future development of Community policy remains to be seen. But there is little doubt that Directive 84/360 on combating air pollution from industrial plants stems predominantly from West Germany's determination to secure decisive intervention with regard to acid deposition. This Framework Directive (EEC, 1984) essentially requires that industrial processes which involve emission of pollution to the atmosphere shall be required to satisfy statutory prior authorisation procedures before being permitted to operate. A series of 'daughter directives' are anticipated which will give specific details to be observed in the authorisation for particular classes of processes, but the Framework Directive specifies the following general conditions which must apply before an authorisation can be made:

1    All appropriate preventative measures against air pollution must be taken utilising the principle of 'best available technology not entailing excessive cost' (**BATNEEC**).

2    Any emission must not create 'significant' air pollution in the sense that it results in demonstrable additional damage to human health, building fabric or the viability of ecosystems.

3    Emission limits values must not be exceeded and air limit values must be taken into account.

This directive seeks to ensure that harmonised and stringent powers to regulate the major sources (power plants, minerals processing, metals production, chemicals manufacture, waste incineration) of air pollution (especially sulphur dioxide and nitrogen oxides but also asbestos) exist throughout the Community. Its impact on the UK needs to be examined, but first it is necessary to explain yet another acronym – BPEO.

## 4.4    *Integrated pollution control*

The fifth report of the Royal Commission on Environmental Pollution (RCEP, 1976), published in 1976, represented an influential and authoritative review of the UK system of air pollution regulation which was then in force, i.e. before the full consequences of UK membership of the EEC took effect. Reference has already been made to RCEP's cautious endorsement of non-statutory air quality guidelines and its opposition to the use of planning powers which encroached upon the Alkali Inspectorate's jurisdiction. Two of its other recommendations have subsequently proved to be of more lasting relevance.

First, the Royal Commission supported the demand by local authorities for effective powers of 'prior control' over those processes which were not scheduled under the Alkali Act 1906, but which were, nevertheless, sources of air pollution. When pollution from such sources amounted to nuisance (especially odour from offensive trade premises) then local authorities were empowered to prosecute offenders under the Public Health Acts. But retrospective action of this sort was generally recognised to be insufficient; what was required was anticipatory control where such sources should be allowed to commence operation only if the local authority were satisfied that adequate safeguards had been observed to prevent nuisance arising.

Secondly and more importantly, the Commission argued that separate legislative controls over pollution of land, the atmosphere and water had arisen through historical accident, had persisted through administrative inertia and ignored current understanding of the interconnectedness of the environment. As an example of a multi-media pollution problem, consider the following: the practice of landfilling hazardous wastes poses a threat to underground waters, as well as denying that land for other uses; a decision to incinerate such wastes entails extra emission to the atmosphere, and reducing this burden by the use of flue gas cleaning systems (wet scrubbers) in turn entails treatment before any scrubber liquor can be discharged to surface water. As originally conceived, **'best practicable environmental option'** (BPEO) represented an extension of the traditional BPM approach to processes where pollution control involves trade-off between different receiving media. It would be exercised by a small, but well qualified, body of scientists and engineers, Her Majesty's Pollution Inspectorate, with the expertise to identify, and the legal powers to insist upon, the disposal option which posed the least threat to the environment as a whole while remaining cost effective. The government took five years to respond to the Commission's proposals and then it saw BPEO as unnecessary and argued there was 'probably not a large number of situations in which major choices exist in practice'(DOE, 1982). It did, however, agree with the Commission that a comprehensive review of air pollution legislation should be carried out.

Before that review took place, interest in the concept of **integrated pollution control** had increased in Europe; the third Community Action Programme on the Environment in 1983 had as one of its priorities the prevention of pollution, but *not* by its transfer to another medium. The year 1984 then saw the adoption of the Framework Directive and, in Britain, the publication of the tenth report (RCEP, 1984) of the Royal Commission on Environmental Pollution in which this body reiterated its call for BPEO to be incorporated into national legislation. Thus by 1986 when the review had reached the consultation stage, there were many issues on which local authorities, industrial and environmental organisations and others were able to comment.

Before the results of this consultation procedure were announced, the government declared in 1987 its belated conversion to the integrated approach by amalgamating the pollution control agencies – the Industrial Air Pollution Inspectorate (the successor to the Alkali Inspectorate), the Hazardous Wastes Inspectorate, the Radiochemical Inspectorate and the Water Inspectorate (three specialised agencies within the DOE) – to form **Her Majesty's Inspectorate of Pollution** (HMIP). The immediate task of HMIP was to continue the statutory and advisory roles of its constituent inspectorates but it also had a brief to further the eventual implementation of BPEO.

## 4.5  *The Environmental Protection Bill 1989*

State intervention in the environment can never be understood simply by reference to the wording of legislation. Only after laws have been implemented and enforced for some time can their true effectiveness be gauged. As has been noted, the central concept of the Alkali Acts was never defined in the statutes but evolved gradually, its interpretation and development falling to successive Chief Inspectors. The Control of Pollution Act 1974 was heralded by the government of the day as a landmark in environmental regulation at the time of its introduction. But in the event, Part II of this Act, concerned with discharges to rivers, sewers and coastal waters, had barely been implemented before it was repealed by the Water Act of 1989. When referring to the 1989 Environmental Protection Bill the point becomes self-evident. At the time of writing (July 1990), the Bill has yet to complete its passage through Parliament and discussion must necessarily be confined to its drafters' intentions in so far as these may be inferred from its numerous clauses.

Whether the 'Green Bill', as it has become labelled, will eventually live up to its proponents' claim to be a watershed in UK environmental management remains to be seen, but it is undeniably an ambitious and intriguing mixture of old and new, foreign and domestic influences. Part I might best be summarised as an attempt to develop a distinctly British model of 'integrated pollution control' in a way that allows the obligations of various EC directives to be fulfilled. It included six principles:

1   prior authorisation;

2   environmental quality objectives;

3   emission limits;

4   BATNEEC, the use of 'best available technology not entailing excessive costs';

5   the use of 'best practicable environmental option' (BPEO) for multi-media pollution problems;

6   a 'residual duty' to apply BATNEEC to any aspect of a polluting process not covered by an explicit condition.

Q   Which of these principles are continuations of existing British approaches and which embody new approaches to meet European obligations, as discussed earlier in this section?

A   1   *prior authorisation*: although used in some parts of the British system since the mid nineteenth century, it was not universal (as was recognised by RCEP in 1976). It has been an EC obligation since 1984.

2   *environmental quality objectives*: although welcomed by the UK as regards water pollution, EQOs were resisted for air pollution, except as a broad target. In fact the Bill will allow the Secretary of State to make EC standards binding in the UK.

3   *emission limits*: this is another EC principle and contrasts strongly with previous UK views of a negotiated BPM.

4   *BATNEEC*: this is effectively an acceptance of the prevention principle originally articulated in Germany, though in British usage the T means techniques rather than technology.

5   *BPEO for multi media*: an extension of BPM into situations where more than one medium is affected. Part of the RCEP's concept of integrated pollution management.

6    *residual duty of BATNEEC*: the idea of a residual duty is a continuation of the British tradition of intervening at any stage of a process and not just over the nature of discharges.

The Bill empowers the Secretary of State to make regulations not only specifying the processes to be subject to the new procedures, but also listing the pollutants to be controlled. From various papers issued for consultation before the Bill was published, it may be inferred that Part I of the new Act when finally approved will apply to:

1    sources of industrial air pollution falling within the terms of the Framework Directive (EEC Directive 84/360; EEC, 1984);

2    processes emitting substances (e.g. mercury and cadmium compounds, organohalogen and organophosphorus compounds) which by virtue of their persistence, accumulation in food chains, and toxicity, are to be subject to stringent control under EEC Directive 76/464 (Dangerous Substances in Water); EEC, 1976;

3    processes which give rise to significant amounts of solid wastes which are toxic or otherwise hazardous to health or the environment.

The local authorities are to gain an increased role in controlling the less dangerous (metallurgical and mineral works) sources of air pollution, but it is Her Majesty's Inspectorate of Pollution to whom the primary enforcement responsibilities will fall. It is this body which will determine applications for authorisation which operators of prescribed processes must secure before commencing operation (i.e. prior authorisation). And it is in the anticipated scope of the conditions of such an authorisation that the mixture of influences is most apparent.

Clause 6(2) of the Bill, as originally drafted, enables conditions to be imposed which have the primary objective of ensuring that BATNEEC is used to prevent the release of prescribed substances into air or water, to minimise releases where total prevention is not practicable, and to render harmless any other substances released.

Conditions can also be used to secure compliance with any relevant emission limits, quality objectives or any other obligation on the UK under Community Treaties or international law (e.g. the Helsinki Convention on substances which cause depletion of stratospheric ozone). Clause 2 of the Bill empowers the Secretary of State to make regulations which would make any EC emission limit or environmental quality standard immediately enforceable under UK law.

It is of interest to note that BATNEEC as understood by the European Community (i.e. best available *technology* not entailing excessive cost) has been replaced in the Bill by the phrase 'best available *techniques* not entailing excessive cost'. The change is not merely semantic for 'techniques' has a wider connotation than 'technology' and encompasses plant design, maintenance procedures and management practices, as well as pollution control devices. The choice of words is perhaps a reflection of a reluctance to bid a final farewell to the ethos of BPM.

Similarly the residual duty (Clause 6(4)), imposing an implicit condition in all authorisations to use BATNEEC in any aspect of the process not covered by specific conditions, can be traced to the British tradition of seeking comprehensive controls over all stages of an industrial process not simply at the point of discharge.

But the requirement which is likely to prove the most contentious is in Clause 6(7): to have regard to the 'best practicable environmental option' in applying BATNEEC to any process involving releases of pollution into more than one environmental medium. BPEO, like its antecedent, BPM, is not defined in the Bill and hitherto has proved no less opaque (and no easier to translate) to our European partners. They will no doubt be anxious to see how this latest concept will develop in practice and whether it will prove to be consistent with *Vorsorge* and the gradual reduction in emissions which that principle requires. They will therefore be looking closely not only at the pilot studies of BPEO which HMIP have commissioned, but also at that body's success in recruiting and retaining high-calibre staff to execute its expanded duties (which include the preparation of advice notes on BATNEEC for those processes which are now subject to control by local authorities).

*Activity 4*

Look out for discussions of the operation of the Environmental Protection Act and reactions of the EC to it. How effective is its combination of British and European approaches?

## 5   Conclusions

BPEO might be seen as the latest refinement of the BPM precept, which originated as a defence available to emitters of dark smoke from furnaces and subsequently evolved into the principal mechanism for exercising anticipatory controls over the more significant sources of atmospheric pollution. But, like its antecedent, BPEO remains a form of state intervention which can be labelled 'direct regulation': it will be incorporated into the conditions of certain authorisations to discharge pollution into the environment. Violation of such conditions renders the discharger liable to penalties which can involve imprisonment. The Alkali Inspectorate was traditionally very loath to resort to prosecution, but whether its successor, HMIP, can maintain that tradition is debatable. In this connection it is of interest to note the apparent readiness of the National Rivers Authority (the body which following privatisation of the water industry is responsible for protecting surface water quality) to prosecute polluters of rivers. Its first prosecution – brought early in 1990 against Shell UK for allowing a 300 000 gallon spillage of oil into the River Mersey – resulted in a £1 million fine plus costs, the highest ever for a river pollution incident. Nevertheless, BPEO and, for that matter, the Environmental Protection Bill as a whole remain yet another addition to UK criminal law and in that respect they might be seen as somewhat outmoded. This is not to suggest that a specialist central inspectorate enforcing technological control over the important pollution sources is no longer necessary. This observation stems more from a recognition of the merit of, as yet untried, alternative approaches to environmental management and of the changed nature of the 'pollution problem'.

*Q*   Refer back to the conclusion of Chapter 4. Do those approaches indicate any forms of environmental policy which would complement regulation?

*A*   Alteration of economic costs through taxation is clearly another route.

Attention in this chapter has concentrated upon the role of central and local government bodies in regulating pollution, and it is easy to overlook the possibility that improvements in environmental quality can arise independently of the efforts of either. A gradual transition to clean fuels by both industry and householders had begun well before the Clean Air Act of 1956 was passed. Since then, the discovery of natural gas (with a very low sulphur content) in the North Sea together with the recession of the 1980s, which saw the demise of our heavy industrial base and a greater reliance on foreign imports of iron and steel, have enabled the long-term decline in emissions of smoke from domestic and industrial sources to be maintained. But if the nature of our industrial base has changed, the need for electricity has not, and indeed has risen. Reduction of acid rain has replaced elimination of smogs as the primary objective of air pollution policy, and attention has in consequence moved away from reducing the pockets of high concentration to a concern to reduce total emissions.

This change in the perception of the problem may explain the apparent willingness of the Department of the Environment to consider the merits of alternative approaches, which can be labelled **'indirect regulation'**. While economists have written endlessly on the pros and cons of pollution taxes, governments have generally shown little enthusiasm for the idea. As was noted earlier, F. A. Russell's simple proposal to boost the sale of anthracite by means of a subsidy raised by a tax on more smoky forms of coal fell on deaf ears. But a century later, the Chancellor of the Exchequer, in one of few instances of the application of economic controls of pollution, reduced the excise duty payable on unleaded petrol relative to that levied on petrol containing lead compounds which are ultimately emitted to the atmosphere. The idea of taxing the carbon content of fuels has also been mooted as a way of reducing total emissions of carbon dioxide and encouraging the use of renewable energy sources and energy conservation.

But it could be argued that the more astute industrialists have needed neither tax incentives nor direct regulation by government to induce them to convert to products and processes which are least damaging to the environment. Regardless of any ethical issues, there are many instances in which such a conversion has resulted in an immediate reduction in costs (pollution prevention pays). For instance, the most recent technology for reducing smelter discharges to the atmosphere has resulted in reduced running costs. Green consumerism represents another contemporary environmental movement which has arisen quite independently of any governmental intervention and which has also proven profitable for the more enlightened industrialists.

Whether such responses can make a lasting and significant contribution is doubtful. There is a growing recognition among the scientific community that the scale of our ecological problems is such that discussion of the short term profitability or practicability of pollution controls merely serves to delay the advent of truly effective counter-measures. What is required goes far beyond the traditional system of consents, inspections and technical advice exercised by a small body of professional civil servants. It requires an environmental dimension to be incorporated into all policies (industry, energy, transport). It also requires both politicians and the public to cease to delude themselves that the ecological catastrophe can be averted without infringing individual liberty.

Because the adoption of more far-reaching policies to tackle more deep-seated problems will require widespread public consent, if not strong public pressure, the next chapter looks at issues which have stimulated public concern. Two of these were provided by the chemical industry itself – fear of catastrophic failure and concern about toxic waste. In discussing these issues, it becomes necessary to confront a question which has been implicit in this chapter: how are issues put on to the political agenda and, once there, how are decisions taken about how they should be handled?

*Q*   From what has been said here, how would you expect these questions to be answered?

*A*   Much of the account here has suggested that public concern is reflected by local and national government and decisions taken which dispassionately weigh the interests of industry against those of a wider public. This is in effect a **pluralist** account of decision-making. However, other factors have been mentioned – notably that government has often been unwilling to press industry too hard and that technical experts seem to have been used to legitimise decisions made in the light of economic as well as technical factors. These suggest that decision-making may not be as straightforward as is sometimes imagined.

## References

ARLIDGE, J. T. (1892) *The Hygiene Diseases and Mortality of Occupations.*

COOKE TAYLOR, W. (1842) *Notes on a Tour in the Manufacturing Districts of Lancashire.*

DEPARTMENT OF THE ENVIRONMENT (DOE) (1981) *Clean Air: Circular 11/81,* HMSO, London.

DEPARTMENT OF THE ENVIRONMENT (DOE) (1982) *Air Pollution Control,* Pollution Paper 18, HMSO, London.

EUROPEAN ECONOMIC COMMUNITY (EEC) (1976) *Directive on pollution caused by certain dangerous substances discharged into the aquatic environment of the Community,* EEC Directive 76/464, Official Journal of the European Community L129 18.5.76.

EUROPEAN ECONOMIC COMMUNITY (EEC) (1980) *Directive on air quality limit values and guide values for sulphur dioxide and suspended particulates,* EEC Directive 80/779, Official Journal of the European Community L229 30.8.90.

EUROPEAN ECONOMIC COMMUNITY (EEC) (1984) *Directive on combating of air pollution from industrial plants,* EEC Directive 84/360, Official Journal of the European Community L188 16.7.84.

FAUCHER, L. (1844) *Manchester in 1844: its present condition and future prospects.*

FRANKEL, M. (1974) *The Alkali Inspectorate,* The Control of Industrial Air Pollution Social Audit, London.

MCLEOD, R. M. (1965) The Alkali Acts Administration 1863–84: the emergence of the civil scientist, *Victorian Studies,* **9(2),** 87.

MILLER, C. E. & WOOD, C. M. (1983) *Planning and Pollution,* Oxford University Press, Oxford.

ROYAL COMMISSION ON ENVIRONMENTAL POLLUTION (RCEP) (1976) *Fifth Report: Air Pollution Control: An Integrated Approach,* Cmnd 6371, HMSO, London.

ROYAL COMMISSION ON ENVIRONMENTAL POLLUTION (RCEP) (1984) *Tenth Report: Tackling Pollution – Experience and Prospects*, Cmnd 9149, HMSO, London.

ROYAL COMMISSION ON NOXIOUS VAPOURS (RCNV) (1878) *Minutes of Evidence*.

SMITH, ST. J. (ed.) (1850) *Public Health Act, Report to the General Board of Health on Darlington*.

WORLD HEALTH ORGANISATION (WHO) (1972) *Air Quality Criteria and Guides for Urban Air Pollutants*, Technical Report Series No. 506, WHO, Geneva.

## Further reading

ASHBY, E. & ANDERSON, M. (1981) *The Politics of Clean Air*, Oxford University Press, Oxford.

BRIMBLECOMBE, P. (1987) *The Big Smoke*, Methuen, London.

HAIGH, N. (1987) *EEC Environmental Policy and Britain*, 2nd edition, Longman, London.

SANDBACH, F. (1982) *Principles of Pollution Control*, Longman, London.

# Answers to Activities

*Activity 1*

Generally the *impact* of air pollution is much greater because it occurs in the milieu in which people live. The quality of the air people breathe must have an effect on their health as well as their general well-being. Since industrial and manufacturing plant is usually cheek by jowl with concentrations of population, the discharge of air pollutants is likely to be all the more significant. This is, of course, not to disregard their damaging impact on local ecosystems, or their contribution to the wider problems caused by acid rain, for example.

By contrast, it is only in quite exceptional circumstances that there have been cases of people contracting diseases by contact with heavily polluted water (usually swimmers), so that the main concern of most human beings is with the purity of drinking water. Rivers are frequently used for the disposal of industrial effluents which, by their nature, may be toxic in themselves, may become toxic as a result of the pH of the receiving water body, may change the pH values of the water, or, because of their fine particle content, alter the suitability of the water as a medium for sustaining biota – all with results like those discussed in Chapter 3, Section 4. Moreover, the disposal of organic material from a manufacturing process can provide food for bacterial micro-organisms, which may increase in their numbers and use up most of the available oxygen in the water, which in turn can have adverse effects on aquatic life. However, the location of industry is usually on the lower reaches of rivers, and water for drinking is frequently extracted closer to the headwaters, so human problems are likely to be minimised. Only rarely does water pollution occur on such a scale as to present a danger to life. Events of this kind are usually the result of accidental spillage of large quantities of highly toxic chemicals. One of the most spectacular of these was the River Rhine incident of 1969 in which a massive discharge of insecticide resulted in the poisoning of forty million fish in 400 km of its length upstream from Rotterdam.

## Activity 2

Smoke is (a) hard to define precisely, and hence to quantify; (b) has been regulated by local authorities, but exempted plants which used best practical means to minimise emissions. Gas emissions, initially hydrogen chloride and sulphur dioxide, are (a) more harmful to vegetation and people than smoke, but chemically more easily detectable. They are (b) regulated by the Alkali Inspectorate, a body of expert chemists employed by central government, but obliged to consider economic as well as technical feasibility.

The existence of two forms of regulation poses obvious possibilities of conflict of view. A proposal for a new factory raises the possibility of a plant which is viewed as satisfactory in itself, but which raises the level of pollution in its neighbourhood to intolerable levels. These problems actually occurred in Cheshire in the 1960s and 70s.

## Activity 3

1    The county council must prepare and periodically revise a development plan, later called a structure plan, allocating land for different uses, in the light of population, economic and technical change. This document must be approved by the Secretary of State for the Environment.

2    Applications for planning permission for new developments:

●    are considered by the district council if consistent with the structure plan;

●    are considered by the county council if not;

●    can be 'called in' by the ministry if it believes that there are reasons for considering it at the centre.

3    Applications which are 'called in' may be referred to a public inquiry, where an Inspector hears evidence from interested parties (from industry, local authorities, pressure groups and members of the public).

4    Final decisions come from the Secretary of State for the Environment (formerly the Minister for Housing and Local Government) who may or may not decide in favour of the conclusions reached by the Inspector.

*NB*   In the examples discussed, there appears to be a division between the industry, the Alkali Inspectorate and expert consultants (who all agreed that the proposed plant would use BPM and therefore be acceptable) and the local public, including their elected representatives, who were all too aware of local impacts and who wanted improvements to environmental quality. Their appeal to WHO standards anticipated the review of British practices which became necessary as a result of growing environmental awareness in the EC.

# 1 Introduction

The aim of this chapter is to extend the analysis of the way that decisions are taken about environmental hazards from the chemical industry. Whereas the previous chapter focused on the chronic problems of air and water pollution from chemical plants and their regulation, this chapter focuses on two kinds of hazard which are less readily apparent: the risk of catastrophic accidents which may endanger life and property outside the plant as well as inside, and the hazards which arise from the disposal of toxic waste. These issues are used to extend the previous chapter's analysis of the development of a regulatory framework, and in particular to clarify three sets of issues:

1 the balance of power between the state and industrial corporations;

2 the role of scientific and technical experts within the decision-making process;

3 the role of the public and of environmental pressure groups in setting the political agenda.

An examination of conflicts surrounding chemical plants reveals two contrasting viewpoints. On the one hand there is the supposedly objective (and therefore rational) process whereby the nature and extent of the risks posed by a given activity are calculated, and on the other hand there is the public perception of such risks and the associated political manifestation of the issues. The weight given by decision makers to each of these approaches to judging risk within the chemicals industry is similar to the balance given in a wide range of environmental issues. This chapter will explore this balance with regard to two elements of the chemicals industry, namely the production and storage of hazardous chemicals at 'major hazard' sites within the Canvey Island area in Essex, and the more general issue surrounding the disposal of hazardous waste.

These problems have been selected to illustrate the second viewpoint. Such hazards are probably less environmentally damaging than routine discharges to air and water but they have aroused greater public concern. Much of this concern has been stimulated by accidents such as the one at Flixborough (UK) in 1974 and the one at Bhopal (India) in 1984, or by the discovery of toxic wastes emerging from dumps, as occurred at Love Canal (USA) in 1978. These events show that while some processes seem contained within the boundary fence of the plant, they can create hazards well beyond it.

# 2   Major hazards

## 2.1   The nature of the risk

The term major hazard is notoriously difficult to define. The term was used
by the Robens Committee as early as 1972 and by HM Chief Inspector of
Factories in 1973, and yet ten years later there was still no adequate,
formally accepted definition of the term. The Advisory Committee on
Major Hazards (ACMH), set up as a direct result of the Flixborough
explosion, applied itself to a study of these installations and has succeeded
in focusing attention on the main hazards that they pose to society (Health
and Safety Commission, 1976, 1979, 1984). The work of the ACMH with
respect to 'major hazards' used the following terms of reference:

> To identify types of installations (excluding nuclear installations)
> which have the potential to present major hazards to employees or to
> the public or the environment, and to advise on measures of control
> appropriate to the nature and degree of hazard.

Because of the wide-ranging nature of these terms, the Committee felt that
it was unable to cover the complete range of such hazards. Recognising its
limitations it decided to focus attention on installations which presented
the greatest risks to the public from catastrophic fire, explosion and toxic
release, although it did recognise that the use of pipelines and inter-site
product transportation also gave cause for concern (Health and Safety
Commission, 1976). Of the three main types of hazard examined by the
Advisory Committee, and listed in Table 7.1, it appears that catastrophic
fire is the most frequent, followed by explosion (which often results in a
conflagration taking place) and then toxic release. By far the greatest
potential for fatalities occurs from the release of toxic gases, due to their
hazard range. Fortunately, the frequency of fatal release for such incidents
is low.

The hazard range of the three events is illustrated in Figure 7.1. Here it
can be seen that fire is generally limited to the effects of thermal radiation,
unless the vapour cloud drifts prior to ignition, when fire could be a major
cause of death. Explosions have an increased hazard range over fire. This is
due to the extent of the blast wave and the dispersion of debris that can
result from the detonation. By far the greatest hazard range is held by toxic
gases as they have the potential to drift over long distances before they
disperse to harmless levels. In all cases the range over which damage can
occur will be largely dependent on the amount of materials involved in the
release and the mode of storage used. Pressurised storage, if breached, will
lead to the faster formation of a toxic/flammable cloud than would a release
of material from a refrigerated storage failure.

## 2.2   The control of major hazard sites

The control of major hazard sites displays the duality that was evident in
the discussion in Chapter 6 of the control of pollution emissions from
factories. Prior to 1974 major hazard sites were under the control of the
Alkali Inspectorate in terms of their day-to-day operations, once planning
permission had been obtained from local authorities. However, evidence

Table 7.1   Main types of hazard event

| Group | Hazard type |
|-------|-------------|
| Catastrophic fire | Pool fire |
| | Fireball |
| | Firestorm |
| | Burning vapour clouds |
| Explosion hazards | Conventional explosives |
| | Unconfined vapour cloud explosion |
| | Confined vapour cloud explosion |
| | Boiling liquid expanding vapour explosion (BLEVE) |
| Toxic releases | Pressurised/refrigerated release |
| | Acute/chronic toxicity |

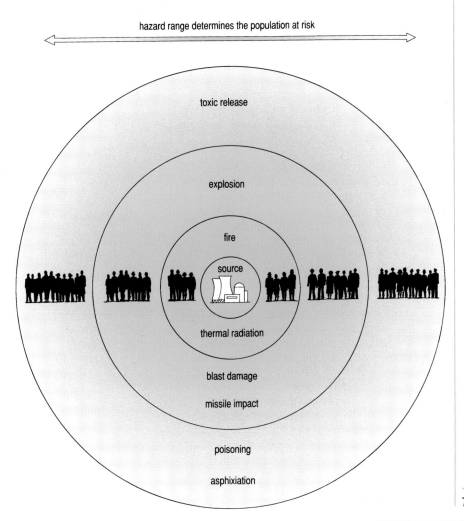

Figure 7.1
The concept of hazard range.

suggests that there were up to nine different statutes concerned with safety and health at work which were administered by five government departments and as many central inspectorates (for a detailed criticism see Robens Committee, 1972). The introduction of the Health and Safety at Work Act (HASAW Act) in 1974 was an attempt to streamline this bureaucracy and was unique in that it provided for the health, safety and welfare of those not actively involved in the industrial process but who might simply be affected by it.

In 1977, following accidents at Beek in the Netherlands (1975), Manfredonia and Seveso in Italy (both 1976), the European Community agreed that there was a need to develop a standardised approach to the control of such installations. This resulted in the publication of a draft directive in 1979 which set out an inventory-based means of control, in a way similar to that proposed by the Health and Safety Commission in 1978. As in the case of the UK, the basis of control lay in the selection of the most hazardous complexes so that available resources could be most effectively utilised.

At present a well-developed regulatory framework is in place for the control of major hazards. These regulations include the Notification of Installations Handling Hazardous Substances (NIHHS) Regulations (1982) and the Control of Industrial Major Accident Hazards (CIMAH) Regulations (1984). Under the NIHHS Regulations the manufacturer must notify the Health and Safety Executive (HSE) if the site stores materials in excess of the quantities listed in the schedule. This notification includes details of the plant's activities and its size, the quantities stored and the local planning authority that has responsibility for development control around the site. The second phase in this control strategy, carried out under the CIMAH legislation, involves the requirement for a survey, more commonly termed a safety case, to be carried out at those sites which store very large inventories of hazardous materials and to be subsequently submitted to the HSE for validation. In addition to the production of a safety case, the manufacturer would also have to formulate an off-site emergency plan and provide information to anyone likely to be affected by the company's industrial operations. This requirement for the release of information was quite unique and was certainly bitterly opposed by the chemical industry, which has always been keen to restrict information dissemination on the grounds of 'commercial confidentiality'.

The CIMAH regulations aim to highlight those sites which present the greatest potential risk to local publics. The installations identified under CIMAH are termed top-tier sites and can be further subdivided into large inventory top-tier sites and small inventory top-tier sites. There are approximately 206 of the former (which correspond to the list released by the HSE in 1986) and over 1000 of the latter. Such a categorisation represents an attempt by the HSE to focus their resources on those sites which represent the greatest potential for catastrophe, determined by the inventories of hazardous materials held in store at the site. It is these large inventory top-tier sites which have been forced to release information to the local public surrounding the plant. Such information concerns the nature of the risks that local residents face and the action that should be taken in the event of an accident. The importance of the CIMAH legislation is that it now allows the public access to information to which they would hitherto have had no rights. However, the degree of information released has proved, in many cases, to have been the minimum required under the regulations and may not have contributed much to developing effective dialogue concerning the nature of the problem.

As already stated, local authorities also have a role to play in determining the location of a hazardous industry in relation to competing land uses and this forms the second strand of major hazard control policy in the UK. At the heart of this policy lies the 1947 Town and Country Planning Act as amended in 1971. This, along with two circulars from the Department of the Environment, offers advice on the strategies to be adopted for major hazard sites. Despite such powers, and the obvious benefits that can accrue from the separation of conflicting land uses, policy makers have stated their reservations about the use of planning to control hazardous industry.

The first of these doubts relates to the argument (referred to in Chapter 6, Section 3.2) that planners cannot effectively exert any control once a plant is in operation. Permission can in theory be revoked in exceptional circumstances; indeed, revocation was a course of action that was seriously considered by the local authority at Canvey Island, as will be seen later. However, this power of revocation is rarely used due to the considerable compensation payments that often have to be made. The second criticism relates to the level of technical competence held by most local authorities to deal with hazard issues. Although this can be overcome by seeking technical advice from the HSE, this procedure has often proved inadequate, and some authorities (notably Cheshire County Council) have attempted to develop their own expertise or have brought in consultants. The main problems facing local and county authorities with regard to major hazard sites are the sheer weight of the 'portfolio of hazards' that they have to face along with the need to balance economic prosperity with increased public safety.

The ultimate aim of the CIMAH Regulations is to provide the HSE, and through them the local planning authorities, with sufficient risk-analytical data on which to base their control strategy. The industrial corporations, with their more complete information about plant and processes, are able to influence decisions by presenting a more structured case than are the other groups. The regulatory agencies themselves have to rely on information received from industry in order to implement their control strategy, and the public are often denied access to information relating to hazard issues on the grounds that it might somehow give away data that would impair an organisation's competitiveness.

The control of information has been a critical component in the development of political conflict surrounding major hazard sites. In many cases local publics have been denied access to important data and then later had their fears dismissed by industry on the grounds of their incomplete data base. (The argument has been that local publics are unable to judge risk levels accurately because they have neither the expertise nor the necessary information to carry out such analyses.) Even in those situations where data have been more generally available, industry has used its greater resource of technical expertise to undermine the credibility of 'pressure group' analyses. Such cases of 'open' information flows are usually restricted to public inquiries where the state waives the argument of commercial confidentiality and generally 'forces' industry to support its case with some form of empirical argument. The most celebrated case in the UK of 'open' decision-making involved a series of decisions surrounding the Canvey Island complex; Section 2.4 will examine this area in more detail in order to illustrate the potential environmental impact that is associated with developments of this nature.

The complexity and spatial diversity of chemical plants obliges decision makers to quantify the levels of risk in order to make some subsequent judgements about their acceptability. The technique used in this process is termed **risk assessment** and is essentially a multi-disciplinary approach which attempts to 'make accidents happen in the imagination', thereby allowing decision makers the opportunity to target scarce resources into those areas which require the greatest attention.

## 2.3   *Risk assessment and its limits*

Risk assessment represents an attempt to make rational decisions about risks. However, the notion of 'rational' decision-making has been severely criticised within the social science literature since the early work by Simon (1945), which argued that total rationality was impossible given the bounds and biases that affect all decision makers. Within the context of risk-based decisions in the chemicals industry, this problem is compounded by the importance of vested interest in shaping the decision-making agenda and also by the role of technocratic expertise within the process of 'risk assessment'.

Unfortunately for those decision makers operating at national, local and corporate levels, the issues arising from the activities of the chemicals industry are not simply those relating to environmental degradation. The economic benefits associated with the industry are central to the economic well-being of any industrial society. This raises the notion of a level of risk acceptability which can be traded off against levels of benefit for certain activities. This can be illustrated by reference to the motor car which results in significant numbers of annual fatalities and causes severe environmental impacts through noise and atmospheric pollution. Despite the level of damage that arises through the use of such technology, any attempts to ban the free use of the car would be met with considerable public opposition because of the benefits that accrue to the individual, and arguably to society, as a result of its use.

In order for decision makers to be able to judge complex technological systems they must first attempt to reduce the problem to manageable proportions, while at the same time not trivialising the problem under consideration. In an attempt to make 'rational' judgements regarding the nature and acceptability of the risks that arise as a result of major hazard operations, both industry and the regulatory agencies rely heavily on the findings of risk assessment. This process involves an analysis of the *probability* and *consequences* of accidents associated with given activities. The initial calculation (termed risk analysis) of the probability of an accident is then used as a basis for determining risk acceptability by weighing the statistically determined risk against an evaluation of the utility associated with a given event. Risk assessment can be considered therefore as an umbrella which covers two distinct, but closely related activities: **risk analysis** (a technical exercise which is concerned with the identification and estimation of risk, along with some assessment as to the likely consequences associated with a given failure event) and **risk evaluation** (a judgemental and normative phase of the process which is concerned with an assessment of the acceptability of the estimated risk levels). The process is shown in a simplified fashion in Figure 7.2 although it is worth noting that, in the process of decision-making, the phases are rarely separable in such a tidy manner. A simple example of risk analysis is described in Box 7.1.

Risk analysis is by nature a truly interdisciplinary synthesis of scientific disciplines and techniques and the sheer range of intellectual traditions involved, along with the variety of the problems under consideration, pose obvious difficulties for the development of risk assessment as a coherent speciality. One problem here lies in the specific forms of communication used within individual disciplines. These can often inhibit the effective transfer of information between one discipline group and another; and between the scientific community as a whole and the various public groups with an interest in the problem.

The phase of risk evaluation is often extremely controversial because of its reliance on value judgements and broader economic and social considerations. Risk analytical data accordingly become one further element in a public or private discussion of the costs and benefits of regulatory action. In addition, there is often encountered a lack of agreement between the 'real' risks of a hazardous situation (as defined by technical experts who may themselves disagree) and the 'perceived' risks of citizens and potential victims. In particular, the public tend to focus on the magnitude of possible accidents even when experts stress the very low probability of the accident occurring.

In reality these functions of a risk assessment are often carried out by different groups of people. Risk analysis is usually the domain of the scientific–technocratic complex which is often affiliated to industry or the regulatory bodies. The acceptability of these estimated risks should be determined by the political process, where the decision-making procedure is seen to mediate between interested, although often opposing, groups. It is here that problems arise in terms of the weightings given to the supposedly objective, scientifically determined risk estimates on the one hand and the supposed 'subjective' perceptions of the public on the other.

At this point a number of observations can be made regarding the objectivity of risk analysis which needs to be challenged given the nature of technocratic decision-making for major hazard sites. Hammond *et al.* (1983) point to three constraints which impinge on the use of 'scientific' data within policy-making. These are seen as (1) the context in which the policy is determined; (2) the bounded rationality and affiliations of policy makers themselves; and (3) the limits of scientific knowledge in coping with problems which cannot be solved by experimentation. These problems will be present, to a greater or lesser extent, within the risk assessment process and, consequently, the findings of such an analysis

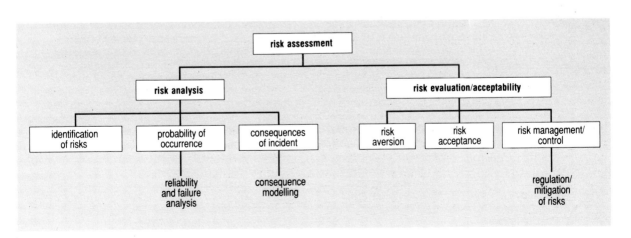

Figure 7.2   The risk assessment process.

should be considered as being bounded by uncertainty. The difficulty in utilising the results of any risk analysis therefore becomes compounded by these uncertainties which are inevitably raised during the acceptability phase of the analysis, as issues of public perceptions and political factors begin to emerge.

In the wake of a series of conflicts surrounding individual plants, a number of writers have claimed that the supposed risks from the chemicals industry have been distorted by the media, with a resulting increase in

---

### Box 7.1   Risk analysis in practice

#### The nature of the problem

A local planning authority have been asked to grant planning permission for the construction of a DIY store at the edge of an urban area. While such a proposal may seem innocuous in itself the proposed site is less than 400 metres from a large industrial complex which includes a major oil refinery, a bottled gas plant and a water treatment works where chlorine is stored in 30-tonne pressurised tanks. It is the latter installation which causes most concern about fatalities within the proposed store.

#### Characteristics of the plant

Chlorine is brought into the plant aboard 20-tonne rail wagons and is stored in three pressurised tanks (Figure 7.3a). In addition there is a network of pipes which feed into and out from the tank. It is possible, therefore, to make some assessment of the likely failure modes for the system and this done in the simplified fault tree shown in Figure 7.3(b).

The 'top event' is a release of chlorine into the environment. This can occur as a result of a number of failure possibilities which can act in unison or independently of each other. If we take the vessels first then it is possible to see two main failure modes. The first is a catastrophic failure of the vessel where the liquid in the tank is released into the bund (a containing embankment surrounding storage vessels). The second form of vessel failure occurs as a leak rather than a total loss of containment. The rate of release here will be a function of the size of the hole and its location. If the hole is above the liquid line within the vessel then the rate of release will be determined by the flow of gas and the rate of liquid evaporation within the vessel. Alternatively if the tank is breached below the liquid line then the rate of toxic cloud formation will be greater as the escaping liquid should vaporise more quickly outside the tank (although this will be dependent on ambient weather conditions).

Another failure mode could be through a pipeline breach which again may be catastrophic (guillotine) or gradual (split and gasket failure). For all cases the ability of plant operators to cut off the flow of chlorine to the point of release will be of importance.

The next two failure possibilities can be considered together as they are concerned with the import and export of chlorine. In both cases, perhaps the greatest risk of release arises as a result of a failure in the transfer hose on the coupling mechanism. There is also the risk of vessel impact (due to road or rail tankers being brought close to the tank) and supply vessel failure (which can be considered in the same way as the pressurised tank itself). Finally, it is possible to consider any other likely initiating events such as pump or vaporiser failure.

#### Risk analysis

Once the fault tree has been drawn up it is then possible to attach probabilities of failure to each event. The data for this part of the risk analysis are usually drawn from reliability data banks which record details of different types of failure of pump, flange vessel, etc. and their frequency. For example, for a catastrophic failure we may find that the rate could be somewhere between $5 \times 10^{-6}$ and $4 \times 10^{-6}$ per vessel per year with each catastrophic failure instantaneously releasing 1 tonne of chlorine. This procedure would be followed for all possible release cases and the resultant data would be inputted into a computer program such as the HSE's RISKAT which would generate the probabilities and likely consequences for a chlorine release from the site. Further calculations would indicate the probability of deaths at different distances from the site, allowing for the density of the population around the site. The proposed DIY store actually increased the probability of a few dozen fatalities by a factor of ten, but there seems to be little increased risk of fatalities in the range of 400 to $10^4$.

concern on the part of the public. As a result it has been argued that public perceptions of the risks are somewhat greater than the 'real risk' as indicated by statistical evidence. This view has also been strongly articulated within the debates surrounding nuclear power proposals. For example, Justice Parker, during his hearing of the inquiry into the accident at Windscale in 1977, stated that no weight could be given to the findings of the various opinion polls relating to the proposal. This technocratic view of decision-making has been called into question by a number of social

◄   Figure 7.3(a)
A chlorine installation (not showing pipe sizes, instrumentation, etc.). Liquid chlorine is pushed from the supply tank by pressure from the padding gas supply through a series of flexible couplings, pipes and valves to one of three storage tanks. Gas given off by the liquid chlorine in the storage tanks can then be piped to the consumer. Tanks and flexible couplings, pipes and valves (joined by gaskets) will each have some propensity for possible failure.

◄   Figure 7.3(b)
A simplified fault tree for a chlorine installation.

scientists (Smith & Irwin, 1984; Fischer, 1980, 1990) who argue that in a democratic society the views of the public are important and should play some role in the decision-making process for major hazard sites.

The problem for policy makers is further compounded by the weight they ought to give to the findings of probabilistic risk assessment in determining the level of acceptable risk. This issue is addressed by Perrow (1984) in his discussion of 'normal accidents'. He argues that all systems are destined to fail by virtue of their interaction with humans who are so obviously fallible. He adds that the complexity of a system, in terms of its hazard potential, will be a result of the system's 'coupling' and 'complexity'. If a technical system is deemed to be 'interactively complex' then it follows that the components within the system are tightly linked and a failure in one part of the system will result in a failure at another point within the system. The problem becomes worse if the system displays what Perrow terms 'tight coupling'. In this case the speed of the interaction between failed components of the system is so short as to make any remedial action difficult to implement.

The arguments articulated by Perrow stand in stark contrast to the technocratic rationale which underpins the process of risk assessment. Here the question is not simply one of the probability of failure but rather a question of *when* the system will fail and *how long* the management structure will have to prevent the system's failure from degenerating into a disaster. This approach to risk analysis adopted by Perrow raises important questions concerning the location of hazardous industry and the political dynamics surrounding such decisions. These issues now need to be considered in the light of the comments made above and by reference to the case of Canvey Island.

*Activity 1*

Review the discussion of the decision-making process and:

(a)  list the problems that could prevent a rational decision based on calculations of the risks created by a proposal to build a large new facility in an existing concentration of chemical plants;

(b)  forecast whether permission will be granted or withheld.

## 2.4    Canvey Island – the most dangerous place in Britain?

The 'Canvey Island' complex is found on the north bank of the River Thames in Essex and represents a line of petrochemical installations which run from Stanford-le-Hope in the west to Canvey Island in the east (Figure 7.4). The area has played host to no less than eight public inquiries over the period 1963 to 1983 and witnessed the UK's first published risk analyses, carried out by a joint HSE/Atomic Energy Authority (Safety and Reliability Directorate) investigating team. The first of these investigations, carried out between 1976 and 1978, revealed data regarding the quantities of materials held in store at the complex which had previously been unavailable in a public forum. If the conventional wisdom concerning the impact of scientific knowledge on decision-making holds true, then one would expect that the risk analyses carried out at Canvey Island would

INDUSTRIAL SITES
A  Fisons Ltd            C  Calor Gas        E  URL site                    G  Occidental                           I  Texaco Ltd
B  Shell UK Oil Ltd      D  Mobil Oil Ltd    F  URL 1965 permission         H  London & Coastal Oil Wharves Ltd     J  British Gas Methane Terminal

Figure 7.4   The location of major hazard installations at Canvey Island.

have provided decision makers with a sound basis for assessing the costs
of further development in the area. However, as the chronology of events
shows (Table 7.2) the main impact of the first risk analysis report (Health
and Safety Executive, 1978) was to heighten conflict and to cause
considerable technical debate amongst the various protagonists.

The main reason for the increase in conflict was that the first Canvey
Report highlighted hitherto unknown facts about the risks from the site in
terms of probabilities of plant failure and inventory levels. These
inventories are shown in Table 7.3 where it can be seen that local residents
were faced with a wide range of potential hazards. If the two proposed
refineries were to be constructed and all existing sites were operating to
capacity in 1978, then the complex would have stored up to 150 000 tonnes
of liquefied energy gas (methane, propane and butane), more than 110
tonnes of hydrogen fluoride, 15 900 tonnes of ammonia, 9300 tonnes of
ammonium nitrate and over 5 380 000 tonnes of petroleum and other
hydrocarbons. As a result of the operations at the complex, local residents
were exposed to high levels of risk and Canvey was branded the 'most
dangerous place in Britain'.

In the period following publication of the first risk analysis report there
was considerable criticism from both industry and the public groups of the
report's findings and methodology. Following this heightened level of
conflict the Secretary of State decided that another public inquiry was
needed in order to evaluate fully the findings of the Canvey analysis. This
inquiry was held in 1980, where the conclusions of the inspector were that
permission could only be granted to United Refineries Ltd (URL) if the
methane terminal (which accounted for one-third of the risks) were to have
igniters installed at its perimeter or to be closed down. This shifted the
balance of the conflict away from the two proposed refineries towards a
state-owned installation which had been operating for over 15 years. The

state was thus presented with an embarrassing problem as it could not be seen to ignore the recommendation of the inspector, given the history of the conflict in the area. Similarly it could not install the igniters (as this would increase the risks to the workforce and therefore contravene the HASAW Act) nor close down the terminal (which served to guarantee continuity of gas supplies for the British Gas Corporation). The government decided that they could not act directly on this recommendation but should hold another public inquiry in order to assess the situation further.

In the period between the URL and methane terminal inquiries, a series of risk analyses were carried out by both the HSE/Safety and Reliability Directorate team and British Gas. This included the publication of the second risk analysis report (Health and Safety Executive, 1981) which suggested that the first report had overestimated many of the risks from the complex. As a consequence of this and other HSE research, the scene was set wherein the weight of the technical evidence was beginning to shift towards the interests of the corporate groups. The result was that those groups which presented a purely qualitative case at the subsequent methane terminal inquiry were disadvantaged compared with the quantitative risk analysis produced by industry and the regulatory agencies.

*Table 7.2   Major public inquiries at Canvey Island 1963–82*

| Date | Inquiry | Outcome |
| --- | --- | --- |
| 1963 | First methane terminal inquiry. | Permission granted. |
| 1965 | United Refineries Ltd inquiry for the construction of a 2 million tonne refinery. | Inquiry recommended refusal of permission. Permission granted by Secretary of State. |
| 1970 | Occidental Refineries Ltd inquiry for a 6 million tonne refinery. | Permission granted. |
| 1970 | URL inquiry for the construction of a 4 million tonne refinery on a new site. | Permission refused. |
| 1972 | URL inquiry for the construction of a 4 million tonne refinery (taking account of the previous inquiry's criticisms). | Inquiry recommends refusal. Permission granted by Secretary of State. |
| 1973 | Collapse of the Conservative government. | |
| 1974 | Flixborough explosion; calls by local residents for a public inquiry. | |
| 1975 | URL revocation inquiry. | Recommends risk analysis. |
| 1976–1978 | First risk analysis carried out by Safety and Reliability Directorate and Health and Safety Executive. | |
| 1980 | URL revocation inquiry. | Recommends the closure of methane terminal or revocation of URL permission. |
| 1981 | Second risk analysis published. | |
| 1982 | Methane terminal inquiry. | Recommends continued operation of terminal. |
| 1983 | Government announces the continuance of the methane terminal and the confirmation of the URL permission. | |

Table 7.3   Existing and proposed bulk storage at Canvey Island up to 1978

| Location | Mode of storage | Material | Quantity |
|---|---|---|---|
| Methane terminal | In-ground tanks (refrigerated) | LNG | 4 × 20 000 tonnes |
|  | Above-ground tanks (refrigerated) | LNG | 6 × 4000 tonnes<br>2 × 1000 tonnes |
|  | Above-ground tanks (refrigerated) | LPG (butane) | 2 × 5000 tonnes<br>1 × 10 000 tonnes |
|  | Pipeline | LPG (butane) |  |
| Shell UK Oil Refinery | Above-ground spherical tanks (pressurised) | LPG (butane) | 4 × 1700 tonnes |
|  | Above-ground spherical tanks (pressurised) | LPG (propane) | 4 × 400 tonnes |
|  | Above-ground cylindrical tanks (pressurised) | LPG (mixed) | 3 × 135 tonnes |
|  | Tank farms | hydrocarbons<br>ammonia<br>hydrogen<br>fluoride | 3 500 000 tonnes<br>14 000 tonnes<br><br>20 tonnes |
| Mobil Oil Refinery | Above-ground spherical tanks and cylinders (pressurised) | LPG | 5 tanks<br>10 cylinders<br>(total capacity 4000 tonnes) |
|  | Tank farms | hydrocarbons | 1 500 000 tonnes |
|  | *Proposed storage*<br>Above-ground spherical tanks (pressurised) | LPG | 4 × 1000 tonnes |
|  | Above-ground (fully refrigerated) | LPG | 1 × 5000 tonnes |
| Calor Gas | Above-ground storage tanks (pressurised) | propane<br>butane | 3 × 60 tonnes<br>2 × 60 tonnes |
|  | Cylinders | mixed LPG | Total 500 tonnes |
|  | Pipeline | LPG | From local refineries |
| Texaco Ltd | Tank farms | petroleum products | 80 000 tonnes |
| London and Coastal Oil Wharves Ltd | Tank farms | petroleum products | 300 000 tonnes |
| Fisons | Above-ground spherical storage | ammonia | 1 × 1900 tonnes |
|  | Tank storage | ammonium nitrate | 9300 tonnes |
| *Proposed storage* |  |  |  |
| Occidental Refinery | Above-ground spherical storage (pressurised) | propane<br>butane | 2 × 750 tonnes<br>2 × 400 tonnes |
| United Refineries Ltd | Above-ground spherical storage (pressurised) | propane<br>butane | 4 × 200 tonnes<br>3 × 900 tonnes |

Source: Health and Safety Executive (1978).

The inquiry into the methane terminal was held in 1982 and from the outset the inspector made it clear that he would give greater weight to the evidence presented by the HSE over that put forward by any other group. This placed the public groups at an immediate disadvantage as they had consistently argued that the HSE's determination of the risks (as expressed in the two Canvey Reports) were too optimistic, and had brought in their own experts to argue their case. The British Gas Corporation (BGC), on the other hand, were in an advantageous position. Having carried out much of the basic research into the risks from the terminal they then passed on the results to the HSE/SRD team who used the data in formulating their own analysis. While the BGC assessment indicated that the risks were generally lower than those suggested by the HSE, there was little danger of their being totally undermined by the public groups given the inspector's stated preference for the HSE's analysis. The power of the technocratic élite was such that it prevented a full democratic discourse:

> Throughout the inquiry the evidence of the opposition was systematically destroyed by British Gas on technical grounds or ignored by the inspector in favour of HSE evidence. Where a qualitative case was presented, the inspector felt that it was incompatible with the conclusions derived by the HSE's quantified analysis; and when the opposition's experts attempted to quantify their arguments, the inspector felt that because they were working with incomplete, or possible inaccurate, data their arguments could not be given the same considerations as those made by the HSE. (Smith, 1990, p. 19)

In this case it is apparent that the use of risk analysis failed to allow the arguments of local publics to be given much weight because of their weaker resource base (in terms of information and technical expertise). The inquiry inspector's final recommendation was that the methane terminal should continue operating and that the URL permission should finally be approved. The government decided to accept the recommendation of the inquiry on this occasion and announced its decision in 1983. So after almost 20 years of public opposition to the proposals and two risk analyses (which cost well over £1 million for the two HSE/SRD analyses and the work by British Gas) the outcome was virtually the same as that envisaged in 1973, i.e. the methane terminal was to remain open and the URL refinery permission granted. However, as a result of the delays caused by public opposition and changes that occurred in the economics of producing oil (which necessitated the construction of bigger refineries than either of the two planned for Canvey Island) neither Occidental (who withdrew in 1979) nor URL constructed their proposed plants.

## 2.5   Summary

Although risk analysis was useful in highlighting the hazards emanating from the Canvey complex it did not appear to be instrumental in affecting the outcome of the decision-making process. Scientific knowledge was less influential than political factors – most notably the refusal of the industry to take 'no' for an answer and its ability to keep pressing until a favourable decision emerged. However, if there is no risk analysis the public are kept largely in the dark about the risks that they are exposed to by virtue of their proximity to a major hazard complex. Unfortunately, as the methane

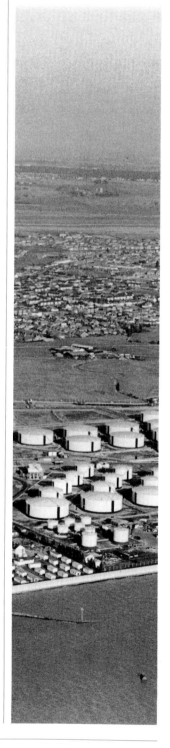

terminal inquiry indicates, the public can also be excluded as a *function* of a risk analysis.

Major hazard sites are not the only source of risk to local residents from the production of chemicals. The disposal of waste raises concern about the potential health effects for those people living close to waste dumps. However, the disposal of hazardous waste has not to date been exposed to the same rigorous risk analyses that have been carried out within the chemical-producing sector of the industry. As a consequence, the levels of data made available to local residents are generally low, the outcome of which is a heightened level of political activity and public activism. The final section in this chapter explores some of these issues in more detail at both the national and international levels.

# 3    Hazardous waste – why should it go in my back yard?

> Just the mention of hazardous wastes and chemical dumps automatically conjures up images of Love Canal, Hooker Chemical Company, and hardworking middle class Americans who found toxic wastes oozing up in their basements. To the average person, the issue is clear-cut. Hooker Chemical is the culprit. The local residents are the victims. Government is the rescuer.    (Yandle, 1989, p. 108)

Perhaps more than any other issue, hazardous waste poses major political problems for the chemicals industry. Hazardous waste is dangerous, in many cases has no value, and its disposal in the past has been shown to be nothing more than a temporary measure due, in the main, to the longevity of the substances involved. In addition there are considerable problems in defining hazardous waste, and in the UK the distinction has been made between hazardous and special (now called notifiable) waste with the latter being the most dangerous. As a result of such uncertainties the waste issue has become the chemical industry's Frankenstein – a 'creation' which it cannot control and which (on the evidence of recent conflicts) seems to strike terror into the hearts of local citizens.

Such an alarmist view of the problem has been engendered by a series of events which occurred in the USA in the late 1970s, followed by similar incidents in Europe during the late 1980s. In both sets of cases the disposal routes initially chosen to deal with the waste stream were subsequently shown to be woefully inadequate under the circumstances and ultimately led to the re-emergence of the wastes into the ecosystem, with potentially damaging consequences. While it is probably true to say that no member of the public has been immediately killed, to date, as a result of direct exposure to such waste 'leaks', their impact on public perceptions has been considerable. There is no doubt that hazardous waste substances have a considerable potential for harm and that exposure to them could result in severe damage to health or even death. The management of such waste is, therefore, an important issue for the chemicals industry and the principal disposal routes that are available need to be detailed here prior to examining the socio-political dimension of the problem.

## 3.1   Waste disposal – the search for the best environmental option

The strategies chosen for the disposal of hazardous waste will vary according to the economic and geophysical characteristics of the host country. However, a number of well-defined disposal routes can be identified and these are shown in Table 7.4. The mix of such technologies used will be dependent on issues of availability, cost, the physical characteristics of the waste and, to an increasing degree, the prevailing political climate at both local and national levels. In the UK, for example, the main disposal route is through landfill, which accounted for some 78% of the 4.8 million tonnes of hazardous and special waste disposed of in 1988. The percentages of waste disposed of by each route will vary over time according to political and economic pressures. Disposal at sea, for example, accounted for some 7% of the 1987 total, but this figure is likely to decrease to zero as a result of a European ban on sea-based incineration.

The question as to which of these routes provides the 'best environmental option' is a contentious one. For certain highly toxic and persistent wastes, such as polychlorinated biphenyls (PCBs), incineration would appear to provide the best option as it has the potential for the virtual destruction of such substances. However, the degree of technical uncertainty surrounding such issues has provided the basis for a series of public debates involving the state, industry, environmental groups and local publics in an attempt to reconcile what are basically irreconcilable differences of opinion. The environmental groups, and Greenpeace in particular, have gone so far as to argue that all the disposal routes on offer are potentially damaging to the environment. Their solution to the problem

Table 7.4   *Disposal routes for hazardous waste*

| Mode | Method |
| --- | --- |
| Landfill | Disposal to land, usually in a 'lined' pit to prevent leakage. |
| Co-disposal | This involves the landfilling of hazardous with municipal waste. Not widely practised although it has been used in the United Kingdom. |
| Land-based incineration | The burning of wastes in a high temperature (1500 °C) incinerator. Favoured for PCBs but requires flue-gas scrubbers to reduce stack-based emissions. |
| Sea-based incineration | As in the land-based process but the waste is burnt at sea in a ship which operates without flue-gas scrubbers. Economically viable but potentially ecologically damaging. The process has been suspended in the North Sea. |
| Sea disposal | The dumping of waste at sea. Favoured for sewage sludge in the UK although it has been strongly criticised by the EEC. |
| Solidification | The encapsulation/fixation of waste to provide physical stability prior to disposal. |
| Chemical treatment/ neutralisation/ oxidation/reduction | Aims to make waste suitable for subsequent landfilling by changing the chemical characteristics of the waste. |

lies in the concept of waste prevention or source reduction. Here, future waste arisings would be significantly reduced, thereby allowing for the minimum of environmental impact. However, the cost implications of this approach have generally conspired to make such an option unattractive to industry in the past. In spite of this, the recent upsurge in public and political concern about the waste issue may promote a more responsive view from industry in the future. Local publics have also expressed their dissatisfaction over a range of waste disposal options, simply on the grounds that they do not want such an operation in their locality. Such opposition has been termed the **NIMBY** syndrome (not in my back yard) and has been characteristic of a number of highly politicised debates in the USA and, increasingly, in the UK.

The role of the state within the context of such conflicts is an interesting one. On the one hand, local government agencies in the UK have recently rejected a series of proposals for waste disposal plants; on the other hand central government has argued the need for continued disposal capacity. At the European Community level, attempts have been made to regulate the international transfers of waste streams, although such moves could be seen as running counter to the philosophy of a single European Market. Throughout the issue of state involvement in waste disposal, the question of the national (or European Community) versus the local interest is of paramount importance. At the local level, the argument has been that waste disposal facilities may discourage future investment in the area as a result of their environmental impacts. At the national level, the view has been articulated that a disposal industry is needed in order to prevent the country being dependent on foreign companies.

From the corporate perspective waste disposal has two aspects. For chemical producers, waste disposal is a cost which has to be kept as low as possible to maintain competitiveness. For waste disposal companies, disposal is a highly profitable venture within which the main barriers to entry are largely political. As a consequence, the industry has been quick to oppose any further attempts to regulate its operations and individual companies have lobbied central government in an effort to overcome local opposition. As a result of the actions of the various groups involved in the debates the issue became highly politicised, at both the regional and international levels, in the latter part of the 1980s. In order to understand fully the nature of the political problem we also have to gain an appreciation of the relationship between the point of waste creation and its eventual disposal.

It is not surprising that the points of hazardous waste arisings tend to follow the pattern of production. Figure 7.5(a) shows the main areas of hazardous waste creation in England and Wales (Scotland is administered separately) with the main concentrations being in the North West, Yorkshire and the Midlands. Cheshire, which, as Chapter 6 made clear, has a long history of alkali production and plays host to much of the UK's modern chemical capacity, is also the main producer of hazardous waste. While many of these areas also dispose of waste within their boundaries (as shown in Figure 7.5b) there are some areas, such as Bedfordshire, Essex and Durham, which are net importers of waste. This is primarily due to the availability of 'suitable' sites for disposal which exist within such areas – often represented by a single site, such as Pitsea in Essex or the Rechem incinerator in South Wales.

This process of 'exporting' waste is replicated at the international level and a well-developed international trade in transfers currently exists, with the UK being a net importer. The current wave of legislation governing

(a)                                                    (b)

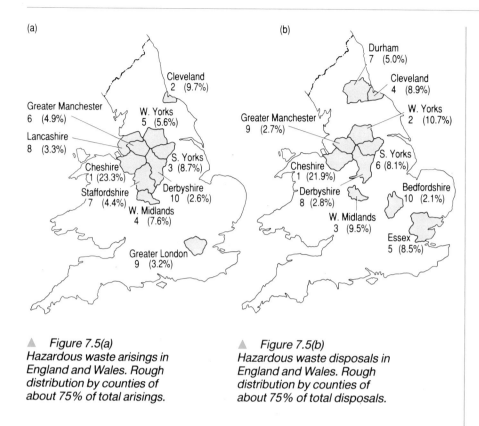

▲    Figure 7.5(a)
Hazardous waste arisings in
England and Wales. Rough
distribution by counties of
about 75% of total arisings.

▲    Figure 7.5(b)
Hazardous waste disposals in
England and Wales. Rough
distribution by counties of
about 75% of total disposals.

such transfers is primarily concerned with providing receiving nations and
counties with detailed information concerning the nature and quantities of
the wastes being imported. Prior to 1988 even such basic information was
not available and this resulted in a number of controversial political
incidents, as waste 'brokers' tried to find a home in the developing world
for wastes from developed countries.

As a result of the complex nature of the disposal cycle, a series of
power bases can be seen to exist at both the national and international
levels. Within nation states conflicts can be seen to occur between industry,
local publics, central government and the local authorities which have
responsibility for waste disposal. At the international level it is possible to
see inter-state conflict occurring at a number of levels.

The first level of interaction can be seen to exist between developed
countries. Here waste is transferred because one country has a well-
developed technological base for the disposal of highly toxic and persistent
wastes (e.g. through high-temperature incineration). The second level of
interaction can again be seen to occur between developed countries. On
this occasion the transfers occur because one country offers a disposal
route which is either cheaper than those available within other developed
countries, or because political/regulatory opposition to specific disposal
routes is lower. The final level of interaction involves transfers between
developed countries and developing or economically stagnant nations
with the latter being eager to take waste as a means of securing foreign
capital.

The resulting framework can be seen in terms of a 'pyramid of
exploitation' as nation states seek to find the route of least political

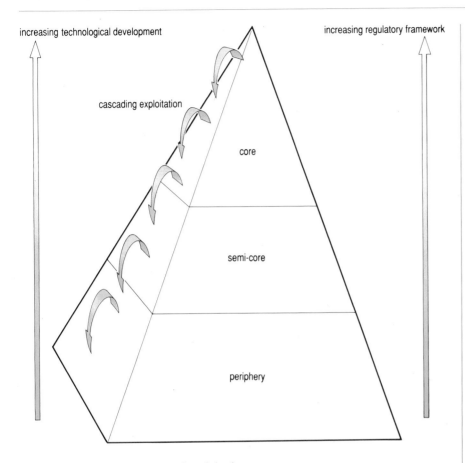

increasing technological development

increasing regulatory framework

cascading exploitation

core

semi-core

periphery

▲   Figure 7.6   The pyramid of exploitation.

opposition through which to dispose of their waste. This system creates three groups, namely core, semi-core and periphery, which can be related to nation states at various stages of economic development (Figure 7.6). The core states are those post-industrial and industrial nations which have highly developed regulatory and technological frameworks which 'control' waste transfer and disposal. The semi-core states are those newly industrialised nations which may seek to export waste as a function of their rapid development, thereby keeping costs down. Alternatively, they may be old industrial nations which have a well-developed chemicals-based infrastructure but do not have the capability to dispose of certain waste streams. The final group, the peripheral states, are developing nations or those countries which are in decline economically. These will include countries such as Nigeria and other West African nations, and countries which made up what was the eastern bloc (e.g. East Germany and Poland) which sought to secure foreign exchange by accepting waste imports. As a consequence, it could be argued that there are three principal driving forces behind hazardous waste transfers: (1) technological development (in providing the means for waste disposal); (2) political pressures; and (3) economic driving forces within the process of production. It is possible to examine the relative importance of these factors by examining the transfers of waste from Italy to Nigeria and from Canada to the United Kingdom.

## 3.2 The international transfer of hazardous waste – the wanderer returns?

It was the export of hazardous waste from Italy to Nigeria, and its subsequent return, that catapulted the issue onto the political agenda in the UK when the vessel *Karin B* sought to offload its toxic cargo here. The waste was originally dumped illegally at Koko Beach in Nigeria, where the landowner was paid the small sum (although not by local standards) of $250 per month to 'store' the waste. Given that the waste had been containerised in temperate northern Italy and then shipped to equatorial Africa, it is not surprising that the barrels became overpressurised and began to show signs of leakage. Following pressure from the Nigerian government and international environmental groups, the waste was eventually put on board the *Karin B* and the *Deep Sea Carrier*, which spent almost three months searching for a country willing to take the waste for disposal. The issue became active in the UK when it was suggested that the waste could be effectively disposed of here as a result of the UK's 'advanced' incineration technology. Although the waste was refused entry into the UK the case served to raise the political profile of the waste disposal industry and provided a foundation for subsequent conflicts at the local level, as Britain became labelled the 'dustbin of Europe'. After refusals from France, the UK, West Germany and Spain the waste was eventually returned to Italy in December 1988, where it also sparked a political protest by local residents who were also fearful of the waste's hazard potential.

While the Nigerian waste was certainly the most infamous, it was not the only dumping incident to occur in West Africa during this period. According to media reports, a total of some 24 million tonnes of waste, which originated in Europe, was either dumped or proposed for dumping in West Africa during the late 1980s. In Guinea Bissau alone proposals were made to dispose of 15 million tonnes of waste at a cost of $120 million, and Benin was offered $12.5 million to take 5 million tonnes of European waste. Such proposals have obvious attractions for developing nations – the Guinea Bissau arrangement, for example, was worth the equivalent of its GNP. European companies also benefit from this trade, due to the low costs of disposal in West Africa, and it is the spatial diversity of disposal costs which drive such an international trade.

However, the transfer of waste from developed to developing countries is only one facet of the global transfer process. Others include developing to developing and developed to developed, with the latter being the more common. The next section illustrates the nature of these transfers by briefly examining the transfers of waste into the UK, paying attention to the attempts in 1989 to import Canadian PCBs for disposal.

## 3.3 Britain – the world's dustbin?

To a large extent the intra-European transfers of waste have been largely overshadowed by what has happened in West Africa. However, this does not imply that the issue is not high on the political agenda of European countries. The scale of the problem in Europe, with some 100 000 waste transfers occurring annually, is such to ensure that the issue will remain politically 'live' (particularly after 1992) until significant action is taken by governments to bring the problem under control. However, events over

Table 7.5    Imports of notifiable waste into the UK, 1989

| Country of origin | Amount/tonnes |
|---|---|
| Netherlands | 14 799 |
| Belgium | 9 225 |
| Switzerland | 5 086 |
| USA | 4 237 |
| Sweden | 1 541 |
| Italy | 1 505 |
| Eire | 1 358 |
| Canada | 1 011 |
| West Germany | 611 |
| Norway | 533 |
| Australia | 280 |
| Austria | 166 |
| Denmark | 166 |
| Portugal | 73 |
| Spain | 64 |
| Brazil | 46 |
| Channel Islands | 30 |
| Philippines | 29 |
| Luxembourg | 17 |
| Finland | 12 |
| Greece | 5 |
| Singapore | 5 |
| Uruguay | 3 |

Source: ENDs Report No. 182, March 1990, p. 26.

1989–90 did little to allay public fears that Britain is becoming the 'dustbin of Europe', if not the world, as companies sought to import waste from around the world for treatment and disposal. The scale of the problem is illustrated by the data in Table 7.5 which show imports into the UK, by country of origin, for 1989. Such figures have served to maintain the public concern and have caused environmental groups to accuse the government of putting economic gain before environmental quality.

The severity of such concerns can be gauged from a brief examination of the conflicts surrounding attempts to import PCB waste into Britain.

In 1989, following a fire in St-Basil-le-Grand, Canada, attempts were made to import PCB wastes to the Rechem plant at Pontypool in Wales for incineration. The waste was shipped in three Soviet-flagged vessels between July and August and culminated in action by local residents, dock workers and port authorities which, in turn, resulted in the waste being denied access to the UK. The outcome of these conflicts was remarkable because of the apparent influence that the local pressure group, Stop Toxic Emissions Action Movement (STEAM), had on the outcome of events. STEAM had lobbied both the UK and Canadian governments and written open letters to the Canadian people playing on the latter's expressed environmental concerns. The actions by STEAM were of considerable political embarrassment to the Canadian government as it had previously given assurances that the waste would not be sent to the UK for disposal. As a consequence of pressure from the Canadian media the government recalled the three vessels carrying the PCBs and refused to let a fourth sail from Canada. The cost of the cancelled contract was considerable. Rechem, who were to dispose of the waste, lost the contract, which was worth around Can\$7.9 million, and also saw their share price fall by some £24 million due to the conflict.

The response from Rechem to this action was to take court action against one of STEAM's key spokespersons who had previously been critical of the company's actions in a BBC radio interview. Rechem stated that they will attempt to recover their losses and have threatened to recover damages from STEAM spokespersons to the value of the company's losses over this period.

The conflict surrounding the Rechem incinerator continued into 1990 with STEAM lobbying extensively for a public inquiry into hazards arising from the site. A blow was dealt to Rechem's plans to expand its site by the publication of a report by the Welsh Affairs Committee which suggested that high-temperature incineration should be located away from urban areas. However, throughout this period Rechem have enjoyed a degree of support from central government – indicated by the state's apparent reluctance to call the matter in for a public inquiry, despite considerable public concern at the local level. The examples of waste transfers and the debates surrounding the conflicts at Canvey Island illustrate the point that there are a number of valid groups within local societies which can intervene in environmental debates of this nature. The question that needs to be addressed relates to their effectiveness in determining the outcome of such conflicts.

# 4   Conclusions

This chapter has explored the ways in which the state attempts to make decisions concerning the control of major chemical hazards and the disposal of toxic wastes. While the political processes surrounding such environmental issues are extremely complex, a number of key points can be made in conclusion.

In the course of the above discussion of the development of hazard and waste regulation it would appear that the involvement of the state has been largely paternalistic, with regulatory interjections being made following public pressure. This process is indicative of a pluralistic framework in which all interested parties have the opportunity to put their views before those people making the decisions. Legislation has ultimately led to significant improvements in environmental quality, although some would argue that the regulations have simply shifted the impact of pollution damage to other areas, e.g. via acid rain and the export of toxic waste. It is also possible to see the perceived problem changing over time, moving from chronic air pollution problems towards the more acute risks associated with major hazards. As the capacity of chemical plants has increased over time so, too, has their ability to cause widespread environmental damage. As a consequence, the state has been forced to develop new legislation and update its regulatory structures to cope with new forms of impact and changes in political demands. The emergence of major hazards illustrates the nature of the problem as the state has put into place new legislation following a series of accidents during the 1970s.

The explosion at Flixborough showed that a problem existed from a public safety perspective and stimulated considerable public concern in areas of chemical production like Canvey Island. In this case the accident prompted a change in the nature of the debates and moved it into a more conflictual setting, as technical expertise became of importance in determining the outcomes of conflicts. From this point on, chemical companies were dragged into the 'democratic limelight' as a result of a whole series of public inquiries prompted by public fears of having potentially dangerous chemical plants 'in their back yards'. The problem for decision makers then became one of reconciling views which were fundamentally opposed to one another. In order to mediate between such opposing factions it was felt necessary to use a rational, supposedly objective decision aid, namely risk analysis, to provide a 'scientific basis' for coping with differing perceptions of risk.

As a consequence of the use of probabilistic risk analysis as a basis for decision legitimation, the debates surrounding chemical complexes such as the one at Canvey Island required the increased use of technical expertise in substantiating opposition or support for a given project or development. The result of such a move was that the debates moved away from a pluralistic framework towards a more structuralist setting where the resource base of the various groups, expressed in terms of available knowledge and expertise, became of importance. A sceptical view might be, therefore, that risk analysis simply favoured those sections of society which had access to data and technocratic knowledge and marginalised any public protest which failed to engage in such technocratic discourse.

Section 2 of the chapter showed that the nature of the risk from chemical plants was a function of location, the scale of operations and the techniques of production and storage. These three elements have been addressed by decision makers, with the Health and Safety Executive being concerned with the issues of technique and scale and the planners focusing on issues of location and the juxtaposition of the plant and potentially incompatible land uses. Much of the political conflict surrounding major hazards has emerged through planning-related issues as local publics have well-defined rights to information in such cases. It is in such contexts that technical expertise has been utilised as a means of legitimating the policy beliefs of industry and central government.

Section 3 demonstrated that the issue of hazardous waste had also emerged on the political agenda in recent years and provided decision makers with a new set of problems to deal with. The issue here was that the initial decisions to dispose of waste were often taken many years previously, as in the case of Love Canal, or even in a different country in the case of the export of waste. As a consequence, the debates almost became one of the 'rights of exploitation'. In the case of waste export, the driving force behind the disposal of waste can be seen to be largely economic as companies search out the cheapest disposal route available to them. In some cases, it would appear that companies have looked for locations in which the disposal of waste would attract little political opposition, as evidenced by the export of Italian waste to Nigeria in 1988.

The issue of waste disposal is also one in which the nature of the problem goes beyond the ability of 'science' to solve in a rational decision framework. It is difficult to determine what damage, if any, is being caused by the disposal of waste and perhaps more difficult to suggest alternative strategies that are available to cope with the growing waste problem. On the one hand a risk assessment might suggest that the incineration of wastes provides the best option currently available, but on the other hand the political dynamics of the issue mean that such a strategy will be difficult to implement, as local publics continue to oppose the siting of such plants in their locality. The question that remains to be answered is: which approach is indeed the most 'rational'?

The use of risk analysis in decision-making does not guarantee an equitable outcome in policy debates over hazardous technologies. This is due primarily to the disproportionate resource base that is available to the producers of chemicals. The exercise of economic power would seem to be an important element in this respect as corporate groups control the flows of information and can use technical expertise to determine political agendas. There are signs, however, that industry is beginning to take notice of environmental impact within their corporate plans. It remains to be seen what influence this will have in the long term on the quality of life of a number of communities that live close to impacting industries.

## References

FISCHER, F. (1980) *Politics, Values, and Public Policy: the problem of methodology*, Westview Press, Boulder, Colorado.

FISCHER, F. (1990) *Technocracy and the Politics of Expertise*, Sage, Newbury Park.

HAMMOND, K., MUMPOWER, J., DENNIS, R. L., FITCH, S. & CRUMPACKER, W. (1983) Fundamental obstacles to the use of scientific information in public policy making, *Technological Forecasting*, **24**, 287–97.

HEALTH AND SAFETY COMMISSION (1976) *Advisory Committee on Major Hazards: First Report*, HMSO, London.

HEALTH AND SAFETY COMMISSION (1979) *Advisory Committee on Major Hazards: Second Report*, HMSO, London.

HEALTH AND SAFETY COMMISSION (1984) *The Control of Major Hazards: Advisory Committee on Major Hazards: Third Report*, HMSO, London.

HEALTH AND SAFETY EXECUTIVE (1978) *Canvey: an investigation of potential hazards from operations in the Canvey Island/Thurrock area*, HMSO, London.

HEALTH AND SAFETY EXECUTIVE (1981) *Canvey: a Second Report. A review of potential hazards from operations in the Canvey Island/Thurrock area three years after publication of the Canvey Report*, HMSO, London.

PERROW, C. (1984) *Normal Accidents*, Basic Books, New York.

ROBENS COMMITTEE (1972) *Safety and Health at Work: Report of the Committee 1970–72*, HMSO, London.

SIMON, H. (1945) *Administrative Behaviour*, Free Press, New York.

SMITH, D. (1990) Corporate power and the politics of uncertainty: Conflicts surrounding major hazard plants at Canvey Island, *Industrial Crisis Quarterly*, **4(1)**, 1–26.

SMITH, D. & IRWIN, A. (1984) Public attitudes to technological risk: the contribution of survey data to public policy-making, *Transactions, Institute of British Geographers*, **9(4)**, 419–26.

YANDLE, B. (1989) *The Political Limits of Environmental Regulation: tracking the unicorn*, Quorum Books, New York.

# Answer to Activities

## Activity 1

(a)  The problems include the following.

- The planning system is more able to prevent building of a new plant than to close an existing one, but the greatest hazards may be posed by existing installations.

- The information and expertise upon which risk analysis is based may be concentrated within the industry, which has a vested interest in minimising the perceived hazards.

- The two regulating authorities, the planning authorities and the HSE, might have different views because one has a local perspective and has to pay heed to the issues of the local economy, while the other is more concerned with issues of risk and views many of the problems from a national perspective. Indeed, a similar application to the development proposed in Box 7.1 was made in an industrial area in the north of England; the decision arrived at was that permission should be given (against HSE advice) in the interests of the local economy.

- Pressure groups might be able to identify experts who would calculate the probability of failure in different ways and reach different conclusions from those of the industry.

- Public anxiety about the magnitude of possible accidents might persuade local politicians to oppose construction 'in their back yard'.

(b)  Beyond the observation that the complexity of the issue might lead to long delays, your forecast of the outcome will depend on your theoretical view of decision-making. Structuralists believe that the state is ultimately dependent on the prosperity of capital and will usually allow proposals which are seen as economically desirable by big corporations. Pluralists believe that the state acts as a neutral referee between interest groups and will decide on the basis of the public good. Both groups would expect a major decision to be taken out of the hands of local decision makers and brought into the hands of central government, either by setting up a public inquiry or through an appeal to the Secretary of State.

# 1 Introduction

You have already encountered the nuclear industry at a number of points in this series. Right at the beginning, in Chapter 1 of *Silvertown & Sarre, 1990*, the controversy surrounding the radioactive discharges from Sellafield was introduced, and in Chapter 4 earlier in this book the problems of identifying and measuring risks from that plant were discussed. In Chapter 1 of this book the process of energy production from nuclear fission was described and nuclear energy was placed in the context of the world's energy balance. Some of the problems with nuclear energy, such as its high cost, limited reserves of uranium, accumulating wastes and the danger of proliferation of plutonium, were considered in Chapter 4.

In terms of risk and potential environmental impacts the nuclear industry has much in common with other large-scale technological systems such as the chemical industry considered in the previous chapter. As we saw, such industries are capable of devastating destruction and widespread impact. The various stages of the nuclear fuel cycle* present different degrees of risk to the environment. In this chapter we shall focus on the 'back-end' of the nuclear cycle: the management of nuclear wastes. In many ways this is the nuclear industry's most intractable problem. Nuclear waste also has some distinctive characteristics which make it as much a political as a technical problem, as we shall see. Our aims will be:

1 To indicate the distinctive features of radioactive waste management compared with the management of other hazardous and toxic materials. The comparison can be partly understood by identifying the environmental impact of nuclear waste. This is a question that can be addressed by scientific inquiry but is also a matter of perception.

2 To identify the sources and characteristics of radioactive waste and to examine in what respects radioactive waste constitutes an environmental problem. A distinctive feature of the nuclear industry and, increasingly, of nuclear waste, has been its political salience. It provides a good example of the ways in which environmental problems become politicised and a cause of conflict.

3 To explain how radioactive waste has shifted from being a non-problem to a technical problem to a political problem. To do this we shall need to look back at the history of the nuclear industry from its military origins in the United States to the development of electricity generation and reprocessing. Contemporary political conflict over nuclear waste management will be examined to understand the local, national and international dimensions of the political problem of nuclear waste. The focus will be on the UK but reference will be made to other countries.

4 To evaluate the political consequences and possibilities of radioactive waste management policies. From the discussion of conflict in the UK

*We use the phrase 'nuclear fuel cycle' in this book without endorsing the nuclear industry view that nuclear materials are best recycled within a closed circuit (after mining). Anti-nuclear groups tend to describe the same process as a 'chain'.

some interesting conclusions can be drawn. It will be clear that political conflict has circumscribed the technical and locational options for radioactive waste management. The nuclear industry has been retreating in the face of political opposition. This opposition has derived its power from an ability to mobilise effective coalitions notwithstanding differing 'political cultures'. Awareness of the potential hazards of nuclear waste has been translated into action that has influenced policy-making.

5    To examine the extent to which the politics of nuclear waste illustrates a developing environmental challenge to conventional political assumptions and arrangements. Radioactive waste is a major environmental problem, presently confined to the 'nuclear nations' but extending down the generations. It indicates the constraints and possibilities of political action both locally and internationally. The political problems surrounding nuclear waste suggest that solutions to this and other global environmental problems will be hard to achieve.

Before beginning our analysis, we should emphasise that because our focus is on the politics of nuclear waste, we only present enough technical information to show what the debates are about. We do not intend to try to resolve the debates or to argue for any particular technical interpretation or solution of the problem of radioactive waste disposal.

# 2    What are radioactive wastes?

## 2.1    The nuclear fuel cycle

In order to understand why radioactive wastes are such a distinctive and possibly intractable political problem we must first define the origins and categories of these wastes. Only by knowing something about the materials we are dealing with, and their environmental implications, can we begin to explain the political significance achieved by nuclear waste. Nuclear wastes are the unwanted by-products of the processes of the 'nuclear industry'. The nuclear industry in this sense includes the civil production of nuclear energy and its attendant facilities, the military production and use of nuclear materials, and the creation of radioactive isotopes for use in industry and medicine. The wastes may be routinely released into the environment, or they may be 'managed', i.e. stored or buried in order to minimise their release into the environment. Radioactive materials are also released as a result of accidents such as Chernobyl, and such releases may, broadly speaking, be regarded as unplanned wastes. Finally, there is the deliberate release of materials from nuclear explosions either through testing or war.

Radioactive wastes are created at each stage of the nuclear fuel cycle (Figure 8.1). You will also find that Figure 2.11 in Chapter 2 can be used to indicate the environmental pathways available at various stages in the cycle. At the first stage, uranium mining and milling, the ore is extracted, leaving tailing piles with long-lived radionuclides that can contaminate wide areas as in, for example, Australia, Namibia, New Mexico or

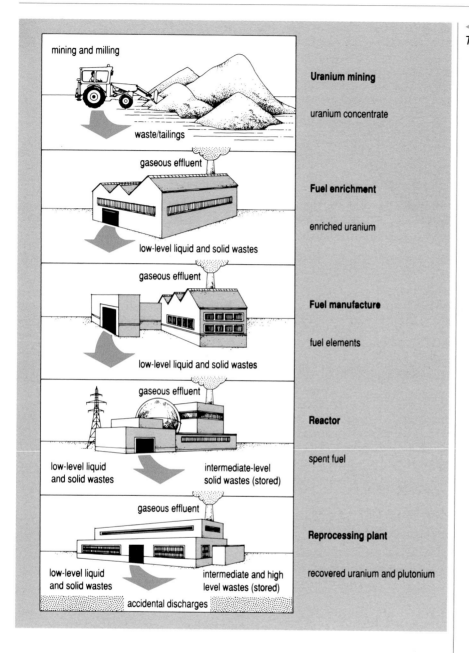

Saskatchewan. Fuel enrichment (not needed for all fuel types) and fabrication, by which the uranium concentrate is converted into fuel elements, create relatively little waste. The main waste-creating processes are *electricity generation* and *reprocessing*. Most countries with nuclear electricity generation have an 'open' cycle without civil reprocessing facilities, hence the fuel rods when removed must be stored as spent fuel. Since they are highly radioactive they are usually stored on site along with other highly contaminated materials such as ion exchange resins (used for purifying the cooling water), sludges and fuel cladding materials. In those countries with reprocessing, notably France (at Cap de la Hague, near Cherbourg, and Marcoule on the lower Rhone) and the UK (mainly at

Sellafield), spent fuel is removed from the power stations and transferred to the reprocessing facilities. The process has been described in Chapter 4, Section 4.4. Reprocessing concentrates the highly radioactive wastes but it also creates large volumes of mildly contaminated trash which must be managed. Apart from radioactive wastes created during the civil nuclear fuel cycle there are those wastes which are produced by military nuclear operations and bomb tests, and wastes from industrial and medical processes. Finally, once nuclear facilities are closed down, the reactors and buildings remain radioactive and are a source of decommissioning wastes. The first of the UK's Magnox power stations at Berkeley, Gloucestershire, was permanently shut down in 1989, leaving a problem of waste management. Recognition that the costs of decommissioning would not be acceptable to the private sector was a factor in the decision taken in 1989 not to privatise the nuclear power stations along with the rest of the electricity industry.

## 2.2   Classification of wastes

The distinctive problem with these wastes and the reason they are an environmental hazard is, of course, that they are radioactive. The process of radioactive decay was explained earlier in Chapter 1, Section 4.5. For the purposes of our present discussion there are two essential points about radioactivity that you need to grasp. The first concerns the measurement of radioactive decay.

Q   Can you recollect how radioactive decay is measured?

A   It is measured in terms of activity and of 'half-life', the time it takes for half the total activity to undergo a nuclear transformation. Activity is measured in becquerels, the number of nuclear transformations per second. Half-lives vary very widely among radioactive elements. As we saw in Chapter 1 of the first book in this series (*Silvertown & Sarre, 1990*), some have a very transitory half-life (e.g. iodine-131 has eight days), while others have half-lives extending over unimaginable gulfs of time (e.g. plutonium-239 has 24 000 years; uranium-238 has 4 510 000 000 years). It is therefore important to know the half-lives of materials being dealt with, particularly of those nuclides with high activity levels.

The second point, also identified in Chapter 1 of *Silvertown & Sarre, 1990*, is the method of classifying ionising radiation.

Q   What are the three types of ionising radiation?

A   They are alpha, beta and gamma radiation. Alpha radiation is the least penetrating but most densely ionising and, if ingested, can cause the most cellular damage. Beta, and particularly gamma radiation, can penetrate more readily causing damage to external body surfaces.

At one time the classification of radioactive wastes in the UK was based on the *method of disposal*. Thus, low-level wastes were those that could be safely disposed of by existing routes. This suggested that the definition of wastes could alter over time as new disposal routes were introduced. To avoid such confusion and to achieve consistency, wastes were classified according to their *activity* and the half-lives of radionuclides. In the United

States classification emphasises the *sources* of the waste, the most dangerous being irradiated spent fuel. There is no internationally agreed system of classification but in Europe and Canada the following three broad categories are recognised:

1   **High-level wastes (HLW).** These are heat-generating wastes in the form of spent fuel or, in those countries with reprocessing, in the form of liquid wastes. Though volumes of such wastes are small they contain around 95% of the total radioactivity and are therefore very dangerous. HLW are technically the major waste management problem and are politically the most contentious, especially in those countries, like the USA, where they are stored in the form of spent fuel at reactor sites.

2   **Intermediate-level wastes (ILW).** These wastes arise from processes closely related to energy production and reprocessing and include fuel cladding, control rods, sludges, resins and filters. They are subdivided into long-lived ILW (mainly alpha emitters with more than 30 year half-lives) and short-lived ILW (predominantly beta and gamma emitters).

3   **Low-level wastes (LLW)** are those wastes which are lightly contaminated, including clothing, paper, plastics, building debris and other materials. Eventually the buildings outside the reactor itself will become LLW. They are high-volume wastes especially where there is labour-intensive reprocessing. Box 8.1 adds some technical information.

The volume of radioactive wastes arising is difficult to estimate and depends on estimates of nuclear electricity generation and decommissioning. One estimate suggests a UK total of about 80 000 cubic metres of ILW by the turn of the century and about a quarter of a million cubic metres by 2030 (NIREX, 1983, 1989). The comparable volumes of LLW are estimated to be around a half million cubic metres by the end of the century and 1.5 million cubic metres by 2030. These volumes will be increased by about a fifth to take into account defence wastes, which are small amounts equivalent to about 2 million tonnes of packaged material by 2030. The total amount of radioactive wastes arising every year is just over a million tonnes comprising 1.0 million tonnes of LLW, 0.16 of ILW, and 0.004 of HLW, in contrast to an annual production of between 5 and 10 million tonnes of industrial wastes containing hazardous materials and 29 million tonnes of domestic wastes that is disposed of every year (House of Commons Environment Committee, 1986, p. xix). The volume of HLW in the UK is much smaller, amounting to around 1200 cubic metres by 2030 which, according to the nuclear industry, is a volume sufficient to occupy a pair of semi-detached houses. For a variety of reasons, including deliberate obfuscation, it is difficult to establish really reliable figures for future radioactive waste arisings. Figure 8.2 gives a visual impression of the volumes of radioactive wastes by type compared with other categories of industrial wastes, against a background of Westminster.

*Box 8.1*

You may recollect that radioactivity is measured in terms of the becquerel (Bq) which has replaced the curie (Ci). In the UK LLW are now defined as wastes not exceeding 4 GBq/tonne of alpha or 12 GBq/tonne of beta or gamma which is about $3 \times 10^8$ Ci/tonne. In the USA all waste not classified as spent fuel, liquid HLW or transuranic (in simple terms, long-lived but non heat-producing) waste is LLW, though this is placed in different subclasses (a, b, c) according to activity.

Westminster to
Victoria Station
**Domestic waste**
40 000 000 m³

Houses of Parliament
**Solid toxic waste**
31 100 000 m³

Buckingham Palace

St James/Whitehall
**Industrial waste**
40 000 000 m³

Lambeth Bridge
to Hungerford
**Liquid toxic waste**
1 400 000 m³

County Hall
**Fly ash**
7 000 000 m³

Row of buses
**Intermediate-level waste**
2000 m³

Car park
**Low-level waste**
44 000 m³

Whitehall/River
**Coal mining waste**
25 000 000 m³

Taxi in foreground
**High-level waste**
30 m³

▲  Figure 8.2
*Volumes of total waste in the UK represented as proportions of central London.*

## 2.3   *The management of radioactive wastes*

If volume was the main concern, the problem of radioactive wastes would
be relatively easy to solve, compared with household refuse for instance.
It is, of course, the activity of the wastes that requires them to be isolated
from the accessible environment. HLW is heat generating with long-lived
radionuclides so that it requires cooling and subsequent safe management
for a period far longer in the future than we believe human civilisation has
existed in the past. Deep geological disposal in a repository with multiple
barriers to prevent escape of the radionuclides is regarded by the nuclear
industry as the most acceptable method of management for HLW and for
the longer lived ILW. Opponents of the nuclear industry argue that it is not
an acceptable solution and they advocate surface storage until a safe
method of management can be agreed.

### Activity 1

Identify some of the arguments for and against deep geological
disposal of HLW.

This debate is at the heart of the political problem of radioactive waste. In
nearly every country with HLW efforts have been made to identify suitable
locations for deep disposal; in every case such efforts have met with
opposition. There is, as yet, no deep repository opened to receive HLW.

By 1990, a purpose-built deep repository in the desert of south-east New Mexico, USA, designed to receive transuranic wastes from the military sites, had been constructed but not opened as a result of technical problems (Figure 8.3). Plans for siting deep repositories in the USA, UK, Germany and elsewhere have been consistently delayed both for technical reasons and as a result of political opposition.

Rather more progress has been made in the management of LLW and short-lived ILW. In the UK, shallow disposal of LLW has been undertaken at Drigg, near Sellafield, since 1959. The need for a further shallow repository was a source of political conflict as we shall see in Section 4. In France LLW is managed in a surface permanent storage facility near the reprocessing works at Cap de la Hague and a new site has been identified east of Paris. In the United States three shallow burial facilities are in operation in South Carolina, Nevada and Washington state and three have been closed as a result of technical problems involving leakage from the sites. The threat of closure of the remaining three sites has precipitated the formation of groupings of states (called regional compacts), and the difficult and controversial task of identifying new sites for the disposal of LLW. In Sweden a purpose-built repository for LLW and short-lived ILW has been opened about a kilometre under the Baltic Sea to the north of Stockholm. This 'Rolls-Royce' solution to the problem has been achieved in a country which has decided to phase out its nuclear energy programme by the year 2010.

## 2.4   The problem of radioactive wastes

In almost every country with a substantial nuclear industry the technical problems of managing nuclear wastes have been compounded by the increasing political difficulty in securing particular solutions. The nuclear industry provokes a pervasive, growing and consistent fear different from the anxiety caused by any other industry. It is not so much the possibility of harm (which may be recognised as remote) but the probability that the consequences will be catastrophic that arouses such fears. Local people are understandably worried about the potential dislocation that may be caused to their community if large volumes of radioactive rubbish is deposited near to where they live.

*Activity 2*

Do you remember the pie diagram in Chapter 1 of Book One of this series (*Silvertown & Sarre, 1990*, Figure 1.13) showing the sources of radiation exposure of the UK population? Before referring back to it can you think roughly how much of the exposure, in percentage terms, came from natural sources? How much came from radioactive waste?

Now check your answers with the diagram. Why should we be cautious in interpreting these statistics?

Over four-fifths of the average radiation dose received by people in the UK comes from natural sources and about a tenth from medical sources (*Silvertown & Sarre, 1990*, Chapter 1, Figure 1.13). Only 1.3% arises from the 'nuclear industry' and defence, of which it is calculated about 0.1% is from

▲   Figure 8.3    The Waste Isolation Pilot Plant near Carlsbad, New Mexico.

nuclear waste discharged into the environment. On this basis it might be supposed that nuclear waste can be dismissed as an environmental problem of any significance. It is the possible consequences of accidental leakage of wastes into the environment, from the repository or during transportation, that causes anxiety. People are anxious about nuclear activity and do not discriminate between the risks or consequences whether from a reactor melt-down or leakage from a low-level waste repository. All radioactivity is perceived to be dangerous regardless of source or intensity.

Q   Why do you think people are so concerned about radioactivity produced as a result of the nuclear fuel cycle? Jot down your answer and compare it with the one given below.

A   The risk from radioactivity produced by the nuclear industry is an *avoidable* risk; there are alternatives to nuclear energy that are less potentially harmful to human health. The claims that nuclear facilities are safe are belied by the evidence of leakages and accidents. The concentrations of radionuclides are such that, if an accident occurs, the consequences are catastrophic and *irreversible* extending over long time-scales because radioactivity cannot be halted. The characteristic of low probability/high consequence risk with irreversible and catastrophic consequences is one that the nuclear industry shares with other high-technology hazardous industries such as chemicals, as discussed in the previous chapter. But, in certain respects, the nuclear industry induces unique anxieties.

Q   Can you think of some of these?

A   Radioactive materials are immune to outside influences; they are
    indestructible and only become harmless through decay, which may
    take thousands of years. Radiation is dangerous by proximity as well as
    by ingestion or inhalation. It cannot be seen, touched or smelled – this
    very invisibility arouses fear. The nuclear industry is perceptibly linked
    to the destructive capability of the atomic bomb. Furthermore, though
    concentrations and activity may vary, radioactivity is perceived to be
    dangerous *whatever its source*. The possible links between leukaemia
    clusters and nuclear activities, discussed in *Silvertown & Sarre, 1990*,
    Chapter 1 and in Chapter 4 of this book, illustrate the increasing
    concern about the health effects of long-term exposure to low levels of
    radioactivity.

Ultimately all nuclear activity becomes radioactive waste. Military wastes
and those from the civil nuclear fuel cycle as well as manufacturing and
medical radioactive wastes must be acceptably controlled either through
containment or, for very low activity wastes, through dilution and
dispersion in the environment. This latter strategy has its own pitfalls. In
the USA, attempts to resolve the disposal problem of low activity, short-
lived radioactive wastes by deeming them 'Below Regulatory Concern'
have fallen foul of the charge that this change of definition is a sleight of
hand to allow such wastes to be co-disposed with household refuse in local
landfill sites. As the nuclear industry has developed and public anxiety has
grown, so it has become increasingly difficult to achieve acceptable
solutions to the management of nuclear wastes. The emergence of
radioactive waste as a political issue is the subject of the next section.

## 2.5   Summary

In this section we have covered the first two aims of this chapter. In certain
respects nuclear wastes are distinctively different from other hazardous
and toxic materials. In particular, the fear of radioactivity from whatever
source has made the management of radioactive wastes increasingly
controversial and a major cause of political conflict. Radioactivity arouses
greater fear than any other form of socially induced risk, and is a unique
problem.

Nuclear wastes are the residual materials from the production of
nuclear electricity, reprocessing, atom bomb manufacture and certain
industrial and medical processes. They constitute an environmental
problem in that they must be managed to ensure that radioactive materials
do not enter accessible environmental pathways and present a health risk.
Radioactive wastes are classified according to source and levels of activity.
These wastes are treated differently from other hazardous wastes. High-
level wastes, in the form of spent fuel or liquid wastes from reprocessing,
though very small in volume, are heat-generating and highly dangerous
and deep geological disposal is the proposed method of management. By
contrast low-level wastes have large volumes but short half-lives with low
radioactivity and are diluted or dispersed or buried in shallow repositories.
Whatever the statistical risks, public concern is now so developed that the
issue of nuclear waste facilities has become a source of political conflict.

# 3   The development of nuclear waste from a non-problem, to a technical problem, to a political problem

## 3.1   Early years: a non-problem

The origins of the problem of radioactive waste are found in the United States where the major military nuclear programme created the first large quantities of nuclear wastes. For centuries indigenous North American (and Australian) peoples used uranium as a colouring agent for glassware, or as an ingredient in paint for warfare or ceremonies. Since the late nineteenth century uranium and other radioactive elements had been used in Europe and North America for scientific experimentation, for medical purposes and for cosmetics. Many small companies dabbled with commercial uses of radioactive materials. As in all businesses, some went bankrupt. But what was left behind in this case was radioactive contamination and a legacy of radioactive residues which, along with those arising from the other uses, particularly laboratory research, created the first nuclear waste 'burden'. At the time these wastes were not regarded as a difficulty – and this perception became part of a later problem.

The problem revealed itself in differing ways over time. First to emerge were the radiation-induced illnesses of the workers and scientists who worked largely unprotected, many contracting various cancers directly attributable to exposure to radioactivity. Although some scientists, such as Marie Curie, an early pioneer in radioactive research, did die of cancer, this did not inhibit her colleagues and peers in continuing this experimentation, such was the fascination of the research. As research continued, radioactive waste built up.

By the mid-1930s, some of the best brains in chemistry and physics were devoted to nuclear science, in Europe, North America and elsewhere. As a result of a coincidence of history, many of these scientists came together in the late 1930s and the early 1940s in the United States and Canada. This collection of scientists made it possible for the United States to develop the atomic bomb, in secret, by 1945 and thereby created the institutional base for the post-war development of atomic energy for military and civil uses.

The American atomic bomb project ('The Manhattan Project') required the setting up of a range of large scale research and development establishments, such as at Los Alamos (New Mexico), Chalk River (Ontario, Canada) and Hanford (Washington state). For reasons of secrecy, primarily, but also safety, these major facilities were located in isolated areas. Following the end of the second world war, the United States also developed nuclear warhead testing sites in the Marshallese and Aleutian Islands in the Pacific Ocean and later in the Nevada desert, north of Las Vegas. Along with a proliferation of other smaller sites across the continental United States, this atomic bomb programme bequeathed an inestimable quantity of radioactive waste and on-site contamination. The problem was being created incrementally and went largely unrecognised and unremarked for some five decades. As a former manager in the US Atomic Energy Commission (the body given responsibility for the management of the project) put it: 'Chemists and engineers were not interested in dealing with waste. It was not glamorous; there were no careers; it was messy, nobody got 'Brownie points' for caring about nuclear waste. The Atomic Energy Commission neglected the problem' (Wilson, 1979).

The extent of the problem of radioactive wastes arising from the Manhattan Project has been the subject of several studies. One of these, published in 1980, indicated that at least 76 separate sites were formerly used in the project and 17 remain operational today. Many sites have high levels of radioactive contamination in the soil or in groundwater, leaving a substantial economic and environmental burden for the United States.

Hanford, a vast nuclear reservation in the sagebrush desert along the Columbia River in the north-western United States, provides an example of the creation of radioactive wastes in these early years. Hanford was the major centre of the plutonium manufacturing process. During the war there was serious consideration of the use of radiological weapons, based on nuclear waste derived from plutonium manufacture, in order to disperse fission products over enemy territory. More disturbing was the revelation that massive quantities of radioactive iodine-131 had been routinely released from exhaust stacks over the Hanford area. In one 1949 experiment, known as 'Green Run', iodine-131 was deliberately released over Hanford, and the resulting 200 by 40 mile plume was secretly measured. This experiment, unknown to the local population, resulted in radioactive contamination which exceeded the US Atomic Energy Commission's own 'tolerance levels' by 11 000 times over Hanford (and those tolerance levels were considerably higher than today's far more conservative permissible-exposure standards).

This casual approach to the risks was also present in the early systems for managing the radioactive wastes produced in Hanford's growing number of nuclear plants. One method was the pumping of liquid radioactive wastes directly into two deep wells that were drilled into the aquifer that passes underneath the site. Other wastes were deposited in earthen ditches, trenches, cribs, ponds, swamps, underground drains, as

---

# Soviet lake is most n-polluted spot

NEW YORK, Aug. 17 (AP)

Karachay lake, a 40-hectare body of water in the Soviet Union, could be "the most polluted spot on the planet", the result of years of radioactive waste dumping, a published report said.

American experts who recently visited a Soviet nuclear weapons production complex found extremely high levels of radioactive contamination and a history of very high doses to production workers, the New York Times reported yesterday.

The Soviets have confirmed that in 1951, atomic bomb makers began pumping radioactive wastes into Karachay lake – about 1,450 km east of Moscow – a practice that continued until the accumulation reached 120 million curies.

That amount is about two and a half times greater than the release from the Chernobyl nuclear accident in 1986.

"This has got to be the most polluted spot on the planet," said Mr. Thomas Cochran, a physicist and senior staff scientist at the National Resources Defence Council, a private environmental group in Washington DC.

The dose rate on the lake shore near the outlet pipe is 600 roengen per hour, according to a new report by Mr Cochran and Mr Robert Standish Norris, also at the Council.

At that rate one hour's exposure would kill a person within weeks, the Times reported.

The Times said Soviet documents described a "sanitary alienation zone" in contaminated areas in which people are forbidden to live or travel.

The size of the zone was not known.

◀ *Figure 8.4*
*Extract from*
*The Hindustan Times,*
*New Delhi,*
*18 August 1990.*

well as double-shelled steel tanks. Mainly arising from the underground disposal of liquid radioactive wastes, both the Columbia River (and areas downstream through which it flowed towards the Pacific Ocean) and the aquifer were seriously contaminated. Hanford has continued to provide a serious problem in the management of radioactive wastes. For example, there was a very serious leak of over 115 000 gallons of liquid radioactive waste from storage tanks in 1973. An official report stated in 1986 that there were over 200 areas within the Hanford reservation alone that were contaminated with radioactive leaks or spillages. Hanford remains the storage site for large volumes of all levels of radioactive wastes from the military programme, and has been earmarked as an appropriate site for the bulk decommissioning wastes from dismantled reactors, both those already on site and others around the USA.

Hanford is just one example, albeit a significant one, of how wastes were managed in the early years. Elsewhere in the United States and in the USSR, France and Britain nuclear defence resulted in the commissioning of plutonium-producing reactors and associated plant and the creation of nuclear wastes. The management of these wastes was a non-problem politically for several decades (Figure 8.4).

> ### Activity 3
>
> Can you suggest reasons why radioactive waste was a non-problem in these early years? Then read the suggested answer at the end of the chapter before continuing.

In these conditions it is possible to give unfettered primacy to the 'positive product' of the production process. The pollution and wastes that result are ignored. In a liberal democratic society such as the United States, such projects as the secret Manhattan Project and subsequent military nuclear programmes illustrate these characteristics. They are also found in centrally controlled economies. Information on the widespread industrial contamination, including toxic and radioactive wastes, was known before the political revolutions in eastern Europe in 1989 but the enormous extent of ecological damage has subsequently been widely publicised.

## 3.2   A matter for the experts

The Soviet Union, United Kingdom and a little later France and China followed the United States in the development of nuclear weapons programmes. By the 1950s these and many other countries had started civil nuclear energy programmes, heralded as the development of 'Atoms for Peace'. Electricity produced from nuclear fission was portrayed as cheap ('too cheap to meter' was a popular slogan at the time), clean and safe. While there was little concern about environmental impacts there was anxiety over the potential dangers of the spread, or proliferation, of military nuclear capability arising from the production of plutonium in civil nuclear programmes. This led to the establishment of international bodies to oversee the spread of civil nuclear technology. After the United Nations Atomic Energy Commission, which had a brief life in the late 1940s, another institution, the International Atomic Energy Agency (IAEA) was established under the wing of the United Nations, with strong support from the United States, in 1957. Regional nuclear bodies, such as the EEC's Euratom and what became the Organisation for Economic Co-operation and Development's (OECD) Nuclear Energy Agency, were established around the same time. Today all three bodies are concerned with the oversight of radioactive waste management strategies, policies and technologies. In the late 1950s radioactive waste was barely mentioned in their 'mission goals'.

During the 1950s, while international and inter-state atomic co-operation developed, exemplified by the Atoms for Peace conferences sponsored by the UN in Geneva, the main focus was upon reactors and fuel development and the diversified uses of atomic energy, not upon the inevitable waste arising. Public concern focused on the possibility of reactor accidents and was fanned by the accidents that actually occurred at Chalk River, Ontario, Canada in 1952, Windscale in 1957, Three Mile Island in Pennsylvania in 1979 and at Chernobyl in 1986. Such accidents can cause widespread contamination. They are dramatic and have contributed to a growing unease about the safety and environmental impact of nuclear energy, as well as providing a damaging blow to the economic case for nuclear reactors. The casualties arising from nuclear accidents are difficult to estimate. In the case of Chernobyl there were over 31 immediate deaths and around 130 000 people were evacuated from a heavily contaminated exclusion zone. The eventual death toll is unpredictable with estimates varying from 180 to 280 000 depending on the assumptions made. It is very difficult to compare the scale of such a disaster with other major industrial accidents. The leakage of methyl isocyanate from the Union Carbide pesticide plant at Bhopal, India, in 1984 caused 2500 deaths and over 250 000 suffering injuries of varying severity.

Nuclear waste accumulates gradually and does not generally give rise to spectacular incidents. Public concern about nuclear waste emerged slowly and developed at local and national level, only later becoming an international political problem. We shall use the example of the United Kingdom to illustrate this process of politicisation, though similar trends may be observed in other western democracies such as the United States, Germany, Sweden and, though to a lesser degree, France.

In the UK low activity liquid and gaseous wastes from atomic facilities were routinely discharged into the air, sea and local rivers. In the mid-1950s the UK Atomic Energy Authority (UKAEA) considered using abandoned mine shafts in the Forest of Dean, about 130 km from its main research centre at Harwell (Oxfordshire), for deep disposal of solid wastes. The plans were opposed by a local group known as the 'Free Miners' who claimed ancient rights to the Forest. This episode was the first example of local reaction in response to a proposal for nuclear waste disposal. This 'not in my back yard' (NIMBY) local protest against a proposal to use a new ('greenfield') site has been a key political component of the opposition to on-land disposal of nuclear waste, as we shall see.

At that time, no civil nuclear programme had yet been developed, so the volumes of waste were small, and the option of sea disposal, with no local opposition to confront, proved attractive. Consequently, the UKAEA withdrew the forest disposal proposal and returned in earnest to sea disposal in the north-east Atlantic Ocean, which had begun in 1949. After a brief and inconsequential public flourish, radioactive waste became once again a technical matter firmly in the hands of experts. For example, the 1955 White Paper, *A Programme of Nuclear Power* (HMSO, 1955) which launched the British civil nuclear programme, dismissed the problem of waste, stating 'the disposal of radioactive waste products would not present a major difficulty.'

Throughout the 1960s and early 1970s the civil and military nuclear programmes in the UK expanded. The Magnox reactor programme of nine power stations was completed and the advanced gas-cooled reactor (AGR) programme, fraught with technical difficulties and delays, was being brought into operation (for locations of nuclear sites in the UK see Figure 8.5). The military designated programme was also expanding and

◀   Figure 8.5
Location of nuclear
facilities in the UK.

Sellafield's operations were increasing. There was no local or national protest against the radioactive waste being concurrently created. The matter was addressed only peripherally in Parliament. While there was popular protest against nuclear weapons (the Campaign for Nuclear Disarmament's Aldermaston marches best exemplifying this) and against the Vietnam War in the late 1960s, the civil nuclear cycle was not a focus of popular opposition at this time.

Political concern for nuclear waste first became fully established during the mid-1970s. This was a decade when 'environmentalism' grew as a social and political phenomenon (*Silvertown & Sarre, 1990*, Chapter 7). It was also a period of energy crisis brought about by the national coal miners' strike in 1972 and the Middle East conflict leading to the rise in oil prices in 1973. Energy shortage brought nuclear energy and attendant reprocessing into greater prominence as a secure source of electricity. But the dangers were gradually becoming articulated, as is illustrated by the extracts from a letter to *The Guardian* signed by 43 senior scientists, environmentalists and former government policy advisers (Figure 8.6).

Q   Why was radioactive waste left mainly to the experts during the period up to the mid-1970s?

A   Attention became focused on the benefits of nuclear energy as the civil nuclear programme developed. Nuclear waste was not regarded as a serious problem, even by most experts. Wastes could be either routinely discharged into the environment, stored on site or disposed of at sea or on land at the low-level site at Drigg near Sellafield. By the mid-1970s some experts were beginning to express concern about radioactive waste, as the *Guardian* letter shows. The outstanding additional question remains: Why did radioactive waste from military programmes still remain in the shadows when civil wastes began to be assessed negatively?

## 3.3   The politicisation of radioactive wastes

The first authoritative and accessible account of the problems posed by radioactive waste in Britain is contained in the Sixth Report of the Royal Commission on Environmental Pollution (RCEP) on *Nuclear Power and the Environment* (HMSO, 1976). Out of 50 recommendations in the Report, 14 were devoted to nuclear waste. Two new organisations were recommended. One, a national waste disposal company, eventually became, in 1982, the Nuclear Industry Radioactive Waste Executive (NIREX), a body formed by partners in the nuclear industry to manage ILW and LLW. The other, an advisory body on waste management, became the Radioactive Waste Management Advisory Committee in 1978. The most oft-cited recommendation of the RCEP Report was:

> . . . There should be no commitment to a large programme of nuclear fission power until it has been demonstrated beyond reasonable doubt that a method exists to ensure the safe containment of long lived, highly radioactive waste for the indefinite future.   (para. 27)

The nuclear opposition took this to support their case that nuclear power should henceforth be halted. The nuclear industry, concentrating on the

# Nuclear dustbins for the centuries

Sir, – The debate, last year, about the choice of reactor system in the development of a nuclear power programme obscured the problems posed by the production of dangerous long-lived radioactive wastes which have to be kept away from the living environment for hundreds, and some for many thousands of years.

We are concerned that the production of electricity by any nuclear fission power plant is inescapably coupled with the production of hazardous radioactive materials and that all known methods of storing the waste require regular supervision. The problem of disposing of them safely has not been solved in spite of some 30 years of nuclear technology. The conversion of liquid wastes into stable solids would merely make storage easier; it will not remove their dangerous properties.

Each reactor continually produces waste for disposal and only stops when it is closed down. Apart from these wastes the commitment to fission involves the containment of vast amounts of radioactive materials in reactors and in processing plants and in transit between plant and storage points at all times.

We noted the Government's decision not to order the American designed light water reactors but instead to adopt the British steam generating heavy water reactor (SGHWR) for the next programme of nuclear power stations and that this programme is a reduction in size on the original proposals.

We were pleased when it was announced in April last year that the Royal Commission on Environmental Pollution was to conduct an inquiry into the safety of the storage and disposal of all radioactive waste from nuclear power stations. The Government did not, however, wait for any report of these inquiries before making its decision to proceed with the nuclear power programme.

We do not think that any society, or its government, can guarantee safety to future generations from these deadly materials for one hundred years, let alone the many thousands that are involved. We cannot guarantee them against foreseeable dangers – we know that the best intentioned men are fallible and can make mistakes; we know that men with bad intentions indulge in acts of sabotage, theft and terrorism and we also know that plutonium is the raw material of atom bombs.

Our nuclear power programme represents a Faustian bargain in which we are jeopardising the safety of future generations and their environment for our own short-term energy benefits and the comforts that go with them. We consider that it is immoral and unwise to pursue a technology which will leave such a dangerous legacy to posterity.

We are, therefore, opposed to the building of any more nuclear power stations at least while there is no safe and proven method of disposing of the long-lived radioactive wastes.

We are convinced that there are other ways of tackling our energy problems. We should be much more economical in the use of the energy already available to us. We should make use of all heat produced and not waste it as we currently do from most of our buildings, power stations and municipal incinerators. Priority should be given to the development of techniques that utilise non-polluting energy sources such as the sun, wind, waves and organic wastes. These are the areas in which we should concentrate our major research and development efforts.

Yours faithfully,

D. Bryce Smith (Professor of Organic Chemistry, University of Reading); Sally Cane (Youth Organiser, Population Countdown); Irene Coates (Chairman, The Conservation Society); Gerry Davis (author and TV script writer, co-author of Doomwatch); P. D. Dunn (Professor of Engineering Science, University of Reading); (Dr) P. N. Edmunds (Consultant Bacteriologist, Fife Health Board); John Foster (Department of Political Economy, Glasgow University); Peter Hain (Former Chairman, Young Liberals); (Prof) John Hawthorn (Department of Food Science and Nutrition, University of Strathclyde); J. Owen Jones (Director, Commonwealth Bureau of Agricultural Economics); T. W. B. Kibble (Professor of Theoretical Physics, Imperial College of Science and Technology); F. Lafitte (Professor of Policy and Social Administration, University of Birmingham); Gerald Leach (Former science correspondent, the Observer; Fellow of the International Institute for Environment and Development); Laurie Lee; (Dr) John Loraine (Medical Research Council, External Scientific Staff, Dept. of Community Medicine, University of Edinburgh); (Dr) Richard Marshall (Department of Physics, University of Keele); (Rt. Rev) Hugh Montefiore (Bishop of Kingston); (Prof.) J. K. Page (Building Science, Sheffield University); (Dr) Kit Pedlar (Opthalmic surgeon; co-author of Doomwatch); (Dr) Robert Perrin (Lecturer in Soil Science, University of Cambridge); Lady Robson (Chairman, Liberal Party Environment Panel); G. F. C. Rogers (Professor of Engineering Thermodynamics, University of Bristol); Richard Sandbrook (Director, Friends of the Earth); (Dr) E. F. Schumacher (Founder-Chairman Intermediate Technology Development Group; President, the Soil Association); Cedric A. B. Smith (Weldon Professor of Biometry, Department of Human Genetics and Biometry, University College, London); (Sir) Kelvin Spencer (Former Chief Scientist, Ministry of Power); M. W. Thring (Professor of Mechanical Engineering, Queen Mary College, London); Graham Tope, and 13 others. London.

words, 'demonstrated beyond reasonable doubt', took it as an endorsement of their intention to continue exploration of practical geological disposal sites for the accumulating nuclear wastes. The RCEP lent support to the latter interpretation by calling for a national land disposal facility for the more highly active wastes but was scathing about waste management policy:

▲ Figure 8.6
A letter to The Guardian, 7 January 1974.

The picture that emerges from our review of radioactive waste management is in many ways a disquieting one, indicating insufficient appreciation of long term requirements either by government departments or by other organisations concerned. In view of the long lead times that will almost certainly be involved in the development of appropriate disposal facilities, we are convinced that a much more urgent approach is needed, and that responsibilities for devising policy and for executing it need to be more clearly assigned.    (para. 427)

The magnitude of the problem was first established by the public inquiry into a planned new reprocessing plant (the Thermal Oxide Reprocessing Plant, THORP); modification of the Magnox reprocessing plant; and construction of a vitrification research plant at Windscale in 1977 (Box 8.2). The role of Sellafield (i.e. Windscale plus Calder Hall) is discussed in *Silvertown & Sarre, 1990*, Chapter 1, and the problem of discharges is considered in Chapter 4 of this book. The THORP plant was designed to process spent fuel from the AGR reactor programme and also (crucially for its economics) spent fuel imported from other countries, raising new questions of international co-operation, trade and cost–benefit assessments. The public inquiry into the Windscale proposals, which lasted 100 days, was the first of three major inquiries into nuclear projects. The other two were the inquiry into the first pressurised water reactor (PWR) proposal at Sizewell, which lasted a record 333 days during 1983–85, and the Hinkley Point C inquiry into the second PWR, lasting 182 days in 1988–89 (for locations see Figure 8.5).

The Windscale inquiry has been described in detail elsewhere (e.g. Pearce *et al.*, 1979; Williams, 1980). If the proposals were to be approved, objectors stressed that they would lead to a manifold *increase* in the volumes of ILW and LLW. There would also be a sevenfold *decrease* in the volume, though not the radioactivity, of HLW. The liquid HLW would be vitrified into blocks that could eventually be buried in a deep repository. The scale of the potential trade and the problems of dealing with imported wastes were controversial and attracted Parliamentary questioning and

## Box 8.2

Reprocessing separates out uranium and plutonium from spent fuel. The liquid high-level wastes that remain are stored in stainless steel tanks. Vitrification is a process whereby the liquid wastes are mixed with glass-making materials and converted into solid glass-like form. These blocks will be stored and cooled and it is intended that they will eventually be emplaced in a deep repository. The Sellafield vitrification plant proposal was similar to the plant operating in France.

*The figure shows volume of waste from spent nuclear fuel before and after reprocessing. Volumes are per year per 1000 MW$_e$ pressurised water reactor.*

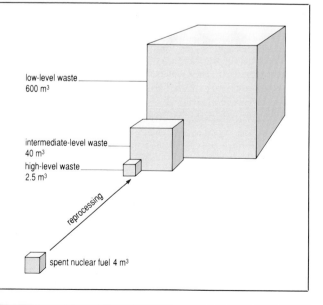

low-level waste
600 m³

intermediate-level waste
40 m³

high-level waste
2.5 m³

reprocessing

spent nuclear fuel 4 m³

some public protest. But the Windscale inquiry was essentially a debate among experts about technical matters which had increasingly prominent political overtones.

Windscale had first achieved notoriety in 1957 when a fire in the plutonium production plant released radioactivity into the atmosphere. Studies released by official sources during the 1980s indicated perhaps between 33 and 200 people may have suffered cancers from this radiation release. In 1973, 35 workers were contaminated by an accident causing a reprocessing plant to be shut down permanently. Concern about reprocessing foreign waste began to interest the Press, provoking such front-page headlines as PLAN TO MAKE BRITAIN THE WORLD'S FIRST NUCLEAR DUSTBIN in the *Daily Mirror* in October 1975. Later, in 1983, the television documentary, *Windscale – the Nuclear Laundry*, drew attention to the possibility of childhood leukaemia associated with the plant.

The public and political debate surrounding Windscale (later renamed Sellafield), beginning in the later 1970s, has had a formative influence on the politicisation of radioactive waste. It provided an opportunity for technical debate of the issues and created a small group of nuclear experts not beholden to the nuclear industry or government who could provide scientific support to opponents of radioactive waste plans in future years. It provided a forum to educate the media who, therefore, could call on journalists with a credible expertise in nuclear waste to conduct investigative research. It also showed that nuclear issues could provide a compelling story line. The planning proposals were eventually approved, but the Windscale inquiry established reprocessing in the media mind and wider public consciousness as an international enterprise creating substantial volumes of low-activity wastes and also underlined the problem of managing HLW. Disposal of HLW was the first of a series of radioactive waste issues which developed during the 1980s in which the nuclear industry and government were forced to retreat in the face of opposition to their plans.

## 3.4   HLW – a victory for local opposition

The Royal Commission on Environmental Pollution's proposal that a comprehensive search should be undertaken to assess the suitability of various geological strata for the prospective deep disposal of vitrified HLW was followed up by the government in the years 1976–81. The UKAEA commissioned the Institute of Geological Sciences to undertake a borehole drilling programme at various sites in crystalline rock formations in Scotland, Cornwall, mid Wales and Northumberland. A range of other sites in different formations in England (Leicestershire, Nottinghamshire and Avon) were also considered but dropped from the programme after objections were raised. Opposition also developed against the programme in the chosen sites.

The conflict over the HLW drilling proposals first established four of the features which subsequently characterised the politics of nuclear waste.

1    The use of specialist counter-expertise to oppose nuclear facilities. The availability of technical arguments to support their case meant that the opposition could confront the nuclear industry on more equal terms, at least in regard to knowledge, if not resources, at inquiries as well as by conducting a campaign through the media.

2     The development of local groups able to mobilise the local community and public opinion against an external threat. Efforts were made to get the support of local councils and the conventional armoury of protests (marches, petitions, newsletters) were used in campaigns. These local pressure groups were inspired by a NIMBY defence of amenity and environment and, in the case of Ayrshire and mid Wales, they had distinct nationalist overtones, too.

3     The ability of these local groups to gain the support and assistance of other opposition groups in different areas of the country to advise on expertise, strategies and tactics of opposition and fund-raising. This empowerment of one local group by others transcended purely local NIMBY concerns and became a major feature of later conflicts over nuclear waste disposal sites.

4     The difficulty of establishing nuclear facilities in 'greenfield' locations. In every case where drilling was proposed in areas without existing nuclear facilities, the plans were vigorously opposed. Only in Caithness, an area heavily dependent on the Dounreay fast breeder reactor plant, was permission to drill granted. As we shall see, after another decade of futile effort to achieve greenfield locations for nuclear waste facilities, the government had to fall back on its 'nuclear oases' where, at least, some support can be secured from communities familiar with and dependent upon the nuclear industry.

The government abandoned its HLW borehole drilling programme in 1981. The conflict had been essentially local although some liaison between opposition groups did take place. The next conflict over radioactive waste brought in a national and international political dimension.

## 3.5   *The end of sea dumping*

For many years Britain had organised the dumping of nuclear wastes (four-fifths British, the rest from Belgium, Switzerland and Holland) in the ocean, first off Alderney and latterly in the north-east Atlantic. Disposal by the United States in the Atlantic and Pacific Oceans had ceased in 1970. In 1972 the Convention on the Prevention of Marine Pollution by Dumping of Wastes and Other Materials (The London Dumping Convention or LDC) was adopted and was ratified by the UK in 1975. The LDC sets the norms, guidelines and recommendations for the disposal of wastes, including radioactive wastes, at sea. It expressly forbids ocean bed 'emplacement' of HLW. The campaign to oppose the dumping of LLW and ILW at sea was initially led from 1978 by Greenpeace, at that time a newly established environmental pressure group which, at first, attempted to blockade ships bringing spent nuclear fuel to Sellafield from Japan. Its campaign was based on a desire to disrupt a trade of which Greenpeace disapproved rather than one it had proof was environmentally damaging.

Greenpeace secured dramatic impact by attempting to stop the dumping in the Atlantic using inflatable dinghies and publicising film of the crew of one dinghy being thrown into the water by a waste barrel dropped from the disposal vessel. There followed a series of 'media stunts' designed to ensure the issue maintained its prominence. Having achieved publicity, Greenpeace then turned its attention to influencing the LDC from its position as an observer using various reports to undermine the credibility of sea dumping. By 1983 the combination of lobbying and spectacular protest was having an effect, and the LDC agreed by 19 votes to 6 with 6 abstentions (the UK opposing) to a two-year moratorium on sea dumping. The UK did not have to accede to the decision but its position was further compromised when the major transport unions, lobbied by Greenpeace and led by the National Union of Seamen, agreed to ban dumping in the Atlantic. Protests against the UK's intended dumping occurred in Spain, Holland, Denmark and New Zealand. In August 1983, the government conceded defeat and abandoned the annual dumping. In 1988 the government formally announced it would not dump drummed waste at sea while keeping an option open on the possible future sea disposal of irradiated waste from closed-down reactors and submarines.

Q    Why did radioactive waste become a political issue during the 1970s?

A    An obvious reason is that the problem was getting physically larger as the nuclear programmes expanded and attention began to turn to the problems at the back-end of the nuclear fuel cycle as Britain began to trade in spent nuclear fuel and waste. At the same time scientific experts and government (for example, the RCEP) were beginning to consider the problem and to formulate policies. The emerging environmentalism created a climate of public concern and debate and the media focused on the problem. Public confidence in the nuclear industry began to weaken and consequently undermined the public acceptability of the proposals for the management of nuclear wastes.

Above all, it was the opportunity presented by specific proposals that established nuclear waste as an issue of political conflict. The Windscale inquiry focused scientific and technical attention on nuclear waste whereas the HLW drilling proposals transformed the radioactive waste into a subject of popular local political protest. The long-established sea dumping of nuclear waste became a suitable target for a campaign led by environmentalists able to exploit the opportunities of media publicity and lobbying.

## 3.6  Summary

The third aim of this chapter is to explain how radioactive waste has shifted from being a non-problem to a technical problem to a political problem. During the early period when nuclear activity was essentially military, radioactive waste was, politically at least, a non-problem. Shrouded in secrecy, the accidental, experimental and routine releases of radioactive wastes were not revealed to the public until much later, if at all. As the civil nuclear programme developed, governments and international agencies formulated guidelines and policies for the management of wastes but these were predominantly a technical matter arousing little political or public interest. This was largely true of the Windscale inquiry, the first occasion in which nuclear waste was subject to open public scrutiny and debate.

Arising from the technical debates of the RCEP and the Windscale inquiry, the HLW borehole drilling programme first precipitated local opposition to nuclear waste. Mutual aid between communities was a factor in increasing support and preventing the drilling programme. Use of publicity and lobbying techniques was a key factor in defeating the sea dumping programme. By 1983 radioactive waste was a subject of open public debate and conflict. The protagonists had become evenly matched and the context for the conflict over on-land shallow disposal of LLW and ILW had been set.

OBSERVER David Austin

WE NEED A ROCK FORMATION WITH NO FAULTS AND A LOCAL ENVIRONMENTAL GROUP WITH A RIFT.

SITES FOR NUCLEAR DUMPING

U.K.A.E.A

# 4   *Radioactive waste – the political consequences*

## 4.1   *A problem of time and place*

With the abandonment of the HLW drilling programme and of sea
dumping of ILW and LLW, the options for radioactive waste management
had been considerably narrowed. Accordingly, the government turned its
attention to on-land disposal of ILW and HLW. In October 1983, less than
two months after the ending of sea dumping, the Secretary of State for the
Environment announced that 'effective disposal, in ways which have been
shown to be safe, is well within the scope of modern technology' (*Hansard*,
25 October 1983, col. 156). NIREX simultaneously identified two sites
which it considered 'most worthy of detailed investigation' (NIREX, 1983,
p. 1). One was a disused anhydrite mine owned by Imperial Chemical
Industries at Billingham on Tees-side for the disposal of long-lived ILW.
The other site was a wartime munitions store at Elstow near Bedford
owned by the Central Electricity Generating Board (CEGB) where a
shallow repository would be constructed for the management of short-
lived ILW and to provide capacity for LLW in addition to Drigg (for
locations see Figure 8.5). This proposal inaugurated a political conflict
lasting nearly four years, 1983–87. This conflict will be used to evaluate the
political consequences and possibilities of radioactive waste management,
the fourth aim of this chapter.

   The fundamental cause of the political conflict is the anxiety about the
effects on the local environment and health extending down the
generations. Radioactive waste raises political problems of equity between
places and between generations.

Q   Can you indicate the nature of these problems of equity? Consider,
   first, equity between places and then equity over time between
   generations. In each case it may help to think in terms of costs and
   benefits.

A   The problem of equity between places may be called the problem of
   *spatial equity*. A radioactive waste facility is a LULU (locally unwanted
   land use) except possibly in those places where such facilities already
   exist and are accepted by the local population. The costs of radioactive
   waste disposal (blighting effects, health risks, and amenity concerns)
   are imposed on specific localities. The benefits of nuclear electricity are
   spread widely over the community in general. Nuclear waste brings
   few local benefits apart from a small number of jobs and, in some cases,
   compensation in the form of community facilities, infrastructure and
   tax relief. Certainly compensation is regarded as a necessary
   component in any radioactive waste management proposal. But, the
   perceived costs outweigh the benefits, a point that is politically
   confirmed by the opposition to nuclear waste facilities at greenfield
   sites, illustrated in the case study that follows.

      Equity between generations is called *intergenerational equity*. The
   benefits of nuclear technology accrue to the present generation and,
   through technology transfer, arguably to immediate future
   generations. There can be little certainty that the technology will
   continue to be of benefit in the future while the cost of waste

management will inevitably fall on generations far into the future. It is easier to estimate short-term benefits than to calculate long-term costs. The needs of the future tend to be discounted or ignored unless they have some palpable impact on the present.

The nuclear industry, governments and environmentalists agree on the need to manage radioactive wastes safely for local communities and future generations. Whereas the nuclear interests argue that safety is assured by the disposal methods proposed, their opponents claim that waste management proposals lack the technical verification necessary for public acceptability. The problem of uncertainty and credibility was at the heart of the conflict over radioactive waste in the UK during the mid-1980s.

## 4.2   A premature proposal

Billingham and Elstow were announced without prior consultation with the communities or any public discussion of the disposal methods and strategy which had led to the particular sites being selected. The two local communities mobilised public opinion and marshalled expertise in order to challenge the proposals on grounds of technology, strategy and acceptability.

The technology of deep burial at Billingham and shallow disposal at Elstow was justified by reference to scientific consensus and experience elsewhere. NIREX argued that 'there is a wide consensus that the use of existing technology can lead to the disposal of radioactive wastes in a very safe manner' (NIREX, 1983, p. 3). However, there was no technology comparable to that proposed in operation anywhere else. In the United States burial of wastes in salt vaults had been debated and a facility was under construction, but not in operation, in New Mexico. As for shallow burial, there was no experience of an engineered repository in a clay formation as proposed at Elstow. The French site was essentially an engineered surface facility and in Sweden an engineered repository was being constructed in crystalline rocks under the Baltic. In the United States where three sites were in operation and three had been closed, shallow burial was undertaken without the protective barriers proposed by NIREX. Drigg was similarly unprotected, though problems with its operation were used by opponents to undermine the credibility of the quite different engineered repository proposed for Elstow.

The selection of specific techniques and sites for disposal in advance of publicly evaluating other options indicated an absence of an overall strategy for radioactive waste management. NIREX and the government were exposed to the criticism that they had acted prematurely on the basis of a pragmatic rather than rational assessment of the possibilities. The fact that the Department of the Environment did not produce its policy statement, *Radioactive Waste Management: the National Strategy*, until the Sizewell B inquiry during 1984, seemed to confirm the absence of a coherent approach to the problem.

The absence of a publicly debated analysis including such factors as risk assessment, volumes and activity of waste arising and management options, enabled opponents to claim that the proposals lacked acceptability. They argued that any public inquiry into specific site proposals must include, and preferably be preceded by, an analysis of the generic issues and a comparative assessment of potential sites. The premature announcement of the two sites enabled the local communities

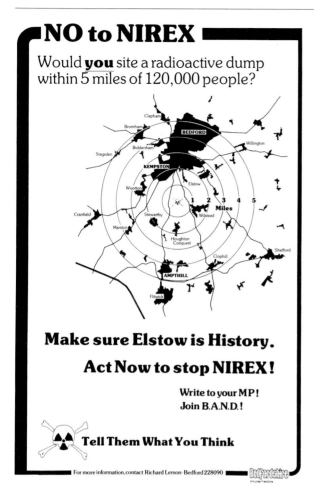

**NO to NIREX**

Would **you** site a radioactive dump within 5 miles of 120,000 people?

**Make sure Elstow is History.**

**Act Now to stop NIREX!**

Write to your MP!
Join B.A.N.D.!

☠ **Tell Them What You Think**

For more information, contact Richard Lemon - Bedford 228090

◀ *Figure 8.7*
*Publicity material used in the campaign at Elstow, Bedfordshire.*

to appeal to general principles rather than simply exhibit a NIMBY reaction. This gave widespread credibility to their campaigns against the proposals (Figure 8.7).

## 4.3 *The power of local action*

Opposition to the proposals in principle was backed by campaigns against the specific choice of Billingham and Elstow. In each community public meetings were held shortly after the announcement, and pressure groups, each with the acronym BAND (Billingham/Bedfordshire Against Nuclear Dumping) were set up. At Billingham the repository already existed, connected by road and rail within a conurbation of half a million people. The proposal to dispose of long-lived alpha-emitting wastes there provoked great anxiety. Billingham's BAND organised a petition of 85 000 signatures, lobbied Parliament, and held vigils, public meetings and demonstrations (Figure 8.8). Imperial Chemical Industries (ICI) who had at first co-operated with NIREX were sensitive to the pressures of local opinion and announced in March 1984: 'Having carefully considered the implications that the proposal would have for its business, ICI has concluded that it would not be in the company's best interests and is

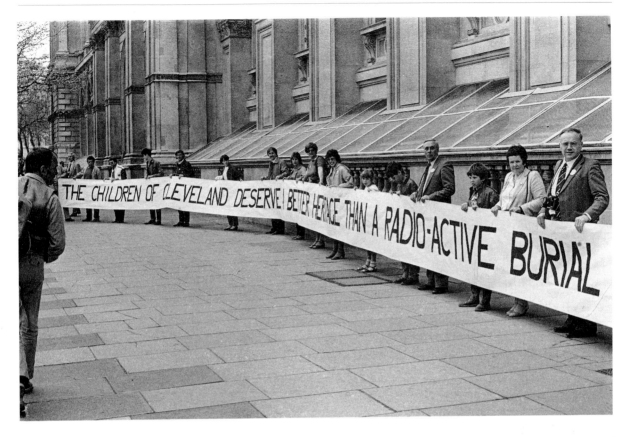

THE CHILDREN OF CLEVELAND DESERVE BETTER HERIAGE THAN A RADIO-ACTIVE BURIAL

▲   Figure 8.8
Billingham Against Nuclear
Dumping take a petition to
Downing Street.

therefore opposed to it.' This was to prove decisive since NIREX was
thereby denied access to the mine and the government would be sensitive
to the power of local opinion.

The conditions in Bedfordshire were different. The Elstow site was in a
rural area, though close to a town of 50 000 people, and its owners, the
CEGB, with no significant investment in the area, a partner in NIREX, and
a major creator of radioactive wastes, were unlikely to capitulate to local
opposition. Moreover, Elstow was destined to take the less dangerous
short-lived ILW and also LLW for which a disposal route at Drigg already
existed. The campaign against the Elstow proposal, after an initial flurry,
lacked the national political impact generated at Billingham. But the
Bedfordshire County Council were employing technical consultants and
developing technical counter-expertise to be used in the event of public
inquiry. In particular they challenged the selection of Elstow on grounds of
hydrogeology, land use and location, arguing that a comparative
assessment of sites should be undertaken.

Billingham's campaign was unequivocally successful. In January 1985
the Secretary of State for the Environment announced that NIREX had
agreed 'not to proceed further with that site'. Bedfordshire's more muted
campaign had secured an important concession that NIREX should 'select
and announce two further sites for investigation in addition to Elstow'.

Q   Reflecting on what you have just read, what do you think were the
main political reasons for the government's abandonment of the
Billingham proposal and its agreement to a comparative assessment of
sites for shallow burial?

A   Whatever the technical arguments, the proposals had been presented
without prior consultation and in the absence of a publicly debated
national strategy. Two specific sites had been selected, one for each
category of wastes, without any reasoned justification of the site
selection process. This provided the local communities with an
opportunity to oppose the sites on grounds of general principles and
the lack of a comparative assessment. They were able to generate
technical expertise, mobilise local opinion and argue on technical and
ethical grounds rather than self-interest. The rationality and political
impact of their arguments persuaded the government to retreat. By
abandoning Billingham, only shallow disposal on land was left as an
option under active consideration.

## 4.4   Collaboration and coalition

It was over a year before three (rather than two) further sites for
investigation were announced in February 1986. They were a CEGB-owned
site in an industrial and port area at South Killingholme on the Humber
estuary; a former airfield owned by the Ministry of Defence at Fulbeck in
the farmlands of south Lincolnshire; and a site near one of the early
Magnox power stations at Bradwell on the Blackwater estuary in Essex (for
locations see Figure 8.5). Local action groups sprang up in each area using
the familiar acronym (HAND, LAND, NAND, EAND; Humberside/
Lincolnshire/Nottinghamshire/Essex Against Nuclear Dumping) and
emulating the tactics – press publicity, petitions, and fund-raising events –
already employed in Billingham and Elstow (Figure 8.9).

The opposition to individual sites was consolidated by alliances
between the four areas which transcended purely local interests. Three of
the county councils (Bedfordshire, Humberside and Lincolnshire) formed a
County Councils Coalition, which pooled technical information, employed
Parliamentary lobbyists and agreed tactics and a longer-term strategy to
defeat the proposals through the public inquiry process. For local political
reasons, the fourth county council, Essex, did not join the coalition. The
four local action groups, together with Billingham's BAND, established a
national organisation, Britain Opposed to Nuclear Dumping (BOND), to
co-ordinate publicity and political action. Both the Coalition and BOND
emphasised the case against the concept of shallow disposal as proposed
by NIREX, leaving the local groups to identify the case against the specific
sites. The political context for success for these alliances proved propitious.

In March 1986 the House of Commons Environment Committee
published a Report on Radioactive Waste which confirmed the Coalition's
view that the UK was 'still only feeling its way towards a coherent policy'
and that the NIREX proposals revealed a 'premature and uncoordinated
approach' (HMSO, 1986, paras 3 and 58). The Report also criticised the
method of classifying wastes, the lack of adequate research and
development into disposal options and the failure to overcome public
anxiety by greater openness and discussion. Not surprisingly the Coalition
was gratified 'to find such an overwhelming weight of opinion coming
round to our way of thinking'.

On 26 April, 1986 the world was transfixed by the disaster at
Chernobyl. The immediate consequences were over 30 deaths and the
evacuation of the surrounding area, while the radiation cloud
contaminated a vast area to the north and west affecting livestock and food

▲  Figure 8.9
Lincolnshire Against
Nuclear Dumping
protesters at Fulbeck.

supplies. The longer term effects are still being calculated but it is already clear that premature deaths and genetic effects will persist far into the future. Public opinion on nuclear energy, already sceptical as a result of the leakages and fears of leukaemia at Sellafield, was further hardened by Chernobyl. In the wake of the disaster and, in the light of the House of Commons Report, the government withdrew its proposals to bury short-lived ILW in shallow repositories.

The government intended to pursue its remaining option, the shallow burial of LLW, by means of a Special Development Order (SDO). An SDO is a device whereby Parliament, not the local authority, gives permission for a development, in this case exploratory drilling at each of the four sites. This decision was regarded by the local communities as a means of avoiding an early debate on the general issues, enabling exploration to identify the best site and to hold a subsequent public inquiry which focused mainly on the comparative advantages of that site.

With the SDO in operation, contractors were appointed to undertake exploratory drilling at each site. When they arrived at South Killingholme, Fulbeck and Elstow in August 1986, and at Bradwell in September, they were confronted by well-organised blockades which prevented entry to the sites. Eventually the contractors secured entry to the sites but not before the blockades had generated sufficient publicity to ensure that nuclear waste became a national political issue.

Members of the County Councils Coalition toured nuclear waste facilities in Sweden, Germany and France and pronounced these countries 'far more advanced than the UK in the development of policies and practices for the disposal of radioactive waste' (County Councils Coalition, 1987, p. 1). They recommended that co-disposal of both ILW and LLW in a deep repository was a cost-effective and safe means of managing nuclear wastes and would command public acceptability.

It was by now clear that shallow burial lacked political credibility. Opposition had been generated crossing political, social and geographical boundaries. Although each site was in a safe Conservative-held constituency, the government was undoubtedly sensitive to the hostility the proposals had generated. Accordingly, on 1 May, 1987, the eve of the announcement of a general election, the then Secretary of State for the Environment, Nicholas Ridley, withdrew the proposals for shallow burial. In an exchange of letters with the Chairman of NIREX he accepted the case for co-disposal of ILW and LLW in a deep repository as 'the responsible course of action'.

> *Activity 4*
>
> Can you suggest why the comparative assessment of four sites weakened rather than strengthened the government's position?

In terms of future policy two points had been established. One was that disposal in a deep repository would be the *technical* solution to the problem. The other was that disposal in a greenfield location was unlikely to be a feasible *political* option.


## 4.5    *Retreat to the nuclear oases*

With the surrender of the shallow burial option, the government and NIREX had to begin all over again in the search for a technically suitable and politically feasible solution. It was evident that certain political lessons had been absorbed when NIREX published a discussion document, *The Way Forward*, towards the end of 1987. It aimed 'to promote public understanding of the issues' (p. 4) by open discussion on site selection, environmental protection and local participation in the development. Although the technical options were limited to deep disposal of ILW and LLW, three concepts (under land, off shore and under sea) were under consideration. Potentially suitable sites were likely to be found in areas of hard rock in Scotland, islands mainly off the Scottish coast and sedimentary rocks stretching down the eastern side of England and down the north-west from the Solway Firth to the Wirral. There was, therefore, a large territory in which to find a politically suitable site.

The consultation revealed, predictably, no unanimity of view. There was general support for the concept of deep disposal in principle but opposition to specific sites. There was a sense of political inevitability in the eventual choice, in March 1989, of Sellafield and Dounreay as sites for further investigation. In *The Way Forward*, Sellafield, as the main source of ILW, was considered 'worth careful scrutiny'. During the consultation the Highland Regional Council had recognised the potential of Dounreay, and Caithness District Council had indicated that NIREX should be invited to test for a repository. Copeland District Council, which includes Sellafield, welcomed the new approach to disposal, and British Nuclear Fuels announced plans to investigate the possibility of an offshore sub-seabed repository. In making the selection of these two remote nuclear oases Nicholas Ridley commented, 'it would be best to explore first those sites where there is some measure of local support for civil nuclear activities' (*Hansard*, 21 March, 1989, cols 505–6) (Figure 8.10).

# Man who hopes to see N-dump under his garden

❏ JOHN VASS

Today, we present one side to the nuclear waste disposal sites controversy and tomorrow the other.

First, the case as put by a leading supporter of a national waste repository at Dounreay – a Highland Regional councillor who expects it to go, not in, but extending under his back garden, for he lives within a mile of the Dounreay reactor.

He is consultant engineer Roy Gilbert, who worked at the Dounreay plant for many years. He claims to have been 30 years in the nuclear industry. He says the prospect of sleeping above a nuclear dump holds no fears for him.

He believes the nuclear power industry has clearly demonstrated there is no supportable objections on safety grounds and that the proposed low and intermediate radioactive waste disposal facility is innocuous in general industrial terms – and quite insignificant, radiologically.

He said: "I have difficulty seeing the hazards suggested by the opponents of the Nirex project. It is an inert material we are talking about, and the low-level waste which is discarded – overalls, gloves and suchlike – is really quite safe to handle. And when the intermediate waste is mixed in cement slurry as it will be, that too will be perfectly safe."

He added: "However, I can understand people being frightened about it because of the very able public-relations campaign run by the groups opposing Nirex.

"People are swayed by all the emotive stuff they put out, but it's codswallop, mainly. Also, they are bombarded with scare stories in the media.

"If people want to oppose the Nirex project on political grounds, that is fine by me but what I cannot accept are those who say their opposition is really for the sake of their children and their children's children."

> **Quote** "From my point of view, I do believe that, if you look carefully at the 'expert opinion' on offer, you will find that a vast majority of that which is anti-nuclear is anything but expert, but is riding a hobby-horse of some political shade."
>
> *Councillor Roy Gilbert*

He went on: "Some 10 to 15 years ago, the protest organisation 'Friends of the Earth' and their militant-offspring 'Greenpeace' embarked on a major long-term campaign to besmirch, denigrate and discredit the nuclear power industry. They have gathered other smaller, less professional but no-less vocal groups around them. This would have been of little consequence but for the enthusiastic attention they received from the mass communications media."

Mr Godfrey went on: "However, it is not good enough to ignore facts in preference to a perception which has been deliberately and pejoratively generated.

For a small budget, the professional protesters – those

who make a comfortable living campaigning against most commercial, industrial or developmental ventures, have been enormously successful in gaining acceptance of their erroneous image on nuclear waste disposal."

But Mr Godfrey accepts that Nirex have to mount a major public relations campaign and put across the proposals in acceptable form to the public to counter the anti-Nirex propaganda.

"The essence of the problems surrounding the Nirex proposals is, quite simply, to be found in public perception," he states.

With Government funding being withdrawn from the prototype fast reactor programme in 1994, and its associated fuel re-processing plants in 1997, the Atomic Energy Authority are desperate for ways to raise money to sustain these.

> **Quote** "I cannot see that a nuclear-waste repository would have the slightest effect on farming and fishing."
>
> *Councillor Roy Gilbert*

Although the AEA feed the National Grid with vast quantities of electrical power, they receive just over a penny a unit – although it costs many times that to produce – so there is no chance of that becoming a money-spinner. Many people in the industry, therefore, see the prospect of a nuclear waste repository as a major source of revenue, as well as a provider of several hundred jobs.

Mr Gilbert says he accepts this is an obvious and strong influence on the thinking of many people in Caithness.

Nirex have not yet started drilling exploratory boreholes at Dounreay, although preparatory work is in hand, said Nirex spokesman Mr Harry Hudson yesterday.

"Drilling is not expected to start for another month," he added. Nirex had intended a series of public meetings to explain their general plans. However, these have been called off because of the sudden illness of the company's managing director.

But in a recent briefing, the company pointed out that a further programme of seismic surveying is planned, together with detailed transport and environmental studies to create a three-dimensional "picture" of the site at Dounreay. They point out these investigations will take them into next year and it could be 1992 before a final decision is taken on the suitability of Caithness as a site.

Similar investigations are under way at Sellafield in Cumbria.

Nirex expect their proposals will go to a Public Inquiry in 1994 and, assuming permission is granted, would expect the repository to be open for business in 2005.

▲   *Figure 8.10   A rare example of pro nuclear waste feelings from* Aberdeen Press and Journal, *31 July 1990.*

In both areas there was nevertheless opposition to the proposals. In Cumbria this was part of a general opposition to Sellafield and the expansion of the THORP plant through imports of spent fuel which would increase the ILW and LLW arisings. In Caithness, the local group Caithness Against Nuclear Dumping (CAND) applied pressure on the local councils to oppose test drilling but was careful to confine its opposition to NIREX rather than the Dounreay fast breeder reactor plant where jobs were being lost as the project was run down. CAND held a referendum of the local population, and in a 58% turn-out there was a three to one majority against a nuclear waste repository in the area. Dounreay and Sellafield, nevertheless, offered the most promising political prospects for a repository and permission to drill was granted by the appropriate Secretary of State. Provided one or other site was found to be technically satisfactory it appeared that a political solution had been found.

Q   In what respects can Sellafield and Dounreay be said to represent a political solution to the problem of radioactive waste? In considering your answer consider why these sites are likely to be publicly acceptable.

A   Three broad reasons can be identified for the emergence of these two sites. (1) The strategy for radioactive waste management had lacked coherence and credibility. Disposal methods had been identified and sites had been chosen before options had been debated. The defeat of the shallow burial proposals left deep disposal as an option which attracted considerable support. Moreover, the consultation provided by *The Way Forward* gave an opportunity for debate about strategy. (2) The conflict over Billingham and also over shallow disposal had demonstrated that it would be politically extremely difficult to secure a greenfield location for the disposal of nuclear waste. (3) Accordingly, it would be prudent to confine the search to places where some solid support for the nuclear industry could be guaranteed. Sellafield and Dounreay fully satisfied this criterion.

Q   What factors weaken the opposition in these areas?

A   Again, there seem to be three factors to consider. (1) The local communities are divided between supporters (usually the workforce and dependents) and opponents of the nuclear industry. (2) A consensus favouring Dounreay or Sellafield will be the natural consequence of the relief felt in all other communities at not being selected. If it is accepted that a solution is necessary then the majority will be grateful that it is found somewhere else. (3) The very success of the campaigns against Billingham and shallow disposal make it more difficult to resist future proposals. Any government would proceed more cautiously, seeking public approval for its actions. Provided there are no technical obstacles and the consensus favouring deep disposal is maintained, Sellafield or Dounreay will remain the most likely candidates for a radioactive waste repository.

## 4.6   Summary

A case study has been used to evaluate the political consequences and possibilities of radioactive waste management policies, the fourth aim of this chapter. After the abandonment of HLW drilling and sea disposal, the government and NIREX turned to on-land disposal of ILW and LLW. Two sites, at Billingham for long-lived ILW, and Elstow for short-lived ILW and LLW, were announced without public consultation before a national waste management policy had been debated. This provided the local communities with an opportunity to oppose the strategy in principle as well as in terms of specific site selection criteria. The Billingham proposal was dropped and a comparative evaluation of four potential shallow burial sites, including Elstow, was agreed. By cooperating in a campaign against the concept of shallow burial the four communities were able to apply combined political pressure culminating in blockades which, eventually, secured the withdrawal of the plans. These events left co-disposal of ILW and LLW in a deep repository as the technical option most likely to achieve public acceptability. The political possibilities suggested the nuclear oases at Sellafield or Dounreay as the likely candidates.

# 5   The political challenge

## 5.1   Parallels and contrasts

There are over 400 reactors in the world producing nuclear electricity, with over two-thirds of them in North America and western Europe. The major producers in these areas are the United States (110 reactors and 98 gigawatts ($GW_e$) installed capacity in 1990), France (52 and 51 $GW_e$), Western Germany (21 and 22 $GW_e$), the UK (41 and 14 $GW_e$), Canada (18 and 12 $GW_e$) and Sweden (12 and 10 $GW_e$). The USSR (45 and 31 $GW_e$) and Japan (38 and 28 $GW_e$) are the only other substantial producers. In addition there are six nations (USA, USSR, UK, France, China and India) with developed nuclear armaments and others with the technical basis for developing them. Nuclear wastes from electricity generation, military programmes and reprocessing are, therefore, a problem confined mainly to the developed countries. But the fallout from bombs, the dangers of proliferation and the possibility of reactor accidents give the nuclear industry, and the residues it creates, a global environmental dimension.

The political response to the environmental problems created by the nuclear industry provides both parallels and contrasts with other global environmental problems. Our fifth aim is to examine the extent to which the politics of nuclear waste illustrates a developing environmental challenge to conventional political assumptions and arrangements. This needs to be considered in two stages. First we must establish how far the political features of nuclear waste in the UK, discussed in the previous section, are paralleled elsewhere. Second, we need to consider whether the politics of nuclear waste are unique or have features in common with other environmental political issues. We can only give a brief outline of these issues here but the book by Blowers *et al.*, referred to in the 'Further reading' section, examines some of them in more depth.

## 5.2   Experience in other countries

The political priorities for nuclear waste depend on the technical nature of
the problem, the political institutions and the political geography of the
country concerned. The contrasts and similarities to the UK's experience
can be illustrated by brief reference to four major producers, United States,
Sweden, France and Germany.

### United States

The politics of nuclear waste in the United States has four key elements.
First is the continental scale of the country which provokes conflict
between the east, with the vast majority of the reactors, and the west,
which harbours most of the remote locations for disposal. Second, the
absence of civil (as opposed to military) reprocessing means that the most
urgent political priority is to find an acceptable location for the deep
disposal of highly radioactive spent fuel. Third, the separation of the
military from the commercial waste streams has meant that political
opposition to nuclear waste projects has focused mainly on the civil
programme, which is most open to constitutional challenge. And fourth,
political challenge to policies is encouraged by the participative nature of
the political institutions of the country.

Search for a suitable site for the disposal of spent fuel has been going
on since the 1960s but the Nuclear Waste Policy Act (NWPA) of 1982 set out
the strategy for developing a deep geological repository. Nine sites in the
west which were under review at the time were reduced, first to a short-list
of five and then to three remote sites: at Hanford in Washington state, and
sites in western Texas and Nevada. A necessary compromise had been that
a site in the east of the country would be identified before construction
could begin at the chosen western site. The announcement of 12 sites in
seven eastern states in 1986 provoked intense opposition, forcing the
federal government to withdraw the proposals. This, inevitably, intensified
opposition from the three western states. State-wide opposition was
sufficient to overwhelm the local support for the project in Hanford. In
Texas there was tough opposition from the local farming community. In
Nevada there was scarcely any local population but the state opposed the
plan. The possibility that the three states could mobilise support from
corridor states through which the waste would be transported was averted
by an Amendment to the NWPA which limited investigation to the Nevada
site, thus limiting the opposition and providing a political solution if the
site proved technically suitable.

Technical problems rather than political opposition were responsible
for the delays in commissioning the Waste Isolation Pilot Project (WIPP)
near Carlsbad in the desert of New Mexico (see Figure 8.3). This new
project was welcomed in an area where the potash industry was failing and
in a state where Los Alamos, the Sandia Laboratories and other nuclear
activities were a powerful interest. Elsewhere nuclear waste projects have
been resisted by state governments, although there may be local support
from dependent nuclear communities.

Low-level nuclear waste has also created political conflict at local and
state level. In South Carolina, Nevada and Washington state, growing
opposition to the three operating shallow burial facilities led to the Low
Level Radioactive Waste Policy Act of 1980. Under the Act the three sites
would eventually be closed and new greenfield sites would need to replace
them. The new sites would receive the LLW arising within each regional

compact set up for the purpose of managing LLW. It has been difficult to
establish the host state for a site within each compact, and political
feasibility will determine the selection of individual sites. The most likely
places will be remote locations, areas in economic decline and areas with
present or past experience of the nuclear industry.

## Sweden

Nuclear power stations at four locations on the coast supply about half
Sweden's electricity. The strength of environmental concern about nuclear
power was demonstrated in the referendum of 1980 which effectively
committed the government to phase out the nuclear programme by around
the year 2010, the end of the life of the latest reactors. The total future
burden of radioactive waste can, therefore, be estimated and plans laid for
its management. Four basic principles are applied to nuclear waste
management in Sweden: very high safety requirements; the use of best
available technology; the highest degree of national independence; and no
burdens on future generations (except some site monitoring).

Plans for waste management include a central store where spent fuel is
cooled prior to disposal in a deep geological repository. ILW and LLW are
disposed of in the purpose-built sub-seabed repository next to the
Forsmark power station about 160 km north of Stockholm. Sweden
exemplifies an approach that applies 'to the entombment of radioactive
waste the sort of devotion that the ancient Egyptians gave to the burial of
their Pharaohs' (*The Times*, 20 May 1986). The 'Swedish solution' has
attracted wide acclaim in other countries but is still treated with scepticism
by opponents of the nuclear industry in Sweden. Despite the efforts to
manage wastes according to rigorous standards, opposition from national
and local environmental groups has focused especially on the test drilling
programme for a HLW repository.

## France

France is also heavily dependent on nuclear energy (around 70% of the
country's electricity) but, unlike Sweden, the state maintains an
aggressively pro-nuclear stance. As the world's second largest producer of
'nuclear' electricity and a military nuclear power, France has the full range
of nuclear cycle facilities located on coasts and rivers throughout the
country. Four potential sites in different rock formations have been
identified for a HLW repository. LLW and short-lived ILW are consigned to
a permanent surface disposal facility at Cap de la Hague, with another one
proposed at Soulaines in the Champagne region east of Paris.

There have been protests against the HLW plans, and the Soulaines
site was challenged in the Supreme Court. But France has not experienced
the continuing and coherent opposition to the nuclear industry that has
been typical in other western countries. There is a strong industry–state
relationship through which the nuclear industry is controlled and
subsidised. Policy is developed through a highly centralised system which
minimises political debate over the implementation of nuclear projects.
Opposition is further limited by the favourable publicity given to nuclear
energy and the investment and inducements that are provided to local
areas which host nuclear plants. Where necessary the state has not been
averse to the use of force to suppress dissent, as in the case of a mass
demonstration against the Superphenix fast breeder reactor in 1977 when a

demonstrator was killed. Opposition to nuclear energy and radioactive waste projects has been slowly emerging but is likely to remain passive in the face of the country's heavy dependence on the nuclear industry for electricity and defence.

### Germany

By contrast western Germany has experienced political convulsions over nuclear energy and waste. It gets around a third of its electricity from nuclear stations but there are no reprocessing facilities. Protest against aspects of the civil nuclear programme is often linked to opposition to the deployment of nuclear weapons and more general environmental concerns. During the 1970s mass protests were held against the construction of new power stations, and during the 1980s consistent protests were a major factor in the cancellation of the Wackersdorf reprocessing project in Bavaria. During these decades there were successful protests against the neutron bomb and Cruise and Pershing missile deployment.

A proposal for a combined reprocessing and nuclear waste facility at Gorleben in Lower Saxony close to the border between East and West Germany provoked a series of demonstrations in a conservative rural area during the late 1970s and 1980s. The reprocessing proposal was withdrawn and proposals for nuclear waste management have been deferred. Evidence that LLW waste consignments exported to Belgium for treatment contained highly radioactive materials revealed a major scandal involving illegal payments and corruption and created additional fears about nuclear proliferation. Consequently, the German government has become highly sensitive to nuclear issues. Protest groups have demonstrated an ability to frustrate the plans and programmes of the nuclear industry.

## 5.3   Summary: political outcomes of radioactive waste

These brief sketches are confined to major western producers of nuclear waste. It is possible to make some general observations about political outcomes but more evidence from a wider range of countries would be needed before generalisations could be made with reasonable assurance. With this reservation in mind we can derive some general conclusions about the politics of radioactive waste.

In nearly every country nuclear waste management policies and proposals have generated opposition once they become known in detail or location. There are contrasts between countries in the character of the opposition. In some cases such as Germany, nuclear waste is one aspect of opposition to the nuclear industry and nuclear weapons. In several countries there are both national environmental groups and local action groups opposed to proposals. In the United States opposition is mainly focused at state and local level and in France the opposition is, as yet, relatively undeveloped. The target of the opposition will depend on the political priorities in individual countries. In countries committed to reprocessing, like Britain and France, HLW is confined to one or two sites and need not be disposed of for several decades. The large volumes of ILW and LLW that are accumulating in these countries are the main waste problem, leading to a search in the UK for appropriate disposal sites. In the United States, Sweden and other countries spent fuel is accumulating at power stations, posing problems of storage space and cost, dangers to the workforce and the risk of proliferation. In these countries the development of a HLW repository has become the political priority for nuclear waste management.

Where it has developed, the opposition to nuclear waste proposals has derived its strength from its broad appeal in two ways. First, it has been able to combine the defence of specific local interests from external threat with an appeal to more general concerns about the long-term threat to the environment. This focus on issues that affect society as a whole has enabled the opposition to generate widespread interest in the problem among the media and the public. Second, the ability of local groups to form coalitions, emphasising the general principles rather than the detailed local aspects of proposals, has endowed the opposition with conspicuous political power, as demonstrated in the UK, for example, during the 1980s. This power has been used to frustrate policies, defer plans and halt the development of specific sites in a number of countries.

A form of political action has emerged outside the realm of party politics that combines the local with the national and international, the short with the long term, and self-interest with the public interest. Centrally determined policies have been undermined by local activists, fighting along a broad front using counter-expertise, publicity and lobbying. Governments have been willing to concede since thereby they may be relieved of politically unpalatable decisions.

The success of the opposition has narrowed the options for radioactive waste management. It has made political calculations pre-eminent in the search for solutions. Governments have been willing to see controversial projects dropped or delayed to avoid political sanctions. The pragmatic retreat to nuclear oases offers a way of minimising the political problem though it may not offer the best technical solution. Deferral leaves decisions to be taken by future generations. On the other hand, decisions once taken remove options for the future. Solutions require heroic assumptions about safety and security of repositories that have no empirical basis. These considerations make continuing conflict over nuclear waste more likely than consensus.

# 6   The future

## 6.1   Prospects for future nuclear waste disposal

Political consensus must rest on an agreement on the appropriate technical means of radioactive waste management. The arguments for and against deep disposal were presented earlier in Activity 1. Some environmentalists argue that disposal of the waste should not be undertaken until the technical problems have been resolved. They advocate continuing on-site storage and monitoring of wastes as the responsible methods of ensuring the safety of the present and future generations. From the anti-nuclear perspective of these groups, on-site storage ensures the visibility of the problem of radioactive waste and emphasises the lack of an acceptable solution. This would act as a brake on the further expansion of the industry.

The interim storage of HLW at a central location is an option being developed in some countries. Sweden has a facility for the storage of spent fuel and the United States has contemplated developing a monitored retrievable storage plant in Tennessee, a state with a large concentration of nuclear plant. In the UK and France HLW from reprocessing is stored and vitrified. In all these countries storage is a preliminary stage for cooling prior to final disposal of the wastes in a deep geological repository.

Deep geological disposal of the most dangerous wastes is now favoured by a broad consensus of government, scientific and public opinion. Deep disposal is justified on the grounds that it concentrates the waste at a few (usually remote) locations where the waste can be monitored and (at least initially) possibly retrieved, although this option involves considerable transportation. By contrast, storage requires permanent routine monitoring at many sites, exposes workers and the local community to the risk of radioactivity and increases the dangers of nuclear proliferation.

Disposal requires the selection of sites that are acceptable on both technical and political grounds. Political acceptability depends partly on the technical criteria adopted and these are likely to become more rigorous under the impact of sceptical public and scientific opinion. The accepted technique is to emplace waste that has been carefully packaged in containers in a repository sealed by multiple barriers in a suitably stable hydrogeological medium.

Technically suitable sites will be increasingly hard to find and, in some countries, the technical standards may be impossible to meet anywhere. We saw in Section 3 how the problem of nuclear waste shifted from being a technical to a political problem. In Section 4 we discussed how the political options were narrowed to a search for nuclear oases where disposal could be achieved either because of the presence of the nuclear industry or the need for economic development. While nuclear oases may offer a pragmatic solution they may not always be available, or, if available, may prove to be technically unsuitable. Nuclear waste does not create many jobs and it brings long-term blight and risk so that it may be unwelcome even in nuclear oases. This is the case in Caithness where community support for the UKAEA's Dounreay plant contrasts with the overwhelming opposition to NIREX.

Any political solution to the problem of radioactive waste will need to consider the principles of spatial and intergenerational equity that we discussed in Section 4.1. Compensation should be provided to those local communities hosting a site regardless of whether they willingly accept a new waste disposal facility. Compensation might be economic (tax relief, local investment), environmental (improvement of the area), or in the form of infrastructure, social and public facilities. Local communities will expect careful monitoring and safety requirements, adequate information and also some participation in decision-making.

Intergenerational equity requires that the burdens imposed on future generations from the actions of the present are minimised. The burden is already unavoidable since nuclear waste exists and is accumulating. An argument for deep disposal is that it spatially limits the future problem. But if it encourages the belief that the problem is solved it may justify the expansion of the nuclear industry. In the prevailing uncertainty about the environmental safety of nuclear waste the only way of minimising the burden on future generations is to limit the further creation of wastes. The development of nuclear energy has already been halted for commercial reasons in the United States and the United Kingdom. The problem of nuclear waste provides a further reason for restraining the growth of nuclear energy. Given the economic and environmental problems and political insecurity encountered with other major sources of energy, abandonment of nuclear energy is not an option likely to be entertained in the near future.

## 6.2    Nuclear, chemical and atmospheric hazards

Here we briefly consider whether the politics of nuclear waste indicate a developing trend in other areas of environmental politics. A comparison can be made with toxic and hazardous wastes, a subject covered in Chapter 7, and with global environmental problems which will be discussed in the last book of this series (*Smith & Warr, 1991*).

1    *Toxic and hazardous wastes.* As with radioactive wastes these are associated with dangerous technologies with low probability/high consequence risks. Disposal of toxic and radioactive wastes creates locally unwanted land uses and there is a need for long term security and surveillance. Fears about local risk and blight, about the dangers to future generations and concern about international trade and dumping have stimulated effective local action and influenced government policies, as we saw in Chapter 7.

Despite these similarities, toxic and hazardous wastes have not generated political movements with the same permanence and power that have emerged in the case of radioactive waste. Toxic and hazardous wastes are not *directly* connected to destructive military purposes. The fear of radioactivity is greater and more pervasive than any other socially induced risk.

2    *Regional and global environmental issues.* These include acid rain, the destruction of the ozone layer and global warming. Like nuclear waste they have achieved considerable political prominence but they are quite different political issues. Regional and global issues, by definition, affect wide areas (perhaps the whole world). While this may cause general anxiety it does not have direct and immediate impact on specific localities, as is the case with nuclear waste. In consequence, regional and global issues do not give rise to local opposition and action; they are handled politically by governments.

These problems tend to raise rather different environmental concerns. They are fundamentally transboundary problems with complex causes and effects that are matters of scientific debate and disagreement. (You might like to refresh your memory on the scientific problems and political implications of transboundary pollution by re-reading Chapter 6, Section 4.3). Solution to such problems requires international control and co-operation. National interests may be in conflict with more general international interests. For example, the UK's refusal to join the 30% Club (those countries that agreed to reduce sulphur dioxide emissions by 30% between 1980–93) was strongly influenced by its unwillingness to pay for desulphurisation when most of the benefits were reaped by other countries.

The chances of achieving co-operation in the event of scientific consensus and political agreement on the need for action to prevent global warming are extremely remote. It will require a major reduction in energy consumption in the developed countries and massive compensation to developing countries who forego the exploitation of their resources. The international political arrangements needed to introduce and monitor such changes barely exist, and are also likely to be subverted by national self-interest. These scientific and political problems are the main focus of the next book in the series (*Smith & Warr, 1991*).

By comparison with these problems, nuclear waste seems an easy problem to solve. It is a distinctive political problem which has produced political outcomes that are not paralleled in other environmental problems. Nuclear waste accumulates at specific sites from identifiable industrial processes. It is under the jurisdiction of individual governments. The management of radioactive wastes can be controlled within countries provided that there can be agreement on the methods.

## References

COUNTY COUNCILS COALITION (1987) *The Disposal of Radioactive Waste in Sweden, West Germany and France*, Prepared for the County Councils Coalition by Environmental Resources Ltd.

HMSO (1955) *A Programme of Nuclear Power*, White Paper, Cmnd 9389, HMSO, London.

HMSO (1976) *Nuclear Power and the Environment*, Sixth Report of the Royal Commission on Environmental Pollution, Cmnd 6618, HMSO, London.

HOUSE OF COMMONS ENVIRONMENT COMMITTEE (1986) *Radioactive Waste*, Session 1985–6, First Report, HMSO, London.

NIREX (1983) *The Disposal of Low and Intermediate-level Radioactive Wastes: the Elstow Storage Depot*, A Preliminary Project Statement, NIREX, Harwell.

NIREX (1987) *The Way Forward: a discussion document*, NIREX, Harwell.

NIREX (1989) *Going Forward: the development of a national disposal centre for low and intermediate-level radioactive waste*, NIREX, Harwell.

SILVERTOWN, J. & SARRE, P. (eds) (1990) *Environment and Society*, Hodder & Stoughton/The Open University, London (Book One).

SMITH, P. M. & WARR, K. (eds) (1991) *Global Environmental Issues*, Hodder & Stoughton/The Open University, London (Book Four).

WILSON, C. L. (1979) Nuclear energy: what went wrong?, *Bulletin of the Atomic Scientists*, June, 13–17.

## Further reading

BLAIR, I. M. (1983) *Taming the Atom: facing the future with nuclear power*, Adam Hilger Ltd, Bristol.

BLOWERS, A., LOWRY, D. & SOLOMON, B. (1991) *The International Politics of Nuclear Waste*, Macmillan, London.

CAUFIELD, C. (1990) *Multiple Exposures: chronicles of the radiation age*, Penguin, Harmondsworth.

HALL, T. (1986) *Nuclear Politics: the history of nuclear power in Britain*, Penguin, Harmondsworth.

PATTERSON, W. C. (1983) *Nuclear Power*, 2nd edition, Pelican, Harmondsworth.

PEARCE, D., EDWARDS, L. & BEURET, G. (1979) *Decision Making for Energy Futures: a case study of the Windscale Inquiry*, Macmillan/SSRC, London.

WILLIAMS, R. (1980) *The Nuclear Power Decisions*, Croom Helm, London.

# Answers to Activities

## Activity 1

*For*   The argument for deep disposal would take the following lines. These are extremely dangerous materials and must be removed from the accessible environment. Deep disposal in engineered repositories in remote areas in stable geological formations will prevent escape of radionuclides into environmental pathways over the necessary periods of time it will take for them to decay to harmless levels. Leaving such dangerous materials as spent fuel scattered over many surface storage sites will require permanent surveillance, will be a hazard to local populations and the workforce and will be vulnerable to terrorist action and the dangers of nuclear theft or war. It would be irresponsible of the present generation to impose such a problem of waste management on subsequent generations. All human activity carries some risks and those from nuclear energy must be weighed against the benefits to present and future generations of a secure energy supply. Similarly the potential dangers of nuclear warfare must be weighed against the benefits of peacekeeping through a nuclear deterrent force.

*Against*   Conversely, it might be argued that over the timescales involved climatic and geological stability is unlikely, and earth movements and the penetration by water of even the most stable formations are a distinct possibility. Political and social changes are inevitable and the permanent monitoring of a hidden danger might become neglected. With surface storage the dangers will remain evident and changes to the storage strategy may be made in good time if necessary. Future generations would be imperilled by the out-of-sight-out-of-mind approach implied in deep disposal. Since the risks from nuclear waste are so large it would be better to minimise waste arisings by ceasing production of nuclear energy now and invest in energy efficiency or more environmentally benign energy sources, and to phase out nuclear weapons production and nuclear-powered submarines.

## Activity 2

About 87% of radiation exposure is from natural sources, mostly from cosmic rays, gamma rays from rocks and soils, radon and thoron seeping into buildings, and from particles absorbed internally from eating, drinking and breathing. About 0.1% comes from nuclear discharges.

In Section 4.2 of *Silvertown & Sarre, 1990*, Chapter 1, it was pointed out that there was great variability in exposure to radioactivity and that the form of exposure varied according to the type of ionising radiation involved. The precise relationship between exposure and harmful effects is little understood. Average statistics convey no information about the *concentration of exposure* ('hot spots') at specific places. The amounts of radioactivity from the nuclear industry may be small but they are concentrated in specific locations and there is the permanent risk of accidental release.

*Activity 3*

One obvious answer is that there was relatively little waste produced in the early years and it could be kept in store near the sites of production. But there are also less obvious political reasons encouraging lenient safety standards and primitive management systems. The lack of concern was induced and reinforced by the characteristic features of the nuclear industry evident at this time. It was a military programme, developed in the utmost secrecy, thus obviating independent oversight and regulation. In such conditions radioactive waste management was a non-problem, possibly a result of considerable ignorance about the dangers of radioactivity. It is also conceivable that the problem was recognised but deliberately suppressed: a case of *negative decision-making*, whereby those with power simply defer a decision or decide not to act, comfortable in the knowledge that inaction cannot be challenged.

*Activity 4*

On the face of it, by accepting the need for a comparative assessment, the government was endorsing a rational strategy. It might also reasonably assume that the opposition would be fragmented, focusing on individual sites. In due course, the relief at the three sites not selected would ensure the isolation of the community at the chosen site. Had the government not capitulated, it is conceivable that the collaboration between the four areas would have foundered once an individual site was selected.

In fact, any hope of a divide and rule strategy was prevented by the united opposition maintained by the four communities. The decision to nominate four sites multiplied the opposition, giving it a national dimension cutting across conventional political boundaries. The Coalition and BOND maintained a united front based on a technical case against shallow burial rather than against individual sites. They were able to put political pressure on the government while providing a coherent alternative which was eventually accepted.

# Acknowledgements

Grateful acknowledgement is made to the following sources for permission to reproduce material in this book:


## Covers

*Front cover, clockwise from top right*: David Parker/Science Photo Library; Roy Lawrance; Martin Bond/The Environmental Picture Library; Janice Robertson; Mike Levers/The Open University; Inco Limited; Information Service of the European Community; Information Service of the European Community; Chris Steele/Perkins/Magnum; *centre*: Janice Robertson; *back cover*: Information Service of the European Community.


## Colour plate section

*Plate 1*: English China Clays Group; *Plate 2*: H. Girardet/The Environmental Picture Library; *Plate 3*: Steven C. Wilson/ENTHEOS; *Plate 4*: British Coal Opencast/Peter N. Grimshaw; *Plate 5*: Cheshire County Council; *Plate 6*: British Coal Opencast/Peter N. Grimshaw; *Plate 7*: Steven C. Wilson/ENTHEOS; *Plate 8*: Steven C. Wilson/ENTHEOS; *Plate 9*: Vanessa Miles/ The Environmental Picture Library; *Plate 10*: P. Glendell/The Environmental Picture Library; *Plate 11*: Forestry Research Institute, The Chinese Academy of Forestry/Steve Newman/ Fountain Renewable Resources; *Plate 12*: D. Taylor; *Plate 13*: R. Everett; *Plate 14*: D. Olivier.


## Figures

*Figures 1.1, 1.2, 1.3, 1.11, 1.13*: from *BP Statistical Review of World Energy*, (1990), British Petroleum Co.; *Figures 1.9, 1.12*: Krenz, J. H. (1980) *Energy: From Opulence to Sufficiency*, Praeger; *Figure 1.10*: from *Energy Technologies for UK* (1979) vol. 1, Department of Energy Paper No. 39, reproduced by permission of the controller of HMSO; *p.2*: © The Graphic Communications Centre Ltd, 1981; *Figure 2.1*: British Coal; *Figure 2.2*: Inco Limited; *Figure 2.3*: John Blunden; *Figure 2.4*: Gilliland, P. (1979) *Atlas of Earth Resources*, Mitchell Beazley; *Figure 2.6*: *New Scientist*, 9 December 1982, p.649; *Figure 2.7*: *Peruvian Times*; *Figure 2.8*: West Air Photography; *Figure 2.10*: Singer, D.A. (1977) *Journal Resources Policy*, 3(2) (June), 127–33; *Figure 3.1*: Aerofilms; *Figure 3.2*: Inco Limited; *Figure 3.3*: Copyright © Commission on Mining and the Environment/Photo supplied by Rio Tinto Zinc Ltd.; *Figure 3.4*: Aerofilms; *Figure 3.5*: Robert Del Tredici copyright © photograph; *Figures 3.6, 3.7, 3.8*: Conroy, N., Hawley, K., Keller, W., LaFrance, C. (Ontario Ministry of the Environment) (1975) Influence of the atmosphere on lakes in the Sudbury area from source (unpublished paper); *Figure 3.9*: Nriagu, J. O. (1984) *Environmental Impacts of Smelters*, John Wiley & Sons; *Figure 3.10*: Troug (1951) *Mineral Nutrition of Plants*, University of Wisconsin Press; *Figure 3.11, left*: Cotswold Water Park, *right*: RMC Group plc; *Figure 3.12*: Inco Limited; *Figure 4.8*: Aerofilms; *Figure 4.9, 4.12, 4.14(b)*: Park, C. P. (1987) *Acid Rain: Rhetoric and Reality*, Methuen & Co.; *Figure 4.10*: Manners, G. (1981) *Coal in Britain*, Allen & Unwin; *Figure 4.11*: Commission on Energy and the Environment (1981), *Coal and the Environment*, reproduced by permission of the controller of HMSO; *Figure 4.15*: Vanessa Miles/Environmental Picture Library; *Figure 5.2*: Saxhof, B., Technical University of Denmark; *p.183*: © The Graphic Communications Centre Ltd, 1981; *Figure 5.7*: JET Joint Undertaking in *Culham Laboratory Annual Report 1988 (CLM-AR26)*, 1989; *Figure 5.9*: copyright © James L. Ruhle and Associates; *Figure 5.10*: North London Waste Authority; *Figure 5.11*: Wind Energy Group; *Figure 5.12(b)*: S.E.A./Lanchester Polytechnic; *Figure 5.13*: Baker, A. C. 'The development of functions relating to cost and performance of tidal power schemes and their application to small scale sites', Symposium on Tidal Power, Thomas Telford Ltd, I.C.E., 1986; *Figure 5.16*: CEGB Evidence to the House of Lords Select Committee on the European Community's Alternative Energy Sources Report, CEGB, 1988; *Figure 5.17*: CEGB; *Figure 5.18*: *Developing Wind Energy for the UK*, 1990, Friends of the Earth; *Figures 6.1 to 6.8*: *Industry Technology: Visual History of Modern Britain*, 1965, Studio Vista, a division of Cassell plc; *Figures 6.11, 6.13*: C. E. Miller; *Figure 7.2*: Rowe, W. D. (1977) 'A hierarchy of risk assessment terminology', *The Anatomy of Risk*, p.45, John Wiley & Sons; *Figure 7.4*: from *Canvey: An Investigation of Potential Hazards from Operations in the Canvey Island/Thurrock Area*, 1978, reproduced with the permission of the Controller of Her Majesty's Stationery Office; *Figure 7.5 (a and b)*: Porteous, A. (1985) *Hazardous Wastes in the UK: An*

*Overview*, Butterworths & Co (Publishers) Ltd; *Figures 8.1, 8.5:* Blowers, A., Lowry, D., Solomon, D. (eds) (1991) *The International Politics of Nuclear Waste*, Macmillan Press, UK, St Martin's Press, New York; *Figure 8.4: The Hindustan Times*, New Delhi, India; *Figure 8.6:* 'Nuclear dustbins for the centuries', *The Guardian*, 7 January 1974, reproduced with the permission of Professor Bryce-Smith on behalf of all signatories; *p.311:* David Austin/*New Scientist; Figure 8.7:* Bedfordshire County Council; *Figure 8.8: Evening Gazette*, Teesside; *Figure 8.9:* copyright © Lincolnshire Echo; *Figure 8.10:* Vass, J. 'Man who hopes to see N-dump under his garden', *Aberdeen Press and Journal*, 31 July 1990.

## Photographs

*pp.168–69:* Peter Thornton/Lakeland Photographic; *p.198:* photographed from *Revue Archaeologique* 1899, i, p.329, plate xii; *pp.280–81:* Echo Newspapers Ltd.

## Tables

*Table 2.1:* Gilliland, P. (1979) *Atlas of Earth Resources*, Mitchell Beazley; *Table 2.2:* Bell, E. from Frosch, R. A. and Gallopoulos, N. E. (1989) Strategies for manufacturing, *Scientific American*, vol 261 (September); *Table 3.4:* adapted from proceedings of an international symposium on waste material sponsored by the Réunion Internationale des Laboratoires d'Essais et de Recherches sur les Matériaux et les Constructions (RILEM), published in *Materials and Structures*, 12(70), 1979; *Table 4.2:* Skea, J. 'Acid Rain and Urban Atmospheric Pollution: Europe', paper presented to the *4th International Energy Conference: Environmental Challenge: The Energy Response*, The Royal Institute, December 1989; *Table 5.2:* Shea, C. P. 'Renewable Energy: Today's Contribution, Tomorrow's Promise' from Worldwatch Paper 81, Worldwatch Institute, January 1988; *Table 7.3:* from *Canvey: An Investigation of Potential Hazards from Operations in the Canvey Island/Thurrock Area*, 1978, reproduced with the permission of the Controller of Her Majesty's Stationery Office; *Table 7.5:* ENDS Report, No 182, March 1990.

## Text

*Box 2.3:* adapted from Gilliland, P. (1979) *Atlas of Earth Resources*, Mitchell Beazley; *Box 3.2:* Winterhalder, K. *Proceedings Third Annual Meeting of Canadian Land Reclamation Association*, Laurentian University, 1978; *Box 3.3:* Lertola, J. from Frosch, R.A. and Gallopoulos, N.E. (1989) Strategies for Manufacturing, *Scientific American*, vol. 261 (September).

# Index